Thermodynamics

AN INTRODUCTION

" *It is not until we attempt to bring the
theoretical part of our training into
contact with the practical that we begin
to experience the full effect of what
Faraday has called 'mental inertia'—not
only the difficulty of recognizing, among the
objects before us, the abstract relations which
we have learned from the books, but the
distracting pain of wrenching the mind away
from the symbols to the objects, and from
the objects back to the symbols. This,
however, is the price we have to pay
for new ideas.*"

JAMES CLERK MAXWELL

*Introductory Lecture at
Cambridge Cavendish Laboratory,
October, 1871*

Thermodynamics

AN INTRODUCTION

Rubin Battino

Wright State University,
Dayton, Ohio

Scott E. Wood

Illinois Institute of Technology,
Chicago, Illinois

ACADEMIC PRESS   New York   London

ACADEMIC PRESS INC.
111 Fifth Avenue, New York, New York 10003

United Kingdom Edition published by
ACADEMIC PRESS INC. (LONDON) LTD.
Berkeley Square House, London W.1

LIBRARY OF CONGRESS CATALOG CARD NUMBER: 68–16513

PRINTED IN THE UNITED STATES OF AMERICA

This work is dedicated to our wives
Charlotte Alice
and
Marie Simmons

Preface

This text was developed for a general introductory course in thermodynamics taught at Illinois Institute of Technology. It treats the basic principles in a general way without being directed toward any specific field. It is thus primarily a text in the field of thermodynamics, per se, with illustrative applications and problems drawn mostly from chemistry. The classical macroscopic approach is followed throughout, operational definitions being adopted for the key concepts.

In many curricula the study of thermodynamics has moved to the sophomore year. Yet it is our experience that students have great difficulty with the subject because of the rapid and sometimes superficial treatment that many books give to the fundamental concepts of temperature, heat, work, and energy. The present book is an attempt to aid students by developing the subject slowly through detailed presentations of these fundamentals, a method especially necessary for a course taught early in a student's career. We have deliberately avoided facile or wordy explanations, permitting the subject to be developed in a more mathematical form.

Calculus is used throughout the text and the properties of exact and inexact differentials and line integrals are utilized in the development of the concepts of heat and work and the definition of the energy and entropy functions. A course in thermodynamics may well be the first occasion where the calculus is applied to variables having physical significance (such as P, V, and T) with an arbitrary choice as to which variables are independent. Also, partial derivatives may be encountered here for the first time. Therefore, after a brief introductory chapter establishing the language of thermodynamics, all of the required mathematics is outlined in Chapter 2. All of the material in this chapter need not be covered immediately, but should be referred to as required. Most of the mathematical concepts so developed are applied in Chapter 3 to equations of state for ideal and real gases.

Chapters 4, 5, and 6 are devoted to operational definitions of the concepts of temperature, heat, and work. These treatments are more complete than those normally found in textbooks at this level. In particular, the concept of work has been developed rather fully since the term "work" can have several different meanings depending on the nature of the process and the manner in which the system and its surroundings are defined.

The first law of thermodynamics is developed in Chapter 7. This is followed by a chapter devoted to the enthalpy function and thermochemistry. In Chapter 9 the first law is applied to real gases.

The second law of thermodynamics is approached first as a generalization of processes as observed in nature in Chapter 10, and then through the entropy function and its properties in Chapter 11. The approach is classical and is based on the differences between reversible and irreversible processes. The entropy function is developed from the Carnot cycle.

There follows the development of the two free energies and the thermodynamics of open systems, and discussion of the conditions for thermodynamic equilibrium and their application to chemical and phase equilibria. Osmotic pressure, electrochemical cells, and the third law of thermodynamics are treated briefly.

It is hoped that individual teachers will be able to enlarge easily on topics or applications of their own choosing. The entire treatment of thermodynamics in the text is general insofar as this is possible. Relatively few equations of a specific nature are developed, although many of the problems require specific equations. Students may be required to develop their own solutions to the problems, based on the fundamental principles given in the text. Some of the problems run as *leitmotifs* through several chapters, growing in complexity as the student's knowledge broadens. Answers to selected problems are provided at the back of the book.

The introductory course in thermodynamics at Illinois Institute of Technology is taken by all students majoring in engineering and by chemistry and biology majors. More advanced courses in thermodynamics and its application to special fields are given in the separate departments, but all are based on the one introductory course. All of the material in this text is covered in a four-credit one-semester course that consists of two one-hour lectures and two one-hour recitations each week.

We thank the Illinois Institute of Technology sophomore class of 1965–66 for bearing with us during the preparation of this text and also for the many suggestions that they made. We wish to thank our colleagues at Illinois Institute of Technology and elsewhere who have contributed suggestions and we also thank Dr. R. J. Tykodi, for his comments on this book.

November, 1967   *R.B.*
Dayton, Ohio   *S.E.W.*
Chicago, Illinois

Contents

Contents

Contents

Thermodynamics

AN INTRODUCTION

1 Introduction

A remarkable thing about our universe is the underlying and discoverable order in it. Whether or not this order has a divine origin is a proper subject only for theological conjecture, but the fact still remains that the order is there and can be uncovered by appropriate experiments, observations, and mathematical manipulations. That the end result of scientific inquiry into the nature of the universe is frequently a simple set of mathematical relations is a subject fit for wonder in itself. In this regard the laws of thermodynamics are much like Newton's laws of motion—they are basic, beautiful, and simple statements describing natural phenomena.

This latter facet of natural laws is of great importance. Natural laws describe natural phenomena; it is misleading to say that phenomena "obey" one law or another. Every experiment that is performed and every observation that is made serves to validate (or refute) the relations that presumably cover the experiment or observation. The history of science contains a number of good examples of laws and theories being disproven. The justification for using the laws of thermodynamics is that they have never yet been controverted. The basic approach used throughout this book will be the empirical one, in which the emphasis is on the experimental and observational basis for the relations developed and the laws used.

Now that thermodynamics has been codified into texts, the tendency is just to accept what is written in the text without any consideration of the historical origins. The concepts of temperature, heat, work, and energy have had their own histories. Although the early controversy surrounding these concepts may be only of historic interest now, the idea that the concepts presented here were once controversial can well be pondered. Substituting a "why" for a quick acceptance can be rewarding.

The mark of thermodynamics can be found almost everywhere, from fundamental studies of the fuel cells carried in satellites to the operation of a household refrigerator to the design of vast steam-generating plants. The physicist makes much use of thermodynamics in low-temperature studies; the biologist, in energy balances in biochemical processes; and the chemist, to predict the extent and feasibility of chemical reactions. A chemical engineer could never transpose a laboratory process to an industrial scale without the application of thermodynamics to mass and energy balances. The liquefaction of atmospheric gases is one area where thermodynamics is effectively applied to engines operating in cycles.

1.1 THE SCOPE OF CLASSICAL THERMODYNAMICS

Thermodynamics involves the study of the interaction of one body on another, the interactions being described in terms of the quantities heat and work. The concepts of heat and work and the laws of thermodynamics have been developed by means of observations and experiments over a long period of years. The laws therefore are based on experiment and are general statements concerning the behavior of systems as observed in nature. There is no independent proof of the laws; however, an experiment has yet to be performed the results of which conflict with the laws.

Many of the original formulations of thermodynamics were made before there was adequate knowledge of the atomistic nature of matter and were based on observations of matter in macroscopic aggregates. Classical thermodynamics, which is the approach used in this book, is concerned with the macroscopic properties of matter and fundamentally not at all with molecular observations. Indeed classical thermodynamics can be developed without the knowledge that matter is composed of atoms and molecules. Statistical thermodynamics, based on statistical mechanics, is essentially a separate discipline which has been developed more recently. It is concerned with the calculation of the thermodynamic properties of matter from the behavior, expressed in terms of the laws of classical or quantum mechanics, of a large collection of atoms or molecules. The advantages of classical thermodynamics are that the thermodynamic properties of systems can be determined experimentally without a complete knowledge of the chemical reactions that may take place in the system or of interactions between the molecules in the system. The limitations are that molecular interactions or possible chemical reactions in a system cannot be determined from classical thermodynamics alone. The edifice of thermodynamics rests securely on the observed behavior of matter in the aggregate: "The justification for the thermodynamic approach is that there is a very large group of phenomena which are adequately treated in terms of macroscopic operations—and if one is inclined to ascribe a greater 'fundamentality' to the microscopic statistical approach, it should not be forgotten that all the basic microscopic operations are ultimately defined in terms of the macroscopic operations of thermodynamics. Logically, so far as the situation can be reduced to logic, the thermodynamic approach seems to be the fundamental one."[†]

Classical thermodynamics is primarily concerned with systems at equilibrium. A more recent development is the application of thermodynamics to systems that are not at equilibrium but are in a steady state, one in which the properties of the system are independent of time although the system is not at equilibrium. When a distinction needs to be made, classical thermodynamics may be called reversible thermodynamics, in contrast to irreversible thermodynamics or thermodynamics of the steady state.

The development of thermodynamics in this book is limited to systems in equilibrium. However, this does not mean that information is not provided about nonequilibrium states. The experimental criteria for equilibrium or for the spontaneity of processes are readily established. The equilibrium conditions for a particular system may be calculated and if the system is not in an equilibrium state, the results of the calculation indicate which direction the change will follow to achieve the equilibrium state. However, time is not a thermodynamic variable and thermodynamics can give no information about the length of time which would be required for a particular process to take place.

For chemical reactions we can use thermodynamics to predict the extent of the reaction, that is, the equilibrium concentrations of all the active species. Although equilibrium concentrations for a given reaction may be calculated, we cannot use thermodynamics to predict how long it will take for the equilibrium state to be attained. Some examples may be helpful. Liquid water at $-20°$ C and 1 atm pressure is unstable with respect to ice at the same

---

[†] P. W. Bridgman, *The Nature of Thermodynamics*. Cambridge, Mass.: Harvard Univ. Press, 1941, p. 65.

temperature and pressure. Water can be supercooled to $-20°$ C and 1 atm pressure and be maintained at that temperature and pressure for a long time. If an ice crystal is dropped into the supercooled water, some of the water immediately freezes. On the other hand, while it is well known that acetylene gas is unstable with respect to graphite and hydrogen gas, no one has ever observed acetylene to decompose spontaneously into graphite and hydrogen. What thermodynamics states is that *if* acetylene were in equilibrium with graphite and hydrogen, then the concentration of acetylene would be extremely small and essentially only graphite and hydrogen would be present. Hydrogen and chlorine gas react explosively to form hydrogen chloride gas if the reaction is initiated by light of appropriate wavelengths. However, the two gases can coexist indefinitely in the dark.

Thermodynamics also permits us to calculate relations between heat and work for particular processes, engines, and reactions. Such calculations give only limiting relations because of the necessity of dealing with systems at equilibrium. For example, we can easily calculate that the maximum efficiency at which a steam engine can operate is 37 percent if the temperature of the steam is 473° K and the heat sink is at 298° K. The efficiency of the real engine will depend on many factors, but no matter how well we design the engine (assuming the aforementioned operating temperatures) the efficiency will not exceed 37 percent. This type of information is obviously valuable.

1.2 THE OPERATIONAL APPROACH‡

Many different approaches may be used to introduce the basic ideas of thermodynamics. The approach we use follows what is called the operational approach. The basis of the approach is that a word used to describe a phenomenon observed in nature has meaning only with reference to the phenomenon itself and that the exact meaning of the word can be obtained only in terms of the operations used to study the phenomenon. Distance, time, and mass are examples of quantities that everyone normally thinks of in operational terms.

Before an example is discussed, a more general discussion of the development of scientific concepts may be helpful. Suppose that we have arrived by direct observation at some idea of a particular natural phenomenon. This

‡ P. W. Bridgman, *Reflections of a Physicist*, Philosophical Library. New York: Macmillan, 1955.

idea is useful for others only after the idea or a description of the phenomenon has been put into words so that it may be communicated to others. In the process of communication we may have to formulate new words; these words then have meaning only in terms of the phenomenon that has been observed. But observation and qualitative description are usually not sufficient, and quantitative studies must be made. To make this possible we define a unit of measurement in terms of the observed phenomenon and the experimental operations used to study the phenomenon. Then we can make quantitative measurements. The concepts may, in fact, be developed gradually over a period of many years and the experimental operations may need to be more carefully defined as knowledge of the phenomenon becomes more exact. Thus a concept evolves to full meaning first through observation, then from description with possible use of new words, and finally to quantitative measurement. In this sense we may say that a word has meaning only in terms of the phenomenon itself and the operations required to study the phenomenon.

As an illustrative but simplified example let us consider the word "length." Each of us in our experience has acquired an idea of the meaning of this word without the use of any definition. We recognize it as a property of a given object. Past observations and measurements have shown that the length of a given object depends upon its temperature. The unit of length is then defined in terms of our concept of length at a particular temperature. In the metric system the unit has been, up to 1960, the length between two marks on a particular bar of a platinum-iridium alloy at 273° K. The operation for measuring the length of an object at a given temperature is fundamentally then the determination of the number of times the bar of unit length can be laid end to end along the length of the object with due consideration of the temperature of the bar. It is only in terms of the concept of length and the operations of measuring length that the "length of an object" has meaning.

The concepts of temperature, heat and work will be defined operationally in the later chapters of this book. Until they are defined we will use the words in terms of their common naive interpretation.

I.3 THE LANGUAGE OF THERMODYNAMICS— BASIC DEFINITIONS

Thermodynamics is a subject that very much depends upon accurate definitions of the terms used and the careful use of these terms within the limits of their definitions. In this regard the use of language in thermodynamics is like the use of language in philosophy. We place great emphasis throughout this book on defining terms and adhering to these definitions.

The *system* is any region of space being investigated. It can be as simple or as complex as we choose but it must be carefully defined. A system may be made up of any number of subsystems. The *surroundings* are considered to be all other matter that can interact with the system. The choice of the system and the surroundings may be quite arbitrary. What might be considered as part of the surroundings of a system at one time or by one person may be considered as part of the system itself at another time or by another person. The important point is that for any particular case the system and the surroundings must be defined. When the effects of the interactions between a region of space and a system of interest are sufficiently small, the interaction is neglected and those regions of space are omitted in considering the surroundings. As an example, the effect of laboratory furniture on a particular system under study in a laboratory is ordinarily neglected and the furniture is then not considered as part of the surroundings. In the second place, we generally devise the surroundings of a system under study to afford us the opportunity of making controlled measurements on the system. We might wish to keep the temperature of the system constant. In order to do so we may devise a thermostat (part of the surroundings) whose temperature is kept constant and then place the system in the thermostat.

The boundary between the system and its surroundings is called an *envelope* or *wall*, the properties of which must be defined. The envelope may be imaginary or real; it may be rigid or nonrigid; it may be a conductor of heat or a nonconductor of heat; it may be permeable to some of the substances in the system or nonpermeable. An envelope that is a conductor of heat is called a *diathermic* wall, while one that conducts no heat at all is called an *adiabatic* wall.

An *isolated* system is one that can have no interaction with its surroundings. This is to be interpreted literally in the sense that an isolated system absolutely and in no way interacts with its surroundings. A *closed* system is one to which matter cannot be added and from which matter cannot be removed. An *open* system is one that permits the removal or addition of matter to a system.

The *state* of a system is defined by ascribing values to a sufficient number of variables called *state variables*. Such variables are macroscopic properties such as pressure, volume, temperature, mass, composition, surface area, position in a gravitational field, and degree of magnetization. Normally, specifying the values of only a few state variables is necessary for fixing or defining the state of a system. In a way, states of systems may be considered to occupy points in an *n*-dimensional space in which the coordinates are the state variables and the points are the states of the system. A *change of state* occurs when the numerical values of the independent variables defining the state of the system are changed or, in the analogy of an *n*-dimensional space, the state of the system moves from one point to another.

Variables are classified as *intensive* or *extensive*. The classification is best explained in terms of an operation. Consider a given system whose state is fixed and let this system be divided into two or more parts without altering the state of the entire system. Those variables whose values remain the same in any part of the system on division are called *intensive* variables. The temperature, pressure, concentration, and density are all intensive variables. Those variables whose values in any part of the divided system are different from the values of the entire system are called *extensive* variables. Thus volume is an example of an *extensive* variable. All extensive variables with which we are concerned in this book have the property that their values are proportional to the mass of the system; that is, if the mass of the system is doubled, with the values of all the intensive variables kept constant, the values of the extensive variables are doubled in magnitude.

State variables are classified also as independent or dependent variables. An *independent* variable is one to which values may be assigned arbitrarily or possibly within limits. *Dependent* variables are those variables whose value depends upon the values assigned to the independent variables. A large number of variables exist in thermodynamics. Fortunately only a limited number need be used as independent variables.

Fundamentally the state of a system is defined or fixed when values are assigned to a sufficient number of *extensive* variables so that the values of all other variables, *extensive* and *intensive*, are fixed. Generally the mass (moles) of each substance contained in the system is used as an independent, extensive variable. However, at least two other variables in addition to the masses must be used. In some cases these additional variables must be extensive and in other cases the temperature *and* pressure or the temperature *or* pressure and one other extensive variable may be used as independent variables. Values may be assigned to a sufficient number of *intensive* variables only in order to fix the values of all other *intensive* variables. But in so doing the state of the system is not defined because the values of the extensive variables are not fixed.

A *process* is the path along which a change of state takes place. Processes

7

can occur under a variety of conditions and these conditions must be carefully specified because many things may depend on the nature of the process. An *isochoric* process is one that occurs under the condition of constant volume. *Isobaric* processes take place at constant pressure. *Isothermal* processes occur under conditions of constant temperature. An iso-anything process occurs at constant "anything."

1.4   CONCLUDING COMMENTS

In this chapter we have presented the beginnings of the language of thermodynamics. In subsequent chapters this language will be enlarged and expanded until your vocabulary is sufficient for you to be conversant with the subject. We consider thermodynamics to have a logical structure and as such this structure and the uses to which it is put rest quite heavily on the exact use of language. The definitions of words like extensive variable, isochoric, isothermal, adiabatic, and diathermic must be memorized. Many of the difficulties you may encounter in the study of thermodynamics can be minimized by recalling the exact definitions of terms. We will emphasize the necessity for relying on accurate terminology throughout this text. Concepts that are initially used in their naive interpretations will be carefully defined later.

Our approach to the development of thermodynamics is classical, since it will be through the macroscopic properties of matter. The development will use the operational approach insofar as this is possible in an introductory course. In this chapter we have discussed the scope and limitations of classical thermodynamics and have indicated some of the many areas where it is useful.

Bibliography

The following books should be of interest to those reading this book. They supply additional information concerning different approaches to many of the topics presented here.

PAPERBACKS

1. Bauman, R. P., *An Introduction to Equilibrium Thermodynamics.* Englewood Cliffs, N.J.: Prentice-Hall, 1966.

2. Klotz, I., *Introduction to Chemical Thermodynamics*. New York: Benjamin, 1964.
3. Mahan, B. H., *Elementary Chemical Thermodynamics*. New York: Benjamin, 1963.
4. Nash, L. K., *Elements of Chemical Thermodynamics*. Reading, Mass.: Addison-Wesley, 1962.
5. Nash, L. K., "Resource Paper on Elementary Chemical Thermodynamics," *J. Chem. Educ.*, **42**, 64–75 (1965).
6. Planck, M., *Treatise on Thermodynamics*. New York: Dover, first American edition.
7. Waser, J. A., *Basic Chemical Thermodynamics*. New York: Benjamin, 1965.

TEXTBOOKS

1. Bent, H. A., *The Second Law*. New York: Oxford, 1965.
2. Callen, H. B., *Thermodynamics*. New York: Wiley, 1960.
3. Glasstone, S., *Thermodynamics for Chemists*. Princeton, N.J.: Van Nostrand, 1947.
4. Hatsopoulos, G. N., and Keenan, I. H., *Principles of General Thermodynamics*. New York: Wiley, 1965.
5. Kestin, J., *A Course in Thermodynamics*. Boston: Ginn (Blaisdell), 1966.
6. Klotz, I., *Chemical Thermodynamics*. New York: Benjamin, 1964.
7. Lewis, G. N., and Randall, M., (revised by K. S. Pitzer and L. Brewer), *Thermodynamics*, 2d. ed. New York: McGraw-Hill, 1961.
8. Moore, W. J., *Physical Chemistry*, 3d. ed. Englewood Cliffs, N.J.: Prentice-Hall, 1962.
9. Reynolds, C., *Thermodynamics*. New York: McGraw-Hill, 1965.
10. Vanderslice, J. T., Schamp, H. W., and Mason, E. A., *Thermodynamics*. Englewood Cliffs, N. J.,: Prentice-Hall, 1966.
11. Zemansky, M. W., *Heat and Thermodynamics*, 4th ed. New York: McGraw-Hill, 1957.
12. Zemansky, M. W., and Van Ness, H. C., *Basic Engineering Thermodynamics*. New York: McGraw-Hill, 1966.

Exercises

1.1 Describe the operational approach for defining concepts. Apply this approach to the concepts of (a) length, (b) mass, and (c) time.

1.2 What is the difference between an intensive and an extensive variable?

Of the following variables, which are intensive and which are extensive? (a) length, (b) mass, (c) time, (d) temperature, (e) pressure, (f) volume, (g) surface tension, (h) viscosity, (i) density, (j) dielectric constant, (k) specific gravity, (l) area, (m) emf of a dry cell, (n) vapor pressure of a liquid, (o) compressibility of a solid, (p) kinetic energy.

1.3 Give definitions for (a) independent variable, (b) state of a system, (c) system, (d) surroundings, (e) diathermic wall, (f) adiabatic wall, (g) process, (h) isotherm, (i) isochore, (j) isobar, (k) thermal equilibrium, (l) chemical equilibrium.

1.4 Discuss the limitations of the thermodynamic approach.

2 Mathematical Background and Preparation

The subject of thermodynamics is inextricably mathematical; indeed mathematics may be said to be the language of thermodynamics. A great part of thermodynamics is concerned with the change of a thermodynamic property with a change of some independent variable. The mathematical operations used in such calculations are simple differentiations, partial differentiations, and integrations. In addition to these operations, a student must be familiar with the ideas of exact differentials, inexact differentials, and line integrals in order to understand the basis of thermodynamics. The mathematics that will be required in this book is reviewed and discussed in this chapter. The material presented in the exercises should be mastered before continuing on to the next chapter. Throughout the chapter it is assumed that the functions discussed are continuous and well-behaved, at least within limits.

2.1 FUNCTIONS, EXPLICIT AND IMPLICIT

A dependent variable u is a function of the independent variables x and y when for every set of values assigned to x and y there is at least one value of u. The symbolism† used in this book for a function u of x and y is

† In thermodynamics the same symbol or letter may be used with as many as four different meanings. For example, the letter P may be used to designate an unspecified number, an independent variable, a dependent variable, or a function. Thus we have such statements as

$u = u(x, y)$. There may or may not be an algebraic expression giving u in terms of x and y. The functions defined in this paragraph are called explicit functions.

As an illustration, we know from experience that the pressure of a pure gas is a function of the temperature T, the volume V, and number of moles of gas n. We then can write $P = P(T, V, n)$. If we choose the volume to be the dependent variable and the pressure as the independent variable, we would write $V = V(T, P, n)$. The van der Waals equation for n moles of a real gas is

$$P = \frac{nRT}{V - nb} - a\left(\frac{n}{V}\right)^2 \tag{2.1}$$

which gives the pressure P as an explicit function of T, V, and n.

An implicit function of several variables is a function of these variables whose value is always zero, independent of the values assigned to the variables. Thus an implicit function of the variables x, y, and z may be written as $f(x, y, z) = 0$. An implicit function can always be written symbolically as an explicit function. Thus, if $f(x, y, z) = 0$, then $x = x(y, z)$, $y = y(x, z)$ or $z = z(x, y)$; of the three variables x, y, and z only two are independent. But given an algebraic expression for $f(x, y, z)$, it is not always possible or convenient to write down the algebraic explicit function. The van der Waals equation, Eq. (2.1), may be written in implicit form as

$$\left[P + a\left(\frac{n}{V}\right)^2\right][V - nb] - nRT = 0 \tag{2.2}$$

or, after expansion, as

$$PV^3 - n(Pb + RT)V^2 + n^2aV - n^3ab = 0 \tag{2.3}$$

---

(1) the pressure exerted by a gas is P atmospheres; (2) the volume of a system is a function of the pressure P; (3) the pressure P of a system is a function of the volume; and (4) the symbol $P(T, V)$ represents a function of the temperature and volume, the value of which for a given set of values of T and V gives the value of the pressure. This multiple use of the same symbol is used to avoid a great complexity of symbols. It should not lead to difficulty once the use is recognized because the meaning of the symbol usually is apparent from its use.

Both Eqs. (2.2) and (2.3) are implicit functions in the four variables n, P, T, and V. It is difficult to obtain a closed algebraic expression for V as an explicit function of T, P, and n because the equation is cubic in V.

It is assumed in thermodynamics that the functions used are well-behaved, single-valued functions between known limits; the functions may be discontinuous at certain points, such as melting points or boiling points, but these points are easily recognized.

2.2 PARTIAL DERIVATIVES

Partial derivatives arise when we differentiate a function having two or more independent variables. A partial derivative is defined as the derivative of the function with respect to one of the independent variables when all other independent variables are kept constant. As an example, let $u = 4x^2 + 2xy - cy^2$. Then the partial derivative of u with respect to x at constant y is

$$\left(\frac{\partial u}{\partial x}\right)_y = 8x + 2y \tag{2.4}$$

and the partial derivative of u with respect to y at constant x is

$$\left(\frac{\partial u}{\partial y}\right)_x = 2x - 2y \tag{2.5}$$

Similarly, for a function with three independent variables there are three partial derivatives. If $u = x^2y - xyz + 3yz^2$, then†

$$\left(\frac{\partial u}{\partial x}\right)_{y,z} = 2x - yz \tag{2.6}$$

$$\left(\frac{\partial u}{\partial y}\right)_{x,z} = x^2 - xz + 3z^2 \tag{2.7}$$

† It is very important in thermodynamics to indicate what variables are held constant (by the use of subscripts) in any partial derivative because the symbol for a partial derivative such as $\partial P/\partial T$ is ambiguous without that. Thus we may have $(\partial P/\partial T)_{V,n}$ where the volume and number of moles are kept constant, or $(\partial P/\partial T)_{E,n}$ where the energy and number of moles are kept constant.

and

$$\left(\frac{\partial u}{\partial z}\right)_{x,y} = -xy + 6yz \qquad (2.8)$$

The partial derivative of a function of two or more independent variables is also a function of the same variables.

The first-order partial derivatives defined above can be differentiated again to obtain second-order partial derivatives. The second-order partial derivatives can again be differentiated to give third-order partial derivatives, and so on. Consider the first-order derivative given in Eq. (2.6). The three second-order partial derivatives are

$$\left[\frac{\partial}{\partial x}\left(\frac{\partial u}{\partial x}\right)_{y,z}\right]_{y,z} = 2 \qquad (2.9)$$

$$\left[\frac{\partial}{\partial y}\left(\frac{\partial u}{\partial x}\right)_{y,z}\right]_{x,z} = -z \qquad (2.10)$$

and

$$\left[\frac{\partial}{\partial z}\left(\frac{\partial u}{\partial x}\right)_{y,z}\right]_{x,y} = -y \qquad (2.11)$$

There are thus nine second-order derivatives of a function having three independent variables.

An illustration of the two first-order partial derivatives of a function having two independent variables is shown in Fig. 2.1. The surface $ABCD$ represents the locus of a series of points P which define the value of u (according to the function $u = u(x, y)$ for values of x and y. u_1 is the value of u for x_1 and y_1. A plane perpendicular to the x axis is passed through the surface at any fixed value of x, say x_2. The curve EF is the intersection of this plane and the surface. The value of the partial derivative $(\partial u/\partial y)_x$, is then the slope of the curve EF. It is apparent from the figure that the value changes along the curve. Other planes can be constructed at other values of x, the intersection of which with the surface $ABCD$ define new curves, the slope of

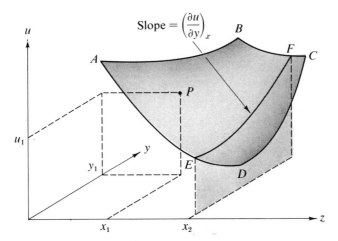

Fig. 2.1. Illustration of first-order partial derivatives.

which would be given by $(\partial u/\partial y)_x$ at various values of x. A similar set of planes and curves may be constructed for constant values of y, to evaluate the partial derivative $(\partial u/\partial x)_y$. It may be seen that both $(\partial u/\partial x)_y$ and $(\partial u/\partial y)_x$ depend on the numerical values of both x and y.

2.3   TOTAL DIFFERENTIALS

The total differential of the function $u = u(x, y)$ is defined as

$$du = \left(\frac{\partial u}{\partial x}\right)_y dx + \left(\frac{\partial u}{\partial y}\right)_x dy \qquad (2.12)$$

where $(\partial u/\partial x)_y$ and $(\partial u/\partial y)_x$ are the two first-order partial derivatives of the function and dx and dy are the differentials of the independent variables x and y, respectively. A graphical representation of the total differential of u is illustrated in Fig. 2.2 where the coordinates are u, x, and y. The shaded surface represents the function $u(x, y)$. The plane is tangent to the surface at the point P, which represents the value of u at x_1 and y_1. The lines a and b lie wholly within the plane and are drawn through the point P parallel to the x axis and the y axis, respectively. Line a then has a slope $(\partial u/\partial x)_y$ and

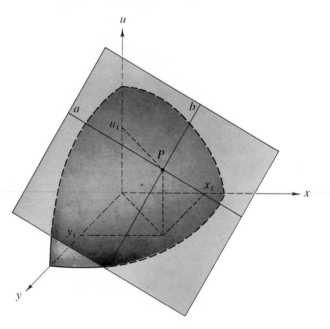

Fig. 2.2. Representation of the total differential of the function $u(x, y)$.

line b the slope $(\partial u/\partial y)_x$. The differential du for given values of dx and dy is thus the difference between the value of the coordinate u in the plane at the point $x_1 + dx$ and $y_1 + dy$ and the value of u at P.

2.4 DIFFERENTIATION OF IMPLICIT FUNCTIONS

Often partial derivatives such as $(\partial y/\partial x)_z$, $(\partial y/\partial z)_x$, and $(\partial x/\partial z)_y$ are required when the implicit function $f(x, y, z) = 0$ is given. In order to obtain such derivatives we consider the differential of the function

$$df = \left(\frac{\partial f}{\partial x}\right)_{y,z} dx + \left(\frac{\partial f}{\partial y}\right)_{x,z} dy + \left(\frac{\partial f}{\partial z}\right)_{x,y} dz = 0 \qquad (2.13)$$

The value of the differential of the function is always zero because the value of the function itself is always zero, a constant. At constant z, dz equals zero. Moreover, when z is constant, the function $f(x, y, z)$ becomes a function of x and y so that $f(x, y) = 0$ or y is a function of x. Then

$$[dy]_z = \left(\frac{\partial y}{\partial x}\right)_z [dx]_z \qquad (2.14)$$

where the brackets and subscript z are used to designate that z is constant. Equation (2.13) may now be written as

$$\left(\frac{\partial f}{\partial x}\right)_{y,z} [dx]_z + \left(\frac{\partial f}{\partial y}\right)_{x,z} \left(\frac{\partial y}{\partial x}\right)_z [dx]_z = 0 \qquad (2.15)$$

with the use of Eq. (2.14). The differential $[dx]_z$ may be canceled and Eq. (2.15) rewritten as

$$\left(\frac{\partial y}{\partial x}\right)_z = -\frac{(\partial f / \partial x)_{y,z}}{(\partial f / \partial y)_{x,z}} \qquad (2.16)$$

The mathematical operations required to get a typical partial derivative involve the differentiation of the function with respect to x at constant y and z and with respect to y at constant x and z.

2.5 RELATIONS BETWEEN PARTIAL DERIVATIVES

To determine the change in the values of the thermodynamic functions caused by a change in one or more state variables, it is necessary to express the partial derivatives of the function in terms of experimentally observable quantities. Certain relations between partial derivatives which facilitate obtaining the required expressions are developed in this section.

First consider the function $u(x, y)$. Its differential is

$$du = \left(\frac{\partial u}{\partial x}\right)_y dx + \left(\frac{\partial u}{\partial y}\right)_x dy \qquad (2.17)$$

If u is a function of x and y, then x is a function of u and y, so that $x = x(u, y)$.

17

The differential of $x(u, y)$ is

$$dx = \left(\frac{\partial x}{\partial u}\right)_y du + \left(\frac{\partial x}{\partial y}\right)_u dy \tag{2.18}$$

When Eq. (2.17) is substituted into Eq. (2.18), the equation

$$\left[1 - \left(\frac{\partial u}{\partial x}\right)_y\left(\frac{\partial x}{\partial u}\right)_y\right] dx = \left[\left(\frac{\partial x}{\partial y}\right)_u + \left(\frac{\partial x}{\partial u}\right)_y\left(\frac{\partial u}{\partial y}\right)_x\right] dy \tag{2.19}$$

is obtained. The variables x and y are independent. If y is constant, $dy = 0$ and Eq. (2.19) becomes

$$\left[1 - \left(\frac{\partial u}{\partial x}\right)_y\left(\frac{\partial x}{\partial u}\right)_y\right] dx = 0 \tag{2.20}$$

But dx may have any value and therefore the coefficient of dx must be zero. The relation

$$\left(\frac{\partial u}{\partial x}\right)_y = \frac{1}{(\partial x/\partial u)_y} \tag{2.21}$$

is thus obtained; that is, a partial derivative is equal to the reciprocal of the partial derivative between the same two variables taken in opposite order, provided the same variables are held constant. If x is constant, $dx = 0$ and the relation

$$\left(\frac{\partial x}{\partial y}\right)_u + \left(\frac{\partial x}{\partial u}\right)_y\left(\frac{\partial u}{\partial y}\right)_x = 0 \tag{2.22}$$

is obtained by the use of the same arguments. Equation (2.22) may be written in several different forms such as

$$\left(\frac{\partial x}{\partial y}\right)_u = -\frac{(\partial u/\partial y)_x}{(\partial u/\partial x)_y} \tag{2.23}$$

or

$$\left(\frac{\partial u}{\partial x}\right)_y \left(\frac{\partial x}{\partial y}\right)_u \left(\frac{\partial y}{\partial u}\right)_x = -1 \tag{2.24}$$

Note that Eq. (2.23) is similar to Eq. (2.16). Such equations are valid for any three variables of which only two are independent. Also note in Eq. (2.24) that each variable appears once in the numerator, once in the denominator, and once as a subscript—and especially note the minus sign.

Consider again the function $u(x, y)$ whose differential is given by Eq. (2.17), but assume that y is a function of x and s so that $y = y(x, s)$. The differential of y in terms of x and s is

$$dy = \left(\frac{\partial y}{\partial x}\right)_s dx + \left(\frac{\partial y}{\partial s}\right)_x ds \tag{2.25}$$

But if $u = u(x, y)$ and $y = y(x, s)$, then $u = u(x, s)$; that is, u is a function of x and s and its differential is

$$du = \left(\frac{\partial u}{\partial x}\right)_s dx + \left(\frac{\partial u}{\partial s}\right)_x ds \tag{2.26}$$

When Eq. (2.25) is substituted into Eq. (2.17), the equation

$$du = \left[\left(\frac{\partial u}{\partial x}\right)_y + \left(\frac{\partial u}{\partial y}\right)_x \left(\frac{\partial y}{\partial x}\right)_s\right] dx + \left(\frac{\partial u}{\partial y}\right)_x \left(\frac{\partial y}{\partial s}\right)_x ds \tag{2.27}$$

is obtained. Equations (2.26) and (2.27) are identities and therefore the coefficients of dx and ds in them must be the same:

$$\left(\frac{\partial u}{\partial x}\right)_s = \left(\frac{\partial u}{\partial x}\right)_y + \left(\frac{\partial u}{\partial y}\right)_x \left(\frac{\partial y}{\partial x}\right)_s \tag{2.28}$$

and

$$\left(\frac{\partial u}{\partial s}\right)_x = \left(\frac{\partial u}{\partial y}\right)_x \left(\frac{\partial y}{\partial s}\right)_x \tag{2.29}$$

19

Equation (2.28) gives the relation between two partial derivatives of the same two variables but with different variables constant when the two constant variables are functions of each other; that is, y is a function of s and x or s is a function of y and x. Equation (2.29) affords a means of introducing a new variable when that variable is a function of the two original independent variables.

Additional relations are obtained when the two original independent variables may be taken as functions of two other independent variables. Thus we may have $u = u(x, y)$ but $x = x(s, t)$ and $y = y(s, t)$. In such a case, u is also a function of s and t, $u = u(s, t)$. The differentials of these four functions are: Eq. (2.17), and

$$dx = \left(\frac{\partial x}{\partial s}\right)_t ds + \left(\frac{\partial x}{\partial t}\right)_s dt$$

$$dy = \left(\frac{\partial y}{\partial s}\right)_t ds + \left(\frac{\partial y}{\partial t}\right)_s dt$$

(2.30)

and

$$du = \left(\frac{\partial u}{\partial s}\right)_t ds + \left(\frac{\partial u}{\partial t}\right)_s dt \qquad (2.31)$$

The substitution of Eqs. (2.30) and (2.31) into Eq. (2.17) yields the relation

$$du = \left[\left(\frac{\partial u}{\partial x}\right)_y \left(\frac{\partial x}{\partial s}\right)_t + \left(\frac{\partial u}{\partial y}\right)_x \left(\frac{\partial y}{\partial s}\right)_t\right] ds$$

$$+ \left[\left(\frac{\partial u}{\partial x}\right)_y \left(\frac{\partial x}{\partial t}\right)_s + \left(\frac{\partial u}{\partial y}\right)_x \left(\frac{\partial y}{\partial t}\right)_s\right] dt$$

(2.32)

Equations (2.31) and (2.32) are identities and therefore

$$\left(\frac{\partial u}{\partial s}\right)_t = \left(\frac{\partial u}{\partial x}\right)_y \left(\frac{\partial x}{\partial s}\right)_t + \left(\frac{\partial u}{\partial y}\right)_x \left(\frac{\partial y}{\partial s}\right)_t \qquad (2.33)$$

and

$$\left(\frac{\partial u}{\partial t}\right)_s = \left(\frac{\partial u}{\partial x}\right)_y \left(\frac{\partial x}{\partial t}\right)_s + \left(\frac{\partial u}{\partial y}\right)_x \left(\frac{\partial y}{\partial t}\right)_s \qquad (2.34)$$

The derivation of similar equations involving three or more independent variables follows the same methods.

2.6 ORDINARY INTEGRATION

The operation of integration is the inverse of that of differentiation, thus the integral of a function of x, $f(x)$, is the function of x whose derivative is $f(x)$. Consider a function $f(x)$ which is to be integrated and let $y(x)$ be the integral of $f(x)$. Then the derivative dy/dx equals $f(x)$:

$$\frac{dy}{dx} = f(x) \qquad (2.35)$$

The differential of y also is given by

$$dy = \left(\frac{dy}{dx}\right) dx \qquad (2.36)$$

The combination of these two equations gives

$$dy = f(x)\, dx$$

Upon integration, the equation

$$y(x) = \int dy = \int f(x)\, dx \qquad (2.37)$$

is obtained. The expression given in Eq. (2.37) is complete except for a constant term. If the function $y(x)$ contains a constant term, that term does not affect the derivative $f(x)$ because the derivative of a constant is zero. Consequently, on integrating the function $f(x)$, the constant term must be added to the integral. For emphasis, Eq. (2.37) may be written as

$$y(x) = \int f(x)\, dx + I \tag{2.38}$$

where I represents the constant term, the integration constant. The constant term can be evaluated if we know the value of $y(x)$ at some value of x, say x_1; thus, from Eq. (2.38),

$$I = y(x_1) - \left[\int f(x)\, dx \right]_{x_1} \tag{2.39}$$

where the subscript on the last term is used to indicate that the integral is to be evaluated at x_1. The integrals obtained by the method discussed in this paragraph are called *indefinite* integrals.

The *definite* integral is the integral of a function $f(x)$ between two limits, an upper and lower limit, which are fixed values of the independent variable. Let x_1 represent the lower limit and x_2 represent the upper limit. The definite integral of a function $f(x)$ between the limits x_1 and x_2 is

$$\int_{x_1}^{x_2} f(x)\, dx = \left[\int f(x)\, dx \right]_{x_2} - \left[\int f(x)\, dx \right]_{x_1} \tag{2.40}$$

where the first term on the right-hand side of the equation indicates that the integral is to be evaluated at x_2 and the second term indicates that the integral is to be evaluated at x_1. By comparison of Eqs. (2.38), (2.39), and (2.40) we see that

$$y(x_2) - y(x_1) = \int_{x_1}^{x_2} f(x)\, dx \tag{2.41}$$

which shows that the value of a definite integral between the limits x_1 and x_2 is the difference in the values of the integral $y(x)$ at the two limits. According to Eq. (2.41) the sign of the definite integral is changed when the order of the limits is reversed. It may be emphasized that an indefinite integration yields a function while a definite integration yields a number.

We may note that the definite integral of a function $f(x)$ between the limits x_1 and x_2 is represented by the area under the curve between the limits when the function $f(x)$ is plotted as the ordinate against the variable x as the abscissa. The curve in Fig. 2.3 represents such a function $f(x)$. The value of

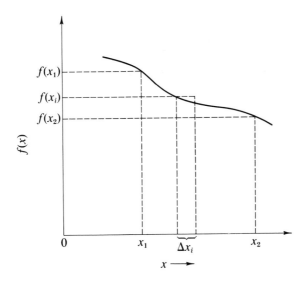

Fig. 2.3. Ordinary integration of $f(x)$.

the integral $\int_{x_1}^{x_2} f(x)\,dx$ is the area under the curve between the lines designated as x_1 and x_2. We may consider that the area between the limits is divided into a large number of rectangles, only one of which is shown in the figure. The area of the rectangle illustrated is $f(x_i)\,\Delta x_i$. The integral is the sum of the areas of all such rectangles in the limit as Δx_i approaches zero.

A combination of the concepts of an indefinite and definite integral is made possible if we set a fixed value to the lower limit, say x_1, and allow the upper limit to be variable. According to Eqs. (2.37), (2.40), and (2.41), the integral could be written as

$$y(x) - y(x_1) = \int_{y(x_1)}^{y(x)} dy = \int_{x_1}^{x} f(x)\,dx \qquad (2.42)$$

23

or

$$y(x) - y(x_1) = \int f(x)\, dx - \left[\int f(x)\, dx \right]_{x_1} \tag{2.43}$$

In this case $y(x)$ is a function of x. Comparison of Eq. (2.43) with Eqs. (2.38) and (2.39) shows that the integral here is the equivalent of the indefinite integral after the integration constant has been evaluated.

The integration of functions of two independent variables which are known to be partial derivatives of another function is basically the same as the integration of a function having a single independent variable. Consider the integration of a function $f(x, y)$ which is known to be the partial derivative of another function $u(x, y)$ with respect to x at constant y. Then

$$\left(\frac{\partial u}{\partial x} \right)_y = f(x, y) \tag{2.44}$$

and the differential of u at constant y is given by

$$[du]_y = \left(\frac{\partial u}{\partial x} \right)_y dx = f(x, y)\, dx \tag{2.45}$$

The indefinite integral is represented by the equation

$$u(x, y) = \int f(x, y)\, dx + I(y) \tag{2.46}$$

In the actual operations the variable y is treated as a constant. Thus the integration constant is actually a function of y and this function may be unknown. As an example, let $f(x, y)$ be

$$f(x, y) = ax^2 + bxy + cy^2 \tag{2.47}$$

This equation can be written as

$$f(x, y) = ax^2 + \beta(y)x + \gamma(y) \tag{2.48}$$

where $\beta(y)$ and $\gamma(y)$ are functions of y and equal to by and cy^2, respectively.

24

The function $u(x, y)$ is then

$$u(x, y) = \tfrac{1}{3}ax^3 + \tfrac{1}{2}\beta(y)x^2 + \gamma(y)x + I(y) \tag{2.49}$$

$$u(x, y) = \tfrac{1}{3}ax^3 + \tfrac{1}{2}byx^2 + cy^2x + I(y) \tag{2.50}$$

The definite integral of a function $f(x, y)$ which is known to be equal to $(\partial u/\partial x)_y$ is represented as

$$
\begin{aligned}
u(x_2, y^*) - u(x_1, y^*) &= \int_{u(x_1,y^*)}^{u(x_2,y^*)} [du]_y \\
&= \int_{x_1}^{x_2} f(x, y^*)\, dy
\end{aligned}
\tag{2.51}
$$

and

$$
u(x_2, y^*) - u(x_1, y^*) = \left[\int f(x, y^*)\, dx \right]_{x_2,y^*} - \left[\int f(x, y^*)\, dx \right]_{x_1,y^*} \tag{2.52}
$$

Here the asterisk is used to emphasize not only that y is held constant in the integration but also that, in order to evaluate the definite integral, y must be assigned a fixed and constant value. Thus the value of the definite integral depends upon the chosen value of y.

2.7   INTEGRATION OF A TOTAL DIFFERENTIAL

The total differential of a function $u(x, y)$ has been defined in Eq. (2.12) to be

$$du = \left(\frac{\partial u}{\partial x}\right)_y dx + \left(\frac{\partial u}{\partial y}\right)_x dy \tag{2.53}$$

The inverse problem is: Given the total differential of a function of x and y as

$$du = M(x, y)\, dx + N(x, y)\, dy \tag{2.54}$$

25

where $M(x, y)$ and $N(x, y)$ are both functions of x and y, find the function $u(x, y)$ by integration. The integral $\int M(x, y) \, dx$, integrated by holding y constant, will give all terms containing the variable x, by Eq. (2.46). The integral $\int N(x, y) \, dy$, integrated by holding x constant will give all terms containing y. However, only those terms containing y alone are retained because the terms containing both x and y are already obtained in the first integral. Finally one integration constant is required. For example, consider the total differential

$$du = \left(2ax + \frac{b}{y}\right) dx - \left(\frac{bx}{y^2} + \frac{2c}{y^3}\right) dy \qquad (2.55)$$

First

$$\int \left(2ax + \frac{b}{y}\right) dx = ax^2 + \frac{bx}{y} \qquad (2.56)$$

Second

$$-\int \left(\frac{bx}{y^2} + \frac{2c}{y^3}\right) dy = \frac{bx}{y} + \frac{c}{y^2} \qquad (2.57)$$

The function $u(x, y)$ is then

$$u(x, y) = ax^2 + \frac{bx}{y} + \frac{c}{y^2} + I \qquad (2.58)$$

We may express the definite integral of a total differential as

$$\int_{u_1}^{u_2} du = \int_{x_1, y_1}^{x_2, y_2} [M(x, y) \, dx + N(x, y)] \, dy \qquad (2.59)$$

If the function $u(x, y)$ is obtained by the method of integration discussed in the previous paragraph, then it is apparent that

$$\int_{u_1}^{u_2} du = u(x_2, y_2) - u(x_1, y_1) \qquad (2.60)$$

and the value of the integral is equal to the difference in the values of the function at the two limits. A second method of integration may be expressed by the equations

$$\int_{u_1}^{u_2} du = \int_{x_1}^{x_2} M(x, y_1)\, dx + \int_{y_1}^{y_2} N(x_2, y)\, dy \tag{2.61}$$

$$\int_{u_1}^{u_2} du = \int_{y_1}^{y_2} N(x_1, y)\, dy + \int_{x_1}^{x_2} M(x, y_2)\, dx \tag{2.62}$$

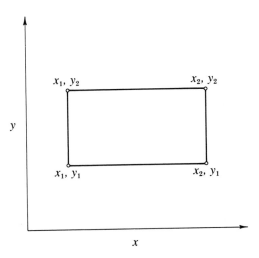

Fig. 2.4. Integration along two different paths.

These two equations correspond to the integration along two different paths, illustrated in Fig. 2.4. In Eq. (2.61), the first integral on the right side is determined between the two points (x_1, y_1) and (x_2, y_1) and the second integral is determined between the points (x_2, y_1) and (x_2, y_2). In Eq. (2.62), the first integral is between the points (x_1, y_1) and (x_1, y_2) and the second integral is between the points (x_1, y_2) and (x_2, y_2). It is also instructive to point out that

$$\int_{x_1}^{x_2} M(x, y_1)\, dx = u(x_2, y_1) - u(x_1, y_1) \tag{2.63}$$

27

and

$$\int_{y_1}^{y_2} N(x_2, y)\, dy = u(x_2, y_2) - u(x_2, y_1) \tag{2.64}$$

so that the sum of the two integrals given in Eq. (2.61) is equal to the integral given in Eq. (2.60). Exactly the same result is obtained for Eq. (2.62). Therefore *the value of the definite integral of a total differential of a function depends only upon the values of the function at the end points and not at all upon the path of integration*. Moreover, if the two end points are identical, the value of the definite integral is zero.

2.8 LINE INTEGRALS

Differential expressions of the form

$$d\phi = P(x, y)\, dx + Q(x, y)\, dy \tag{2.65}$$

for two independent variables are often met in the physical sciences and engineering. The quantity $d\phi$ is a small increment, when dx and dy are small, of some quantity ϕ, which may or may not be a function of x and y. (In Section 2.7 u was known to be a function of x and y.) The integral of such expressions between two points (x_1, y_1) and (x_2, y_2) can be determined along some particular path connecting the two points, since $d\phi$ can be calculated from Eq. (2.65) for each part of a specific path. The integral is the summation of the quantities, $d\phi$, obtained as one moves along the curve. Such integrals are called line or contour integrals.

The value of a line integral between two points depends in general upon the path followed in determining the integral. As an example, let us evaluate the line integral

$$\int (y\, dx - x\, dy) \tag{2.66}$$

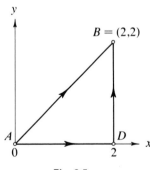

Fig. 2.5

from A to B in Fig. 2.5 along the two different paths $A = (0, 0)$ to $B = (2, 2)$ and $A = (0, 0)$ to $D = (2, 0)$ to $B = (2, 2)$. Along the line AB, $y = x$ and $y\,dx - x\,dy = x\,dx = 0$, so that $\int_{AB}(y\,dx - x\,dy) = 0$. Along AD, $y = 0$ and $dy = 0$, so that $y\,dx - x\,dy = 0$. But along DB, $x = 2$, $dx = 0$, and $y\,dx - x\,dy = -2dy$. Thus

$$\int_{ADB} (y\,dx - x\,dy) = \int_{DB} -2dy = \int_0^2 - 2dy = -4 \qquad (2.67)$$

It is readily shown also that the value of a line integral depends upon the path of integration when the curve of integration can be expressed as a function of one independent variable. Consider the integral

$$_L\int_{x_1,y_1}^{x_2,y_2} d\phi = {}_L\int_{x_1,y_1}^{x_2,y_2} [P(x, y)\,dx + Q(x, y)]\,dy \qquad (2.68)$$

along some path L. However, let y be a function of x so that $y = y(x)$ and $dy = (dy/dx)\,dx$. Equation (2.68) becomes

$$_L\int_{x_1}^{x_2} d\phi = \int_{x_1}^{x_2} \left[P(x, y(x)) + Q(x, y(x))\frac{dy}{dx} \right] dx \qquad (2.69)$$

The line integral has now been reduced to an ordinary integral with one independent variable. But the value of the integral depends upon the particular function chosen for $y(x)$.

A line integral of special interest occurs when the path of integration is a closed curve, that is, the initial and final points are identical. Such integrals are called *cyclic* integrals and the symbo' used is generally $\oint$. Thus the cyclic integral of the differential expression given by Eq. (2.65) is represented as

$$\oint d\phi = \oint [P(x, y)\,dx + Q(x, y)\,dy] \qquad (2.70)$$

The value of the integral is determined by traversing the closed curve, usually in a counterclockwise direction. Green's theorem states that under certain conditions

$$\oint_L [P(x, y)\, dx + Q(x, y)\, dy] = \int_S \int \left[\left(\frac{\partial Q}{\partial x} \right)_y - \left(\frac{\partial P}{\partial y} \right)_x \right] dx\, dy \qquad (2.71)$$

The right-hand side of Eq. (2.71) represents the double integral over the surface enclosed by the curve.

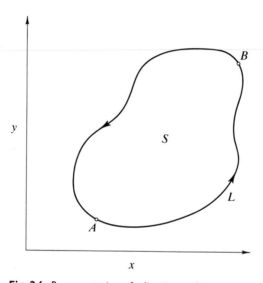

Fig. 2.6. Representation of a line integral.

These concepts are illustrated in Fig. 2.6 where a closed curve L is drawn in the x-y plane. The two points A and B are any two points on the curve, chosen arbitrarily. If we start at point A, the cyclic integral represented by Eq. (2.70) is evaluated by traversing the curve from A in the direction indicated by the arrows back to A. Green's theorem states that the cyclic integral is equal to the double integral taken over the surface S enclosed by the curve L. The conditions for this to be true are that $P(x, y)$, $Q(x, y)$, $(\partial P/\partial y)_x$, and $(\partial Q/\partial x)_y$ are continuous functions of x and y both along the curve L and in the surface S.

2.9 EXACT AND INEXACT DIFFERENTIALS

A special case occurs when the cyclic integral of a differential expression given by Eq. (2.65) equals zero for every closed curve. According to Green's theorem, $(\partial Q/\partial x)_y$ must then equal $(\partial P/\partial y)_x$. When such conditions hold, the differential expression is said to be *exact* and $d\phi$ is said to be an *exact differential*. Otherwise the differential expression is said to be *inexact*. These concepts can be developed further by referring to Fig. 2.6. If

$$\oint d\phi = \oint [P(x, y)\, dx + Q(x, y)\, dy] = 0 \tag{2.72}$$

the line integral of this same quantity from A to B is equal and opposite to the line integral from B to A, so that

$$L\int_A^B d\phi = -L\int_B^A d\phi \tag{2.73}$$

If this condition is true for any cyclic path, the line integral from A to B, $L\int_A^B d\phi$, must be independent of the path and its value can depend only on the two points A and B. The definite integral of a total differential of a function of x and y has been shown in Section 2.7 to be independent of the path. We therefore conclude that if $d\phi$ is an exact differential, then $d\phi$ is the differential of a function of x and y. The condition of exactness is that

$$\left(\frac{\partial Q}{\partial x}\right)_y = \left(\frac{\partial P}{\partial y}\right)_x \tag{2.74}$$

from Green's theorem.

It may readily be proved that the condition (2.74) is equivalent to Euler's reciprocity relation. If ϕ is a function of x and y, the total differential of ϕ is given by

$$d\phi = \left(\frac{\partial \phi}{\partial x}\right)_y dx + \left(\frac{\partial \phi}{\partial y}\right)_x dy \tag{2.75}$$

If $d\phi$ is given by the differential expression

$$d\phi = P(x, y)\, dx + Q(x, y)\, dy \qquad (2.76)$$

and ϕ is known to be a function of x and y, then

$$P(x, y) = \left(\frac{\partial \phi}{\partial x}\right)_y \qquad (2.77)$$

and

$$Q(x, y) = \left(\frac{\partial \phi}{\partial y}\right)_x \qquad (2.78)$$

The condition of exactness is given by Eq. (2.74). Therefore

$$\left[\frac{\partial}{\partial y}\left(\frac{\partial \phi}{\partial x}\right)_y\right]_x = \left[\frac{\partial}{\partial x}\left(\frac{\partial \phi}{\partial y}\right)_x\right]_y \qquad (2.79)$$

which is Euler's reciprocity relation.

The concepts of line integrals, exact differentials, and inexact differentials may be summarized as follows:

We are concerned with the differential expression

$$d\phi = P(x, y)\, dx + Q(x, y)\, dy$$

The integration of such an expression is carried out along a designated path or curve between two points (x_1, y_1) and (x_2, y_2) or along a closed curve.

If the line integral $_L\int_{x_1,y_1}^{x_2,y_2} d\phi$ depends upon the path along which the integration is performed, or if $\oint d\phi$ is not equal to zero, then the expression is inexact. There is no function $\phi(x, y)$ whose total differential is given by $P(x, y)\, dx + Q(x, y)\, dy$.

If the line integral $_L\int_{x_1,y_1}^{x_2,y_2} d\phi$ does not depend upon the path along which the integration is performed, or, if $\oint d\phi$ equals zero for every cyclic path, then

$d\phi$ is an exact differential. A function $\phi(x, y)$ does exist. The total differential of the function is equal to $P(x, y)\, dx + Q(x, y)\, dy$. If $d\phi$ is exact, then $(\partial P/\partial y)_x$ must equal $(\partial Q/\partial x)_y$.

In order to distinguish between exact and inexact differentials symbolically in this book, a bar is drawn through the d of the differential sign of an inexact differential as $đ\phi$ (see Chapter 5).

2.10   EXACT DIFFERENTIALS AND THERMODYNAMIC PROPERTIES

Let us consider some of the properties of the exact differential $dG(x, y)$ and the function $G(x, y)$. First the integral of $dG(x, y)$ between any two points will be a function of the end points only and will be independent of the path. This may be represented as

$$\int_A^B dG(x, y) = G(x, y)\Big|_A^B = G_B - G_A = \Delta G \tag{2.80}$$

The term ΔG is then just $G_B - G_A$ and its value is dependent on the difference $G_B - G_A$ and not on the path in between. Further, the cyclical integral becomes

$$\oint dG(x, y) = \int_A^B dG(x, y) + \int_B^A dG(x, y) = 0 \tag{2.81}$$

or

$$\int_A^B dG(x, y) = -\int_B^A dG(x, y) \tag{2.82}$$

Any property of a system the differential of which is an exact differential is called a *thermodynamic property*. In Chapter 1 in discussing the idea of the state of a system, we indicated that states may be considered to be points in an n-dimensional space where the coordinates are the macroscopic properties or state variables. In this analogy a thermodynamic property is one that can be considered to be characteristic of a given state. Then a change in a thermodynamic property $\Delta G = G_B - G_A$ is the difference in that property between the two states. This difference, being independent of the path between the states, is a measure of the change in the thermodynamic property in going from one state to another. For example, the potential energy of a mass in a gravitational field is a function of height, but is not dependent on the path followed in raising the mass to any given height.

2.11 COMMONLY USED DERIVATIVES, INTEGRALS, AND MISCELLANEOUS RELATIONS

For the convenience of the student we reproduce here some commonly used derivatives, integrals, and miscellaneous mathematical relations.

Derivatives

1. $\dfrac{d(au)}{dx} = a\dfrac{du}{dx}$ (a is a constant)

2. $\dfrac{d(u + v)}{dx} = \dfrac{du}{dx} + \dfrac{dv}{dx}$

3. $\dfrac{d(uv)}{dx} = v\dfrac{du}{dx} + u\dfrac{dv}{dx}$

4. $\dfrac{d(u/v)}{dx} = \dfrac{\left(v\dfrac{du}{dx} - u\dfrac{dv}{dx}\right)}{v^2}$

5. $\dfrac{df(u)}{dx} = \left(\dfrac{df(u)}{du}\right)\left(\dfrac{du}{dx}\right)$

6. $\dfrac{dx^n}{dx} = nx^{n-1}$

7. $\dfrac{de^x}{dx} = e^x$

8. $\dfrac{da^u}{dx} = (a^u)\left(\dfrac{du}{dx}\right)(\ln a)$

9. $\dfrac{dx^x}{dx} = x^x(1 + \ln x)$

10. $\dfrac{d(\log_a x)}{dx} = \dfrac{1}{x \ln a} = \dfrac{\log a^e}{x}$

Integrals (Fundamental Forms)

1. $\displaystyle\int a\, dx = ax$

2. $\displaystyle\int af(x)\, dx = a\int f(x)\, dx$

3. $\displaystyle\int \dfrac{dx}{x} = \int d\ln x = \ln x$

4. $\displaystyle\int x^m\, dx = \dfrac{x^{m+1}}{m+1}$ (when $m \neq -1$)

5. $\displaystyle\int e^x\, dx = e^x$

6. $\displaystyle\int (u+v)\, dx = \int u\, dx + \int v\, dx$

7. $\displaystyle\int u\, dv = uv - \int v\, du$

8. $\displaystyle\int u\dfrac{dv}{dx}\, dx = uv - \int v\dfrac{du}{dx}\, dx$

35

Miscellaneous Mathematical Information

1. $\ln = \log_e$ (and will be used this way throughout the book)

2. $\log = \log_{10}$

3. $e = 2.318$

4. $\log e = 0.4343$

5. $\ln 10 = 2.303$

6. $2.303 \log x = \ln x$

2.12 CONCLUDING COMMENTS

This chapter contains the mathematical background that is necessary for work in thermodynamics. Most derivatives that are used in thermodynamics are partial derivatives and the majority of mathematical operations involve simple differentiation and integration. The problem is to keep track of what variables are independent and what variables are dependent in any given problem.

We shall see that the concepts of line integrals, exact differentials, and inexact differentials are important in understanding the mathematical distinctions between heat and work on one hand and the thermodynamic functions on the other. The differential quantities of heat and work are inexact differentials. The concept of exact differentials and the condition for exactness will be used in defining the energy function and the entropy function and in deriving certain relations between specific partial derivatives.

Exercises

2.1 Write expressions for the total differential for each of the following functions: (a) $u = u(x, y, z)$; (b) $A = A(B, C)$; (c) $M = M(P, Q, R, T)$; (d) $P = P(V, T, n)$; (e) $V = V(r, \theta)$.

2.2   Test the following expressions for exactness:

(a) $P\,dx + Q\,dy = (3x^2 + 2xy^3)\,dx + (3x^2y^2 + 2y)\,dy$.

(b) $P\,dx + Q\,dy = (x^3 + 12x^2y)\,dx + (2y + 4x^3)\,dy$.

(c) $P\,dx + Q\,dy = (x^2 + y^2)(x\,dx + y\,dy)$.

(d) $P\,dx + Q\,dy = (x^3 + 2x^2y^2)\,dx + (3x^2 + 4x^2y^2)\,dy$.

(e) $P\,dx + Q\,dy = (xy)\,dx + (xy)\,dy$.

(f) $P\,dx + Q\,dy = (x + y)\,dx + (x + y)\,dy$.

(g) $P\,dx + Q\,dy = (2x + y^2)\,dx + (x^2 + 2y)\,dy$.

2.3   Given that $z = ax^2y + by + cxy^3$ where a, b, and c are constants, show that

(a) $\left(\dfrac{\partial z}{\partial x}\right)_y = 2axy + cy^3$;

(b) $\left(\dfrac{\partial z}{\partial y}\right)_x = ax^2 + b + 3cxy^2$

(c) $\left(\dfrac{\partial x}{\partial y}\right)_z = -(ax^2 + b + 3cxy^2)/(2axy + cy^3)$;

(d) dz is an exact differential;

(e) $\left(\dfrac{\partial z}{\partial x}\right)_y \left(\dfrac{\partial y}{\partial z}\right)_x \left(\dfrac{\partial x}{\partial y}\right)_z = -1$.

2.4   Given that

$$P = \frac{RT}{V} + \frac{a + bT}{V^2}$$

where R, a, and b are constants, show that

(a) $\left(\dfrac{\partial P}{\partial T}\right)_V = \dfrac{R}{V} + \dfrac{b}{V^2}$;

(b) $\left(\dfrac{\partial P}{\partial V}\right)_T = -\dfrac{RT}{V^2} - \dfrac{2(a + bT)}{V^3}$;

(c) $\left(\dfrac{\partial V}{\partial T}\right)_P = \dfrac{R + (b/V)}{P + (a + bT)/V^2}$.

(d) dP is an exact differential;

(e) $\left(\dfrac{\partial P}{\partial T}\right)_V \left(\dfrac{\partial T}{\partial V}\right)_P \left(\dfrac{\partial V}{\partial P}\right)_T = -1.$

2.5 The differential dz is given as

$$dz = ax^2 y\, dx + \left(\frac{ax^3}{3} + c\right) dy.$$

Integrate the expression to obtain

$$z = \frac{ax^3 y}{3} + cy + I$$

where I is a constant. Prove the result by differentiation.

2.6 Given $dz = (x + y)\, dx + y\, dy$, (a) show that this differential is not exact; (b) obtain the integral of this expression between the limits z_2 and z_1 and x_2 and x_1 under the conditions that (i) $y = ax$ and (ii) $y = bx^2$.

2.7 Given A as a function of any two of the variables B, C, and D, prove that

$$\left(\frac{\partial A}{\partial C}\right)_B \left(\frac{\partial C}{\partial B}\right)_D = -\left(\frac{\partial A}{\partial D}\right)_B \left(\frac{\partial D}{\partial B}\right)_C$$

2.8 Consider circular segments of radius r and width θ (in degrees, and less than 360 deg). The area is given by $A = \pi r^2 \theta/360$ and the perimeter by $P = 2\pi r\theta/360$. Evaluate the following partial derivatives:

(a) $\left(\dfrac{\partial A}{\partial r}\right)_\theta$; (b) $\left(\dfrac{\partial A}{\partial \theta}\right)_r$;

(c) $\left(\dfrac{\partial \theta}{\partial r}\right)_A$; (d) $\left(\dfrac{\partial P}{\partial r}\right)_\theta$;

(e) $\left(\dfrac{\partial \theta}{\partial r}\right)_P$; (f) $\left(\dfrac{\partial P}{\partial A}\right)_\theta$;

(g) $\left(\dfrac{\partial P}{\partial A}\right)_r$; (h) $\left(\dfrac{\partial A}{\partial r}\right)_\theta\left(\dfrac{\partial r}{\partial \theta}\right)_A$.

(i) Is dA an exact differential?

2.9 Given

$$du = (2ax + byz)\,dx + (bxz + 2cyz)\,dy + (bxy + cy^2 + 2ez)\,dz$$

show that

$$u = ax^2 + bxyz + cyz^2 + dy + ez^2 + I$$

where I is an integration constant.

2.10 Given $ax^2y + bxy^2 + c = 0$, (a) obtain x as an explicit function of y; (b) obtain an expression for the derivative dy/dx in terms of x and y.

2.11 Given the function $S(T, P)$, show that

$$\left(\frac{\partial P}{\partial T}\right)_S = -\frac{(\partial S/\partial T)_P}{(\partial S/\partial P)_T}$$

2.12 Given the functions $S = S(T, P)$ and $P = P(T, V)$, show that

$$\left(\frac{\partial S}{\partial T}\right)_V = \left(\frac{\partial S}{\partial T}\right)_P + \left(\frac{\partial S}{\partial P}\right)_T\left(\frac{\partial P}{\partial T}\right)_V$$

2.13   Given $u = u(x, y, z)$; $y = y(x, s)$; $z = z(x, t)$, show that

(a) $\left(\dfrac{\partial u}{\partial x}\right)_{s,t} = \left(\dfrac{\partial u}{\partial x}\right)_{y,z} + \left(\dfrac{\partial u}{\partial y}\right)_{x,z}\left(\dfrac{\partial y}{\partial x}\right)_{s} + \left(\dfrac{\partial u}{\partial z}\right)_{x,y}\left(\dfrac{\partial z}{\partial x}\right)_{t}$;

(b) $\left(\dfrac{\partial u}{\partial s}\right)_{x,t} = \left(\dfrac{\partial u}{\partial y}\right)_{x,z}\left(\dfrac{\partial y}{\partial s}\right)_{x}$;

(c) $\left(\dfrac{\partial u}{\partial t}\right)_{x,s} = \left(\dfrac{\partial u}{\partial z}\right)_{x,z}\left(\dfrac{\partial z}{\partial t}\right)_{x}$.

2.14   Given the implicit function $f(x, y, z) = 0$, prove

(a) $\left(\dfrac{\partial x}{\partial z}\right)_{y} = -\dfrac{(\partial f/\partial z)_{x,y}}{(\partial f/\partial x)_{y,z}}$;

(b) $\left(\dfrac{\partial y}{\partial z}\right)_{x} = -\dfrac{(\partial f/\partial z)_{x,y}}{(\partial f/\partial y)_{x,z}}$.

3 Equations of State—Ideal and Real Gases

For the purpose of accurately describing the behavior of systems in nature we have recourse to finding mathematical relations between characteristic determinable properties of systems. The extension of a spring can be readily related to the force exerted on the spring. Within the realm of thermodynamics we will find that the mathematical relations are a bit more complicated than for the case of a spring, and that some of the phenomena examined are removed from direct observation and determinable only through derived or secondary relations. This characteristic of thermodynamics will present little difficulty if you adhere to the careful definition of terms and ideas.

Many of the properties of one-component single-phase systems such as gases, liquids, or solids are describable in terms of four variables: pressure, P; volume, V; temperature, T†; and number of moles, n.‡ A mathematical expression relating these four variables is called an equation of state. The mathematical relations developed in Chapter 2 are applied in this chapter to equations of state. General relations are first discussed and then specific equations of state for ideal and real gases are presented.

† The concept of temperature and the definition of the Kelvin or absolute temperature scale is presented in the next chapter. For the purposes of this chapter, a knowledge of the Kelvin temperature scale is assumed.

‡ The mass is the actual quantity measured experimentally. The number of moles is calculated by dividing the mass by the appropriate molecular weight.

3.1 GENERAL CONSIDERATIONS

If the four variables P, V, T, and n are related by an equation of state, three of the four variables are independent while the fourth is dependent. Four different ways of expressing the equations of state are possible, depending upon what variables are chosen as independent. Thus we may write

$$P = P(V, T, n) \tag{3.1}$$

$$V = V(P, T, n) \tag{3.2}$$

$$T = T(P, V, n) \tag{3.3}$$

or

$$n = n(P, V, T) \tag{3.4}$$

These four equations state that the pressure of the system is a function of its volume, temperature, and the number of moles contained in the system; the volume of the system is a function of its pressure, temperature, and number of moles; the temperature of the system is a function of its pressure, volume, and number of moles; and finally the number of moles of substance in the system is a function of the pressure, volume, and temperature. The experimental measurement of three of the variables permits the calculation of the value of the fourth when a suitable algebraic expression for the equation of state is known.

The total differentials of the functions given in Eqs. (3.1), (3.2), (3.3), and (3.4) are

$$dP = \left(\frac{\partial P}{\partial T}\right)_{V,n} dT + \left(\frac{\partial P}{\partial V}\right)_{T,n} dV + \left(\frac{\partial P}{\partial n}\right)_{T,V} dn \tag{3.5}$$

$$dV = \left(\frac{\partial V}{\partial P}\right)_{T,n} dP + \left(\frac{\partial V}{\partial T}\right)_{P,n} dT + \left(\frac{\partial V}{\partial n}\right)_{T,P} dn \tag{3.6}$$

$$dT = \left(\frac{\partial T}{\partial P}\right)_{V,n} dP + \left(\frac{\partial T}{\partial V}\right)_{P,n} dV + \left(\frac{\partial T}{\partial n}\right)_{P,V} dn \tag{3.7}$$

and

$$dn = \left(\frac{\partial n}{\partial P}\right)_{T,V} dP + \left(\frac{\partial n}{\partial V}\right)_{P,T} dV + \left(\frac{\partial n}{\partial T}\right)_{P,V} dT \qquad (3.8)$$

As the total differentials in Eqs. (3.5) to (3.8) are obtained from functions, we know that they are exact and that the condition of exactness, Eq. (2.79), must be satisfied for any pair of the partial derivatives appearing in any single equation. Each of the partial derivatives in the above equations may be expressed as a function of three of the four variables appearing in the equations. These new functions for the partial derivatives might be determined from experimental studies.

Also, because we know that dP in Eq. (3.5) is exact, we know that

$$\oint dP = 0 \qquad (3.9)$$

and

$$\int_{P_A}^{P_B} dP = P_B - P_A = \Delta P \qquad (3.10)$$

where P_A and P_B represent the pressure of the system in two states A and B. Similar relations are valid for each of the other three equations.

3.2 COEFFICIENTS OF EXPANSION AND COMPRESSIBILITY AND THE THERMAL PRESSURE COEFFICIENT

Three of the six partial derivatives that appear in Eq. (3.5) through (3.8) are of special significance. These are the ones that can be rather easily measured experimentally under the appropriate conditions.

The partial derivative $(\partial V/\partial T)_{P,n}$ when divided by the volume is called the isobaric coefficient of thermal expansion or more briefly the coefficient of expansion, α, so that

$$\alpha = \frac{1}{V}\left(\frac{\partial V}{\partial T}\right)_{P,n} \qquad (3.11)$$

This coefficient measures the fractional change of a unit volume of substance with temperature at constant pressure and mass. The units of α are (degrees)$^{-1}$.

The isothermal coefficient of compressibility, β, is defined as

$$\beta = -\frac{1}{V}\left(\frac{\partial V}{\partial P}\right)_{T,n} \tag{3.12}$$

The minus sign is used so that the value of β will be positive because when pressure increases (positive dP), the volume always decreases (negative dV). Compressibility thus measures the fractional change of volume per atmosphere. The units of β are (atmosphere)$^{-1}$.

The partial derivative $(\partial P/\partial T)_{V,n}$ is called the thermal pressure coefficient, γ, and is

$$\gamma = \left(\frac{\partial P}{\partial T}\right)_{V,n} \tag{3.13}$$

It is apparent from the relation

$$\left(\frac{\partial T}{\partial P}\right)_{V,n}\left(\frac{\partial V}{\partial T}\right)_{P,n}\left(\frac{\partial P}{\partial V}\right)_{T,n} = -1$$

that

$$\gamma = \frac{\alpha}{\beta} \tag{3.14}$$

3.3 THE IDEAL GAS EQUATION OF STATE

An ideal gas is defined† as one whose pressure, volume, temperature, and mass are related by the equation

$$PV = nRT \tag{3.15}$$

where R is the gas constant (to be defined in Section 3.7).

---

† In Chapter 7 a second requirement will be discussed, namely, that the energy of an ideal gas is a function only of the temperature of the gas and not of the volume.

The laws of Boyle, Charles, and Gay-Lussac are incorporated in Eq. (3.15), which states that the pressure-volume product of a constant mass of gas is proportional to the Kelvin temperature, the constant R being the proportionality constant. The behavior of no real gas follows the ideal gas law exactly. The advantage of the law is its simplicity and the fact that all real gases approximate the behavior of the ideal gas at low pressures.

For an ideal gas, α, β, and γ are evaluated as

$$\alpha = \frac{1}{T}, \qquad \beta = \frac{1}{P}, \qquad \gamma = \frac{P}{T} \tag{3.16}$$

However, the values of α, β, and γ must be determined experimentally for all real substances.

3.4 P-V-T SURFACE FOR AN IDEAL GAS

We now discuss the P-V-T surface for an ideal gas. Solving the ideal gas equation for P and V we get $P = nRT/V$ and $V = nRT/P$. By holding n constant we can construct the graphs of P versus V, P versus T, and V versus T, shown in Fig. 3.1. The curves in Fig. 3.1(a) are isotherms; in Fig. 3.1(b), isochores; and in Fig. 3.1(c), isobars. The curves in Fig. 3.1(a) are hyperbolas and those in Figs. 3.1(b) and (c) are straight lines. The direction of increase of the third variable is presented in each graph. Figure 3.1(d) shows the P-V lines for constant temperature but with each line of a different number of moles. The curves could be called "isomoles" and are isomolar.

Figure 3.2 illustrates the P-V-T surface for a constant number of moles of an ideal gas. The surface is the locus of the numerical values of P for all possible values of V and T within the range of Fig. 3.2. The four curves shown in the graphs in Fig. 3.1(a), (b), and (c) are labeled aa, bb, cc, and dd for ease of identification on the P-V-T surface. Careful study of the surface should indicate the way in which it is constructed and should also verify the projection of the isolines on each of the planes. Similar surfaces to the one shown can be drawn for other values of n.

Figure 3.3 gives a graphical presentation of the first-order partial derivatives as tangents to the P-V-T surface of an ideal gas. The heavy straight lines drawn through the point Q on the surface represent the tangent lines. The angles a, b, and c are related to the partial derivatives, evaluated at Q

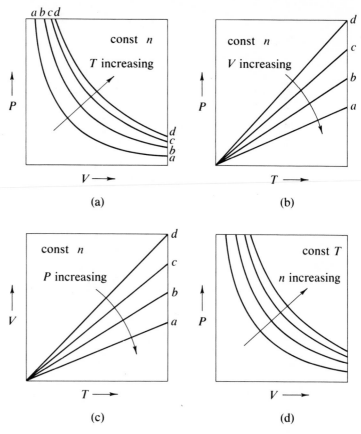

Fig. 3.1. Projections of an ideal gas P-V-T surface on (a) P-V plane; (b) P-T plane; (c) V-T plane; and (d) the P-V plane for constant T but variable n.

by the equations

$$\left(\frac{\partial V}{\partial T}\right)_{P,n} = \tan a; \qquad \left(\frac{\partial P}{\partial T}\right)_{V,n} = \tan b; \qquad \left(\frac{\partial P}{\partial V}\right)_{T,n} = -\tan c \qquad (3.17)$$

Similar tangents can be drawn at other points on the surface; the values of the slopes of the lines vary from point to point.

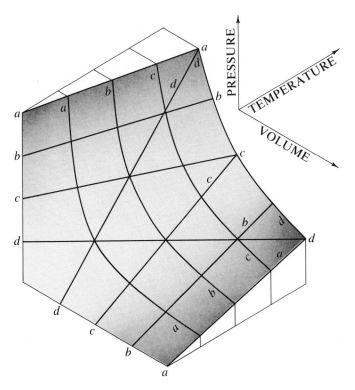

Fig. 3.2.   *P-V-T* surface for an ideal gas.

3.5   EQUATIONS OF STATE FOR REAL GASES

Equations of state for a real gas may be developed from the experimental study of the *P-V-T* relations of a constant quantity of the gas. This requires the measurement of all four variables (*P*, *V*, *T*, and *n*), followed by the development of an equation relating the four variables so that values of one variable, taken as dependent and calculated by means of the equation from the values of the other three variables taken as independent, agree with the experimental data. In many cases the form of equation may be dictated from theory but the values of the coefficients in the theoretical equation must

47

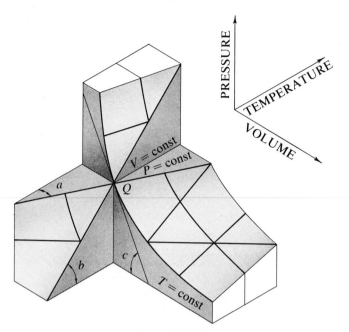

Fig. 3.3. The geometrical meaning of partial derivatives: $(\partial V/\partial T)_{P,n} = \tan\ a$; $(\partial P/\partial T)_{V,n} = \tan\ b$; $(\partial P/\partial V)_{T,n} = -\tan\ c$

be determined, in general, from experimental measurements. The experimental study of the three coefficients α, β, and γ may also lead to suitable equations of state on integration.

Many different equations of state have been developed, some of them being strictly empirical and some based on theory. In 1873 the Dutch physicist van der Waals derived the equation

$$\left(P + \frac{an^2}{V^2}\right)\left(V - nb\right) = nRT \tag{3.18}$$

which bears his name as credit to him. In Eq. (3.18), the van der Waals equation, a and b are constants; Table 3.1 gives the values of a and b for some representative gases. The units of R must be consistent with those of a and b (see Section 3.7). The van der Waals equation gives a reasonably good description of the behavior of real gases when the deviations from ideality are moderate.

Table 3.1 The van der Waals Constants a and b for Some Representative Gases

Gas	a, in liter^2 atm mole^{-2}	b, in cm^3 mole^{-1}
He	0.0341	23.7
H_2	0.244	26.6
N_2	1.39	39.1
CO	1.49	39.9
O_2	1.36	31.8
CO_2	3.59	42.7
H_2O	5.46	30.5

Equation (3.18) may be written as

$$PV = \frac{RT}{1 - (b/V)} - \frac{a}{V} \qquad (n = 1) \tag{3.19}$$

to give the PV product for one mole of gas. All gases approach ideal gas behavior when the pressure goes to zero. If we decrease the pressure at constant temperature, the volume approaches infinity as the pressure goes to zero. It is apparent that Eq. (3.19) reduces to the ideal gas equation of state as V goes to infinity.

Berthelot's equation is

$$\left(P + \frac{n^2 A}{TV^2} \right) \left(V - nB \right) = nRT \tag{3.20}$$

where A and B are constants evaluated from P-V-T data for the gas. This equation is particularly useful at pressures around 1 atm.

The virial type of equation of state, first suggested by Kammerlingh-Onnes, expresses the PV product as a power series in either P or $(1/V)$. The form as a power series in P is

$$PV = A + BP + CP^2 + DP^3 + \cdots \qquad (n = 1) \tag{3.21}$$

for one mole of gas. The constants $A, B, C, D \cdots$ are called the first, second, third, and fourth virial coefficients, respectively, and are functions of the temperature. Some values of the virial coefficients for two gases are given in Table 3.2. As P goes to zero Eq. (3.21) must reduce to the ideal gas equation

Table 3.2 Virial Coefficients for Hydrogen and Nitrogen[a]

Gas	$T°$ K	A	$B \times 10^2$	$C \times 10^5$	$D \times 10^8$	$E \times 10^{11}$
Hydrogen	273	22.414	1.3638	0.7851	-1.206	0.7354
	773	63.447	1.7974	0.1003	-0.1619	0.1050
Nitrogen	273	22.414	-1.0512	8.626	-6.910	1.704
	473	38.824	1.4763	2.775	-2.379	0.7600

[a]For one mole of gas; P in atmospheres; V in liters.

of state so that $A = RT$ (for $n = 1$). The virial equation can be written as a power series in the volume as

$$P = \frac{nRT}{V} + B'\left(\frac{n}{V}\right)^2 + C'\left(\frac{n}{V}\right)^3 + D'\left(\frac{n}{V}\right)^4 + \cdots \qquad (3.22)$$

The first virial coefficient in Eq. (3.22) is RT. C' and D' are not the same as C and D in Eq. (3.21) although B and B' are the same (for $n = 1$).

The nonideality of a gas may be represented by using a function called the compressibility factor Z, which is defined as

$$Z = \frac{PV}{nRT} \qquad (3.23)$$

Equation (3.23) affords a means of comparing the general behavior of a real gas with an ideal gas. The curves given in Fig. 3.4 are for hydrogen, but the behavior of any real gas is similar. For an ideal gas the value of Z is 1. The Boyle temperature is defined as the temperature at which $(\partial Z/\partial P)_{T,n}$ equals zero in the limit of zero pressure. It is evident from the figure that for hydrogen this temperature lies between 80° K and 150° K. Below the Boyle temperature and at sufficiently low pressures the values of Z are all less than 1, but at

higher pressures the values become greater than 1. The values of Z are greater than 1 for all pressures when the temperature of the gas is above its Boyle temperature. At temperatures somewhat below 35° K, a liquid-vapor equilibrium would appear.

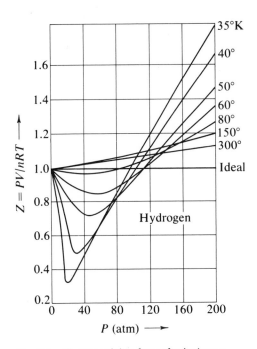

Fig. 3.4.   Compressibility factor for hydrogen.

3.6   EQUATIONS OF STATE FOR REAL SOLIDS AND LIQUIDS

The P-V-T behavior of real solids and liquids can also be described theoretically by equations of state relating P, V, T, and n, but no general form of an equation suitable to liquids and solids has been developed. The coefficients α, β, and γ are defined in the same way for solids and liquids as they are for gases. However, the volume change of liquids and solids with change of temperature or pressure is very much smaller than that for gases.

The coefficient of thermal expansion of a liquid may be positive, negative, or zero, and is a function of both temperature and pressure. For example, liquid water at 1-atm pressure contracts from 273° K to 277° K and then expands as the temperature is increased. The isothermal compressibility for liquids and solids is also a function of both temperature and pressure.

3.7 EVALUATION OF THE GAS CONSTANT R

The experimental evaluation of R is based on the approach of the behavior of all gases to that of the ideal gas as the pressure is decreased. Figure 3.4 shows that the value of Z goes to unity at zero pressure for all gases. If values of (PV/T) were plotted instead of Z, the value of (PV/T) would be equal to R at zero pressure for all temperatures, according to Eq. (3.23). Moreover it is experimentally determined that the same value of R is obtained when similar graphs are drawn for other gases. Thus R is found to be independent of the particular gas used in the experiment.

Equation (3.21) may be used to illustrate how the value of R has been determined precisely. With A equal to RT and the equation written for n moles of gas, we find

$$PV = nRT(1 + \alpha P + \beta P^2 + \gamma P^3 + \cdots) \tag{3.24}$$

The number of moles of gas contained in a vessel of volume V is determined from the mass m and the molecular weight M. The density of the gas, $\rho = m/V$, may then be expressed as

$$\rho = \frac{MP}{RT(1 + \alpha P + \beta P^2 + \gamma P^3 + \cdots)}$$

The limiting value of ρ/P as P goes to zero is then M/RT. Measurements have been made of the density of oxygen as a function of the pressure at 0° C. Prior to 1961 the molecular weight of oxygen was defined to be 32.000 and therefore the value of (RT) at 0° C was determined. This value is 22.414 liter atm deg^{-1} mole^{-1}. When 273.15° K is taken as the Kelvin temperature at 0° C, the value of R becomes 0.082058 liter atm deg^{-1} mole^{-1}. Table 3.3 gives the values of R in several different units. Memorization of the value of R in several units can facilitate conversion from one energy unit to another.

Table 3.3 Values of the Gas Constant

Units	R
liter atm mole^{-1} deg^{-1}	0.082058
cc atm mole^{-1} deg^{-1}	82.058
calories mole^{-1} deg^{-1}	1.9872
joules mole^{-1} deg^{-1}	8.3143
ergs mole^{-1} deg^{-1}	8.3143×10^7

3.8 CONCLUDING COMMENTS

An ideal gas is defined as one whose behavior is accurately described by the ideal gas equation of state, $PV = nRT$. The behavior of real gases must be determined experimentally, and this behavior is described to varying degrees of accuracy by the equations of state presented. The mathematical relations given in Chapter 2 are applicable to ideal and real gases, and problems involving these relations and real gas equations of state can be found in the exercises.

The operational definition of an ideal gas consists of measuring P, V, T, and n for a gas over a range of values of the variables, and then determining by direct calculation whether PV equals nRT for these measurements within the desired degree of accuracy. This last factor is important because for certain applications the ideal gas equation may give satisfactory results, but for others a more exact equation of state may be required. The normal criterion is that a gas is considered operationally to be an ideal gas if its behavior is described by the ideal gas equation of state within the accuracy desired. It is sensible to use the least complicated tools (including equations!) needed to solve any particular problem.

Exercises

3.1 Express 10^9 ergs in joules, calories, liter-atmospheres, kilocalories, and cubic centimeter-atmospheres. (*Hint:* Use the value of R in different units as an aid in converting from one unit to another.)

3.2 Is the gas constant R a universal constant in the same sense that π is? How would you go about finding out the errors in the R values listed in Table 2.3?

3.3 The differences between the ideal gas, van der Waals, and virial equations of state can be illustrated by a sample calculation for one mole of nitrogen gas at 273° K. Tabulate for pressures of 10, 100, and 1000 atm the value of PV calculated for each of the aforementioned equations of state. Also tabulate values of the compressibility factor, using the values of the volumes calculated from each equation of state. (*Note:* For the van der Waals equation you will have to devise a method of successive approximations based on Eq. (3.19). Also use the virial equation of state only through the third virial coefficient.) Graph PV and Z versus the pressure for each equation of state.

3.4 Evaluate the following partial derivatives for the ideal gas, van der Waals, and virial equations of state:

(a) $\left(\dfrac{\partial V}{\partial T}\right)_{P,n}$; (b) $\dfrac{1}{V}\left(\dfrac{\partial V}{\partial T}\right)_{P,n}$; (c) $\left(\dfrac{\partial V}{\partial P}\right)_{T,n}$; (d) $-\dfrac{1}{V}\left(\dfrac{\partial V}{\partial P}\right)_{T,n}$;

(e) $\left(\dfrac{\partial P}{\partial T}\right)_{V,n}$.

3.5 The equation of state for one mole of a certain gas is $PV = RT(1 + (B/V))$, where B is a constant. Evaluate for this gas the same partial derivatives as in Exercise 3.4.

3.6 Demonstrate that dP is an exact differential, when $P = P(T, V, n)$, for the ideal gas, the van der Waals, and the virial equations of state. You may assume that $n = 1$ and is constant. Could dP be other than exact if the functions $P = P(T, V, n)$ exist?

3.7 Assuming that air behaves like an ideal gas, calculate the weight in grams of the air in a room which is 18 ft long, 10 ft wide, and 9 ft high at a pressure of 1 atm and a temperature of 300° K. The average molecular weight of air may be taken to be 29 g mole^{-1}.

3.8 Sketch graphs of the following for an ideal gas where the first term in each pair is the ordinate and the second is the abscissa:
(a) PV versus P, constant n but three different T.
(b) PV versus T for three different n.
(c) P/T versus P, constant n, but three different V.

3.9 Given the three equations

$$\left(\frac{\partial P}{\partial T}\right)_{V,n} = \frac{nR}{V - nb}$$

$$\left(\frac{\partial P}{\partial V}\right)_{T,n} = -\frac{nRT}{(V-nb)^2} + \frac{2an^2}{V^3}$$

and

$$\left(\frac{\partial P}{\partial n}\right)_{T,V} = \frac{RT}{V-nb} + \frac{nRTb}{(V-nb)^2} - \frac{2an}{V^2}$$

(a) Show that the conditions of exactness applied to Eq. (3.5) are satisfied by these relations.

(b) Integrate Eq. (3.5) with the use of these relations and obtain the equation of state.

4 Temperature and Temperature Scales

Temperature may be said to have been "discovered" by Santorio Santorre (commonly called Sanctorius) some time in the years near 1610. This may appear to be a very unusual statement. After all, everyone knows about temperature, for it gets mentioned in all weather forecasts and most households contain thermometers of one sort or another. Moreover, people have been experiencing the effects of temperature and suffering in the cold of winter and the heat of summer for eons past. How, then, can temperature be discovered?

Temperature is an operational concept and as such would take on meaning only when the set of operations describing it were followed. Santorio discovered temperature because he was the first person to *measure* temperature. It makes little difference to the significance of this discovery that Santorio's device for measuring temperature had many faults (Section 4.4); the leap of imagination involved was the recognition (explicitly understood or otherwise) that temperature was measurable in some reproducible way. Temperature could then be defined as that property which Santorio's measuring device measured. Although it required several hundred years to achieve a full understanding of temperature, the launching point was associated with a device for measuring, and an implied way of using this device.

In operational language, temperature is that property of a system which a thermometer measures. If we were to indulge in circular reasoning, we would then state that thermometers are devices which measure temperature. This is what thermometers do, but to break the circle of reasoning it is necessary to describe how a thermometer is constructed and also to give an operational meaning to the scale on the thermometer.

The definition of temperature requires utilization of one property of a standard substance and the definition of the size of the unit of temperature by the assignment of an appropriate set of numbers. Thus the concept of temperature is tied to thermometers and temperature scales.

4.1 DEVELOPMENT OF A TEMPERATURE SCALE

Our first interaction with temperature is a physiological one, and our physiological responses yield a qualitative description of how "hot" or "cold" a substance is. We can utilize these physiological responses to give a direction to temperature in the sense that we can say from touching them that one body is hotter or colder than another. The difficulty here is that not only are our responses qualitative, but also they are imprecisely discriminatory in a quantitative sense (at room temperature a metal object *feels* colder than one made of wood). A more precise way of measuring the degree of hotness of a substance is required.

There are many physical properties of substances which change measurably with temperature; for example, the volume of a fluid, the length of a wire, the viscosity of a liquid, and the electrical resistance of a metal. By measuring the change in any one of these properties, it is possible to construct a temperature scale. The general procedure requires the choosing of one property of one substance, and an interpolation formula which links the property to temperature. This is illustrated by the change in volume of liquid mercury.

A mercury temperature scale may be quite arbitrarily defined by an equation such as

$$V_\tau = V_0(1 + \alpha\tau) \tag{4.1}$$

where V_τ is the volume at the temperature τ, V_0 is the volume where $\tau = 0$, and α is a constant. Other equations could have been used; for example,

$$V_\tau = V_0(1 + a\tau^2) \quad \text{or} \quad V_\tau = V_0(1 + b\tau + c\tau^2) \quad \text{or} \quad V_\tau = V_0(1 + de^\tau)$$

where a, b, c, and d are appropriate constants. The advantages of Eq. (4.1) are that it is simpler than the other equations, and it establishes a linear

57

relationship between volume and temperature. This equation contains two constants, V_0 and α, and therefore two equations are required for their evaluation; that is, the volume must be measured at two different temperatures. In addition, numerical values must be assigned to these two temperatures.

The two temperatures and the values assigned to them may be chosen in a most arbitrary manner, within certain limitations. In the case of a liquid mercury scale, the two temperatures must lie between the normal boiling and freezing points of mercury. If the temperature scale is to be reproducible, the two temperatures must be reproducible experimentally; that is, they must be fixed points. Fortunately, there are certain conditions which yield reproducible temperatures. When two phases of a pure substance are in equilibrium at some specified constant pressure (say, 1 atm), the temperature is fixed and invariant. The pairs of phases normally used are liquid and solid (freezing point), and liquid and vapor (boiling point). The triple point of a pure substance at which the solid, liquid, and vapor phases are in equilibrium is also a fixed temperature. (The testing of the reproducible nature of a fixed point does not require a temperature scale. The student might work out the details of such an experiment.)

The volume of mercury can be measured at the two convenient conditions of the normal freezing point of water, τ_f, and the normal boiling point of water, τ_b. This yields the two equations

$$V_f = V_0(1 + \alpha\tau_f) \quad \text{and} \quad V_b = V_0(1 + \alpha\tau_b) \tag{4.2}$$

These equations are solved simultaneously for V_0 and α to give

$$V_0 = \frac{V_f\tau_b - V_b\tau_f}{\tau_b - \tau_f} \quad \text{and} \quad \alpha = \frac{V_b - V_f}{V_f\tau_b - V_b\tau_f} \tag{4.3}$$

Numerical values are assigned to τ_b and τ_f, V_b and V_f are measured, and from this information α and V_0 are calculated. Substituting the expressions α and V_0 from (4.3) into (4.1) and solving for τ give

$$\tau = \frac{V_b\tau_f - V_f\tau_b}{V_b - V_f} + \frac{\tau_b - \tau_f}{V_b - V_f} V_\tau \tag{4.4}$$

Equation (4.4) now gives the temperature as a function of the volume.

By appropriate choices of the numerical values assigned to τ_f and τ_b, Eq. (4.4) is simplified. If the number zero† is assigned to τ_f, then $V_f = V_0$ and Eq. (4.4) reduces to

$$\tau = \frac{\tau_b(V_\tau - V_0)}{V_b - V_0} \tag{4.5}$$

Since our numbering system is based on 10, possible choices for τ_b might be 1, 10, 100, or 1000. The choice of 1 for τ_b would result in the use of fractions for environmental temperatures, and 1000 would result in large numbers for these same temperatures. A more reasonable choice would be to set τ_b equal to 100, which would make this a "centigrade" type of scale. Equation (4.5) then becomes

$$\tau = 100 \times \frac{V_\tau - V_0}{V_{100} - V_0} = \frac{1}{\alpha} \times \frac{V_\tau - V_0}{V_0} \tag{4.6}$$

since α is $(V_{100} - V_0)/100 V_0$. The value of α for mercury is 1.8260×10^{-4}. This means that the volume increases 1.8260 percent between the freezing point of water and the boiling point of water. It is well to emphasize that the value of α for the thermometric substance depends upon the two fixed temperatures and the numerical values assigned to them. Once these quantities are assigned, the value of α is fixed and constant over the full range of temperatures which can be measured with the use of the thermometric substance.

The centigrade scale (now called the Celsius scale) defined the normal freezing point of water as $0°$ and the normal boiling point of water as $100°$. But for many years neither a standard thermometric substance nor its property was defined. A precise definition of the Celsius scale is given in Section 4.3.

The way in which the physical properties (or for that matter, any property) of a substance change as a function of temperature depends on the temperature scale against which the property is measured. In devising the mercury scale, only *one* property of *one* substance was used and the variation of this property with temperature was defined to be linear. Other properties of mercury (for

---

† Prior to 1954, $0°$ Celsius was defined as the temperature at which pure ice is in equilibrium with air-saturated water at 1-atm pressure.

example, surface tension, viscosity, or vapor pressure) need not be linear functions of the temperature on the mercury scale. If a linear temperature scale were based on the viscosity of mercury, the other properties of mercury, including the volume, probably would be nonlinear functions of the temperature on the viscosity scale.

A particular temperature scale is limited to the range over which the physical property being measured is well behaved and continuous. (A scale based on the volume of liquid water would run into difficulties around 4° C). Beyond this range the temperature scale must be redefined in terms of either a different physical property of the same substance or some physical property of a new substance. The temperature range can be greatly extended by the proper choice of physical property and substance, for example, the volume of nitrogen gas. The definition of a temperature scale which is independent of the nature of the thermometric medium is developed in Chapter 10.

4.2 TEMPERATURE SCALES WITH ONE FIXED POINT

By making a simple transformation it is possible to define a temperature scale having only one fixed point. Referring to Eq. (4.1) let $\tau' = 1/\alpha$ and $\mathbf{T} = \tau + \tau'$, where τ' is a constant (since α is a constant) and $\mathbf{T}$ is the temperature on a new scale. Equation (4.1) becomes

$$V_\tau = V_0\left(1 + \frac{\tau}{\tau'}\right) = V_0\left(\frac{\tau' + \tau}{\tau'}\right) = V_0\left(\frac{\mathbf{T}}{\tau'}\right) = \mathbf{T}\left(\frac{V_0}{\tau'}\right) \tag{4.7}$$

Since both V_0 and τ' are constants, Eq. (4.7) may be written

$$V_\mathbf{T} = k\mathbf{T} \tag{4.8}$$

Equation (4.8) shows that the volume is directly proportional to the new temperature $\mathbf{T}$, and this equation contains only one constant. At some single fixed temperature $\mathbf{T}^*$, the volume will be V^*, and k is given by

$$k = \frac{V^*}{\mathbf{T}^*} \tag{4.9}$$

The volume at any temperature **T** is then given by

$$V = \left(\frac{V^*}{T^*}\right)T \tag{4.10}$$

Any one of the fixed points mentioned earlier can be chosen as the fixed temperature **T***.

The transformation from a two- to a one-fixed-point scale is accomplished by a change of variables and the choice of a single fixed point which defines the incremental change in the property measured as a function of the new temperature **T**. If **T*** is assigned a positive numerical value, the resulting scale has only positive temperatures and a natural lower limit of zero. By an appropriate choice of the number assigned to **T*** a new scale could have only negative values and could be made to coincide with or diverge from the two-point scale. One-point fixed temperature scales are frequently called absolute temperature scales.

4.3 THE IDEAL GAS TEMPERATURE SCALE

A temperature scale based on the volume or pressure of a gas has two distinct advantages over those based on the volume of a liquid: the effects of temperature changes are easily measured and the scale can be defined over a very broad range of temperatures. The volume of a gas is a function of the pressure, temperature, and number of moles, n; pressure is a function of the volume, temperature, and n; the pressure-volume product is a function of the temperature and n; all three are functions of the nature of the gas. A gas temperature scale can be defined, then, by using any one of the following relations:

$$V = V_0(1 + \alpha_V \tau) \qquad (\text{const } P, n) \tag{4.11}$$

$$P = P_0(1 + \alpha_P \tau) \qquad (\text{const } V, n) \tag{4.12}$$

$$(PV) = (PV)_0(1 + \alpha_{PV} \tau) \qquad (\text{const } n) \tag{4.13}$$

By analogy with Eq. (4.3), and with the use of a two-fixed-point scale with the assignments τ(ice point) $= 0$ and τ(steam point) $= 100$, the α's are given by

$$\alpha_V = \frac{V_{100} - V_0}{100V_0}, \qquad \alpha_P = \frac{P_{100} - P_0}{100P_0}, \qquad \alpha_{PV} = \frac{(PV)_{100} - (PV)_0}{100(PV)_0}$$

$$(4.14)$$

The values of the α's for real gases at moderate pressures vary from gas to gas, although the differences are not very large. Table 4.1 gives values of

Table 4.1 α_V, α_P, and $\lim\limits_{P \to 0} \alpha_{PV}$ for Various Gases[a]

Gas	$\alpha_V \times 10^2$	$\alpha_P \times 10^2$	$\lim\limits_{P \to 0} \alpha_{PV} \times 10^2$
Air	0.36716	0.36711	0.36604
Argon	0.36717	0.36724	0.36604
Helium	0.36613	0.36591	0.36608
Hydrogen	0.36627	0.36603	0.36604
Neon	0.36628	0.36606	0.36604
Oxygen	0.36735	0.36746	0.36604

[a] The value of P_0 in columns 2 and 3 is 1 atm.

α_V and α_P for several gases. The experimentally determined values of the α's as P_0 approaches zero (or V_0 approaches infinity) are the same for all gases, within experimental error. This behavior is illustrated by the last column in Table 4.1, which shows the limiting value of α_{PV} as $P \to 0$; that is,

$$\lim_{P \to 0} \alpha_{PV} = \frac{\lim\limits_{P \to 0}(PV)_{100} - \lim\limits_{P \to 0}(PV)_0}{100 \lim\limits_{P \to 0}(PV)_0}$$

The Celsius temperature scale is a centigrade scale which is based on assigning the temperature $0°$ C to the ice point and $100°$ C to the steam point. The thermometric medium is the ideal gas. The symbol t is normally reserved for Celsius temperatures and will be used from here on.

By using the methods described earlier, a temperature scale using only one fixed point may be constructed. For a constant-volume gas thermometer this can be done by setting $t' = 1/\alpha_P$, and $T = t + t'$. Making these substitutions in Eq. (4.12) gives

$$P = P_0\left(1 + \frac{t}{t'}\right) = P_0\left(\frac{t' + t}{t'}\right) = P_0\left(\frac{T}{t'}\right) = T\left(\frac{P_0}{t'}\right) \qquad (4.15)$$

Since both P_0 and t' are constants, Eq. (4.15) reduces to

$$P = kT \qquad (4.16)$$

The constant k is determined experimentally by measuring the pressure P^* at some fixed temperature T^*, or

$$k = \frac{P^*}{T^*} \qquad (4.17)$$

Prior to 1954 the experimental determination of the limit of α_{PV} as P goes to zero defined the ideal gas temperature scale by the use of Eq. (4.13). The most accurate values of α, after correction for the nonideality of the gases used in the experiment, ranged from 0.366085 to 0.36610. The reciprocals of these values are 273.16 and 273.15. If the value of 273.16 is taken, Eq. (4.13) may be written as

$$(PV) = \frac{(PV)_0}{273.16}(273.16 + t) \qquad (4.18)$$

When the Kelvin temperature scale is defined as $T = 273.16 + t$, the equivalence of Eq. (4.18) with the ideal gas equation of state is established with the observation that $(PV)_0/273.16$ equals nR.

In 1954, the Tenth Conference of Weights and Measures† adopted the suggestion of Kelvin, made in 1854, and of Giauque, in 1939, of using a scale defined in terms of one fixed point. The temperature of the triple point of water was chosen as the fixed point and was assigned the value of 273.16° K and 0.0100° C on the Celsius scale. Thus the zero point on the Celsius scale is 273.15° K, $T = 273.15 + t$, and $t' = 273.15$. For an ideal gas, then, the Kelvin

† See "International Temperature Scale of 1948, Text Revision of 1960," Natl. Bur. Standards Monograph 37; H. F. Stimson, *J. Res. Natl. Bur. Std.*, **65A**, 139 (1961).

temperature is given by

$$T = \frac{273.16}{P_{273.16}} P \tag{4.19}$$

This defines the value of α_P, Eq. (4.12), as $1/273.15$, and thus the temperature at which $P = 0$ is $-273.15°$ C or $0°$ K. The ice point and the steam point are no longer defined points, but must be measured. The best measurements to date show that the ice point is within 0.0001 deg of the zero point on the Celsius scale.

4.4 THE HISTORICAL DEVELOPMENT OF TEMPERATURE SCALES†

Temperature has been measured for only a relatively short period of time: Santorio Santorre is generally credited with the development of the first thermometer for use as a scientific instrument some time near 1610. Santorio's thermometer was what we would now call a thermobaroscope, that is, it responded to changes of both temperature and pressure. The device consisted of a glass bulb with a long stem extending downward into a vessel containing water. The stem was partly filled with air. A scale marked off in degrees " at pleasure " was attached to the stem. This was, of course, a crude thermometer, but it did establish the principle of employing a change in a physical property of a substance as a means of measuring temperature. (Galileo Galilei is sometimes credited with the development of the first thermometer, but the evidence† seems to lie in Santorio's favor.)

The next significant advance in thermometry was taken by the Grand Duke of Tuscany, Ferdinand II, who developed in or before 1641 the first sealed liquid-in-glass thermometer. This device responded only to changes in temperature. D. G. Fahrenheit greatly improved on the design of thermometers and was the first to make generally thermometers with mercury as the

† D. Roller, *The Early Development of the Concepts of Temperature and Heat.* Cambridge, Mass.: Harvard University Press, 1950, gives a good account of the development of the thermometer, and also of the concepts of heat and temperature. However, the recent and very readable study by W. E. Knowles Middleton (*A History of the Thermometer and Its Uses in Meteorology*, Baltimore, Maryland: Johns Hopkins Press, 1966) describes the results of the most up-to-date scholarship on the history of the thermometer and is the principal reference for this section.

thermometric fluid. The advantages of using mercury (not all recognized by Fahrenheit) are that it remains liquid over a wide range of temperatures, has a high thermal conductivity relative to other liquids, is readily purified, and improves the readability of thermometers. It is an interesting point that the early makers of thermometers had difficulty in comparing alcohol and mercury thermometers. It took a very long time to recognize that their "dilatations" were different.

Slowly the idea developed that fixed points and an interpolation formula were necessary to define a temperature scale. The early "fixed points" ranged from "the greatest summer heat" to the melting point of butter to the "normal human body temperature." Carlo Renaldini is generally credited with suggesting in 1694 that the freezing and boiling points of water could serve as fixed temperatures. When it was discovered that these points are pressure-dependent, the pressure was specified to be one standard atmosphere, and this defined the ice point and the steam point. Various sets of numbers were assigned to ice and steam points: on the Fahrenheit scale they were 32 and 212, on the centigrade scale 0 and 100, and on the Réaumur scale 0 and 80.

As time went on it became apparent that a standard temperature scale was needed and that this scale should depend on one property of one substance. In the nineteenth century H. V. Regnault showed that the constant-volume hydrogen thermometer was especially suited for this purpose, and this in combination with the centigrade scale was used as the practical standard until 1927.

4.5 THE ZEROTH LAW OF THERMODYNAMICS

Temperature is the way of determining whether or not one system is or has the potential of being in thermal equilibrium with another. If the systems are in thermal contact with each other (or can act on each other in such a way as to be able to alter the temperature of either system), and if the temperatures of both systems are the same, the two systems are said to be in thermal equilibrium.

The zeroth law of thermodynamics states that two systems in thermal equilibrium with a third are in thermal equilibrium with each other. In other words, if two systems A and B have the same temperature as a third system C they have identical temperatures.

The zeroth law may be regarded as the basis for all temperature measurement. Thermometers, after all, only measure their own temperature. We can state only that the temperature of a given system is the same as that we read on a thermometer if the system and the thermometer are in thermal equilibrium. In practice we check for equilibrium between a thermometer and a system by studying the temperature as a function of time and as a function of position in the system.

4.6 THERMOMETRY

The methods of measuring temperature are so intimately associated with the concept of temperature that a brief description of these methods is in order. It will develop later that the thermodynamic temperature scale which is the fundamental scale for thermodynamic use is identical with the ideal gas scale. Consequently the basic instrument for determining temperature is the gas thermometer. This usually takes one of two forms: the constant-pressure gas thermometer, which requires the measurement of volume, and the constant-volume gas thermometer, which requires the measurement of pressure. Constant-volume thermometry has been the preferred approach, but these instruments are still rather difficult to use routinely.

The liquid-in-glass thermometer where the liquid is mercury is the most common form of thermometer in use. Mercury thermometers are useful from the melting point ($234°$ K) to the boiling point ($630°$ K). Some liquid-in-glass thermometers are filled with alcohol, and for use at low temperatures some thermometers are filled with propane.

One of the most precise ways of determining temperature is to measure the electrical resistance of a metal such as platinum or nickel. The resistance of metals usually increases as the temperature increases. Thermistors made of semiconductors, such as oxides of Mn, Ni, Co, Cu, U, and other elements, show a marked decrease in resistance as the temperature increases. This greater sensitivity to temperature and the possibility of fabricating thermistors in many sizes and shapes, including very small beads, has led to the widespread use of thermistors as thermometers.

Seebeck found in 1821 that electric current flowed in a closed circuit of two dissimilar metals when the two junctions were maintained at different temperatures. The thermoelectric thermometer is better known as the thermocouple. In practice, one junction is kept at some constant reference temperature such as the ice point of water and the other junction is used as the temperature probe. The emf of a thermocouple for precise work is measured by a potentiometer, a device which balances the unknown emf of the thermocouple against a known emf. In this procedure no current passes through the detecting circuit. A commonly used thermocouple is fabricated from one wire made of copper and the other from a copper-nickel alloy known as constantan.

There are many other methods of measuring temperature, but they are all based on the consideration that a physical property of some substance or combination of substances changes with temperature.

4.7   THE INTERNATIONAL PRACTICAL TEMPERATURE SCALE OF 1948

The International Practical Temperature Scale (IPTS) is the *practical* scale which makes it possible for laboratories the world over to measure temperatures reproducibly on the same basis. The IPTS uses six fixed points and interpolation formulas for specified types of thermometers for four temperature ranges. The fixed points are given in Table 4.2. The temperatures of

Table 4.2   Defined Fixed Points on the International Practical Temperature Scale (1948)

Defined Fixed Point	Temperature, °K
Temperature of equilibrium between liquid oxygen and its vapor (oxygen point)	90.18
Temperature of equilibrium between ice, liquid water, and water vapor (triple point of water)	273.16
Temperature of equilibrium between liquid water and its vapor (steam point)	373.15
Temperature of equilibrium between liquid sulfur and its vapor (sulfur point)†	716.75
Temperature of equilibrium between solid silver and liquid silver (silver point)	1233.95
Temperature of equilibrium between solid gold and liquid gold (gold point)	1336.15

† In place of the sulfur point it is recommended to use the temperature of equilibrium between solid zinc and liquid zinc (zinc point) with the value 692.655°K.

the fixed points, which are *defined* on the IPTS scale, are actually determined as accurately as possible on the ideal gas thermometer scale. The pressure, except for the triple point of water, is one standard atmosphere. Notice also that the IPTS is not defined below the oxygen point. The fundamental defined point is the triple point of water which has been assigned the value 273.16° K.

The interpolation formulas and their respective temperature ranges of applicability are:

1. From 0° C to 630.5° C (antimony point) the temperature t is defined by the formula

$$R_t = R_0(1 + At + Bt^2)$$

where R_t is the resistance at temperature t of the wire resistor of a standard platinum resistance thermometer, and R_0 is its resistance 0° C. The constants R_0, A, and B are to be determined from the values of R_t at the triple point, at the steam point, and at the sulfur point.

2. From the oxygen point to 0° C, the temperature t is defined by the formula

$$R_t = R_0[1 + At + Bt^2 + C(t - t_{100})t^3]$$

where R_0, A, and B are determined in the same manner as in (1) above, the constant C is determined from the value of R_t at the oxygen point, and $t_{100} = 100°$ C.

3. From 630.5° C to the gold point the temperature t is defined by the formula

$$E = a + bt + ct^2$$

where E is the electromotive force of a standard thermocouple of platinum and platinum-rhodium alloy when one of the junctions is at 0° C and the other at the temperature t. The constants a, b, and c are to be determined from the values of E at 630.5° C (compared against a standard resistance thermometer), at the silver point, and the gold point.

4. Above the gold point the temperature t is defined by the formula

$$\frac{J_t}{J_{\mathrm{Au}}} = \frac{\exp\left[\dfrac{C_2}{\lambda(t_{\mathrm{Au}} + T_0)}\right] - 1}{\exp\left[\dfrac{C_2}{\lambda(t + T_0)}\right] - 1}$$

where J_t and J_{Au} are the radiant energies per unit wavelength interval at wavelength λ, emitted per unit time per unit solid angle per unit area of a black body at the temperature t and the gold point, respectively; C_2 is the second radiation constant with the value $C_2 = 0.01438$ meter deg; λ is in meters; and $T_0 = 273.15$ deg.

In addition, certain physical characteristics and the purity of the materials used in the thermometers are specified. To facilitate calibration of thermometers a set of secondary reference points is defined. There are differences between the thermodynamic and IPTS scales, but in the range between the oxygen point and the sulfur point these differences do not exceed 0.05° C. In the laboratory it is difficult to measure absolute temperatures within 0.01 deg although, of course, differential temperature measurements of greater sensitivity are relatively easy to achieve.

4.8 CONCLUDING COMMENTS

The temperature scales in most common use are the Celsius, Kelvin (or absolute Celsius), Fahrenheit, and Rankine (or absolute Fahrenheit) scales. In practice, they are all defined in terms of the IPTS. The relations among the scales are summarized in the following set of equations:

$$T° K = 273.15 + t° C \tag{4.20}$$

$$T° R = 459.67 + t° F \tag{4.21}$$

$$T° R = \frac{9}{5} T° K \tag{4.22}$$

The Celsius and Kelvin scales are the ones most frequently used in scientific work; the Rankine scale is frequently used by chemical and mechanical engineers.

It should be kept in mind that many arbitrary choices are made in defining a temperature scale. With respect to the physical properties of substances, it is important to remember that the way these properties change as a function of temperature is related to the temperature scale against which they are measured.

In this chapter the concept of temperature has been developed, using the operational approach. From this point on when we refer to temperature we are explicitly referring to the set of operations by which temperature scales have been defined and by which temperature is measured.

Exercises

4.1 (a) Knowing that the ice point is 0° C and 32° F and that the steam point is 100° C and 212° F, find a relationship between the Celsius and Fahrenheit scales. (b) Find the temperature at which the Celsius and Fahrenheit scales have the same numerical value. (c) Is there any temperature at which the Kelvin and Rankine scales have the same numerical value? (d) On a hot summer day the temperature may be 95° F and on a cold winter day it might be 0° F. The average normal human body temperature is 98.6° F. Convert these three temperatures to °C, °K, and °R.

4.2 A numerologically inclined scientist decided one day to devise a temperature scale based on the number 4. As his thermometric medium he chose to use the pressure of an ideal gas at constant volume. He chose to use two fixed points to define the scale and assigned the value 4 to the ice point and the value 4^2 (or 16) to the steam point. (a) Find a linear relationship between the pressure and the temperature (in °N) on the numerological scale. (b) What is the numerical value of the Kelvin absolute zero on this scale? (c) If the pressure at the steam point were 10 atm, what is the pressure at 0° N, and what is the temperature (in °N) when the pressure is 1 atm? (d) Find a relationship between °N and °K.

4.3 A temperature scale is defined in terms of the volume of carbon tetrachloride confined in glass. The fixed points are chosen to be 0° C and 75° C and these are also the numerical values assigned to the fixed points. Later the volume of carbon tetrachloride is determined as a function of the Celsius scale with the use of a mercury-in-glass thermometer and it is found that the volume of the carbon tetrachloride is given by the equation

$$V_t = V_0(1 + 1.838 \times 10^{-3}t + 0.8988 \times 10^{-6}t^2 + 1.3514 \times 10^{-8}t^3).$$

Calculate the difference between the carbon tetrachloride scale and the Celsius scale at 10°, 30°, and 50° C.

4.4 Review the steps by which temperature may be defined operationally.

4.5 The isobaric coefficient of thermal expansion of ethanol is given by

$$\alpha = 1.04 \times 10^{-3} + 1.57 \times 10^{-6}t + 5.15 \times 10^{-8}t^2 = \frac{1}{V_0}\left(\frac{\partial V}{\partial T}\right)_P,$$

where t is the Celsius temperature. If $0°C$ and $50°C$ are taken as defined points on a centigrade ethanol scale, what will be the reading of the ethanol thermometer when an ideal gas thermometer reads: (a) $30°\,C$? (b) $75°\,C$?

4.6 Use Eq. (4.13) as the basis of setting up a temperature scale using the two fixed points of the ice point and the steam point. Also set up a temperature scale using Eq. (4.13) and the triple point of water as the single fixed point.

4.7 The first centigrade scale devised by Anders Celsius (ca. 1741) assigned the value $0°\,C'$ to the steam point and $100°\,C'$ to the ice point of water. (The centigrade scale as we now know it was turned " right side up " not later than 1745 by the great botanist Linnaeus.) (a) Using an ideal gas as the thermometric medium find a relationship for a constant-volume thermometer between $°C'$ and the pressure. (b) What is the numerical value of the absolute zero for the temperature scale devised in part (a)? (c) Find a relationship between $°C$ and $°C'$ for the conditions in (a). (d) At what temperature are the $°C$ and the $°C'$ scales numerically equal? (e) Find a relationship between $°F$ and $°C'$ for the conditions in (a). (f) What is $200°\,K$ in $°C'$?

5 Heat, Heat Capacity, and Calorimetry

A qualitative notion of heat is acquired by everyone through his ordinary everyday experience. Just as our ideas of temperature can be misleading before they are quantified, so can our ideas of heat. The most frequent misconception is to treat heat as a substance that can be added to or removed from objects. This notion of heat was so prevalent at one time that heat as a substance was given† the name "caloric." In this chapter we will proceed from a qualitative concept of heat to a quantitative one. The quantitative measurement of heat will be developed in terms of the properties of a standard substance. In so doing we will define more clearly the nature of diathermic and adiabatic walls. The related areas of heat capacity and calorimetry are discussed at the end of the chapter.

5.1 A QUALITATIVE APPROACH TO HEAT

The concept of heat is based primarily on experience and experiment. We know from experience that when two bodies having different temperatures are placed in contact with each other in a certain manner, the two temperatures approach each other and in time become equal. We describe the phenomenon by saying that *heat has flowed from one body to another*. The change of temperature of a body when another body of different temperature is

† See D. Roller, *The Early Development of the Concepts of Temperature and Heat.* Cambridge, Mass.: Harvard Univ. Press, 1950.

placed in contact with it gives us the basic concept of heat. An extension of the concept to changes of phase such as melting and evaporation is discussed in Section 5.4.

5.2   DIATHERMIC AND ADIABATIC WALLS

In the preceding section, the expression "in a certain manner" was used. Here we discuss what is meant by that expression. We know from experience that the rate at which the temperatures change when the two bodies are placed in contact depends to a large extent upon the type of contact made between the two bodies. If the two bodies are metallic and actually touch each other, the rate is rapid. However, if the two bodies are separated by some ceramic material, asbestos paper, or similar substance, the rate of temperature change is quite slow.

Materials differ in their heat conductivity, that is, in the rate at which heat flows through them under a temperature gradient. Those materials which have very high heat conductivity are called diathermic materials and walls made from such materials are called *diathermic walls*. Materials which have very small heat conductivities are called heat insulators or adiabatic materials, and walls made from such substances are called *adiabatic walls*. An ideal adiabatic wall would permit no heat to flow through it. Thus, if two bodies whose temperatures are different are completely separated from the surroundings and are separated from each other by an ideal adiabatic wall, the temperature of the two bodies would remain the same and no temperature changes would occur.

In actual practice, no wall is truly diathermic or adiabatic. However, in this book we restrict the term "diathermic wall" to one which is made of a substance that has a relatively high heat conductivity, so that when two bodies are separated by a diathermic wall the temperature equilibrium is rapidly attained. *The term "adiabatic wall" is restricted to an ideal wall so that no heat can pass through the wall.* Thus, when a system is separated from the surroundings by an adiabatic wall, *no* heat can flow into or out of the system.

5.3   A QUANTITATIVE APPROACH TO HEAT

In order to arrive at a quantitative definition of heat, we must make quantitative measurements of the phenomena that were described in the

73

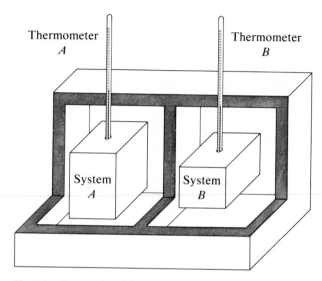

Fig. 5.I. Systems A and B isolated from each other.

preceding section. Let us consider two systems A and B as shown in Fig. 5.1. (For convenience, the systems may be considered to be metallic, but the particular substances composing the systems are not important for the present.) The two systems are separated from the surroundings by a rigid, adiabatic wall and from each other by another adiabatic wall. A thermometer is associated with each system. The systems are allowed to attain thermal equilibrium individually, and we represent the initial temperature of system A by T_{Ai} and that of system B by T_{Bi}. Now the adiabatic wall between the two systems is removed and the systems are brought into thermal contact as shown in Fig. 5.2. If the two initial temperatures are the same, thermal equilibrium already exists and the temperatures of both systems remain the same. When T_{Ai} is greater than T_{Bi} the temperature of system A decreases and that of system B increases. When T_{Ai} is less than T_{Bi} the temperature of system A increases and that of system B decreases. (Phase changes are excluded in this discussion.) After a period of time the two systems are again separated by an adiabatic wall, as in Fig. 5.1, and each system is allowed to obtain thermal equilibrium individually. Let the final temperatures be indicated by T_{Af} and T_{Bf}. Examination of a collection of data in which the initial temperatures or final temperatures or both are varied shows that the

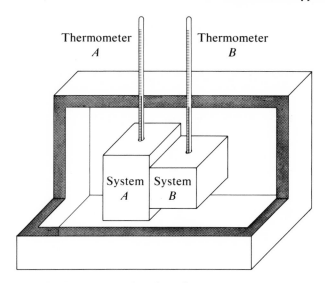

Fig. 5.2. Systems A and B in thermal contact.

data can be expressed by the equation

$$C_A(T_{Af} - T_{Ai}) = C_B(T_{Bi} - T_{Bf}) \tag{5.1}$$

within experimental error, provided the temperature changes are not too great. In this equation C_A and C_B are proportionality constants. Neither of the two constants can be evaluated from such experiments; however, the ratio (C_B/C_A) can be evaluated.

The words used to describe the changes which take place in such experiments are "heat has transferred" from one system to another. We therefore relate heat quantitatively to both sides of Eq. (5.1) by writing

$$Q_A = C_A(T_{Af} - T_{Ai}) \tag{5.2}$$

$$Q_B = C_B(T_{Bf} - T_{Bi}) \tag{5.3}$$

and

$$Q_A = -Q_B \tag{5.4}$$

75

In Eqs. (5.2) and (5.3), the difference between the temperatures is taken as the final temperature minus the initial temperature. The proportionality constants are defined to be positive. The numerical value of Q is therefore positive when the final temperature of a system is greater than its initial temperature. In such a case heat is said to be absorbed by the system. When the numerical value of Q is negative, heat is said to be removed from the system. The symbol Q itself always refers to *heat absorbed by a system*, but the numerical value may be positive or negative. Equation (5.4) states that, in the experiments discussed, the heat absorbed by one system is equal and opposite to the heat absorbed by the other system.

The properties of the quantities C_A and C_B must be explored further in order to make them quantitative measures. When the mass of system B is varied with constant mass of system A, the ratio (C_B/C_A) is found to vary directly with the mass of B. Similarly, when the mass of A is varied with constant mass of B, the ratio (C_B/C_A) varies inversely with the mass of A. Therefore C_A and C_B vary directly with the masses of A and B, respectively.

A preliminary definition of a unit quantity of heat can now be obtained. As has been indicated, the ratio of C_B/C_A can be determined experimentally. If one of the systems, say A, is taken as a standard substance, the value of C_A per unit mass of A can be assigned any arbitrary value. With such an assigned value a quantity of heat, Q_A, can be calculated by Eq. (5.2). Also, the value of C_B is determined from the value of the ratio of C_B/C_A. In actual practice, water has been chosen as the standard substance and the value of C_A assigned the value of 1 cal per gram degree Celsius (cal g^{-1} deg^{-1}). Thus, when the temperature of 1 g of water is raised 1° C, 1 cal of heat is absorbed by the water.

Precise measurements have shown that the C quantities used in Eqs. (5.1) through (5.3) are actually functions of the temperature and also are functions of the pressure or volume. In the past, various units of the calories have been used. The 15-deg calorie, which is the most widely used, is the heat absorbed by 1 g of water when its temperature is raised from 14.5° to 15.5° C. For the 20-deg calorie, the temperature change is from 19.5° to 20.5° C. The average calorie is one-hundredth of the quantity of heat required to raise the temperature of 1 g of water from 0° to 100° C. In all such definitions, the pressure is approximately 1 atm.

In more recent calorimetric work, electrical resistors have been used to increase the temperature of a system. It is thus possible to define a calorie in terms of electrical work. The present accepted calorie is defined by international agreement and is

$$1 \text{ cal (defined)} = 4.1840 \text{ absolute joules} \tag{5.5}$$

This value agrees as close as possible with the original 15-deg calorie. Although the concept of work is not discussed until the next chapter, it should be noted that Eq. (5.5) defines the relation between units of heat and units of work.

5.4   HEAT ASSOCIATED WITH CHANGES OF PHASE

The basic idea of heat developed in Section 5.1 involves a change of temperature in both phases. Phase changes of pure components, such as melting or freezing and evaporation or condensation, take place at constant temperature under a fixed pressure. The concept of heat can be extended to include such phase changes by means of operations similar to those already discussed.

As an example, consider two systems A and B. System A is composed of a known mass of water at some initial temperature, T_{Ai}, greater than $0°$ C in a container C. System B is composed of a mixture of a known mass of ice and a known mass of water at $0°$ C. The pressure is 1 atm. The two systems are isolated from the surroundings by a rigid adiabatic wall. They are then connected by a diathermic wall (Fig. 5.3). The temperature of system A decreases while some of the ice melts. After a period of time and before the temperature of system A becomes $0°$ C, the two systems are separated by an adiabatic wall, as in Fig. 5.1, and allowed to come to thermal equilibrium individually. The final temperature T_{Af} of system A is measured and the mass of ice melted is determined. The quantity of heat absorbed by system A is

$$Q_A = C_A(T_{Af} - T_{Ai}) \tag{5.6}$$

and is negative because T_{Af} is less than T_{Ai}. Thus heat actually has been evolved by system A. The only interaction between the two systems has been through the diathermic wall. Consequently we may say that system B has absorbed heat. The final temperature of system B is still $0°$ C, provided some ice remains, and therefore the only change that has taken place is the melting of a measured mass of ice. If the initial and final states of the diathermic wall are the same the quantity of heat Q_A must have been absorbed by system B.

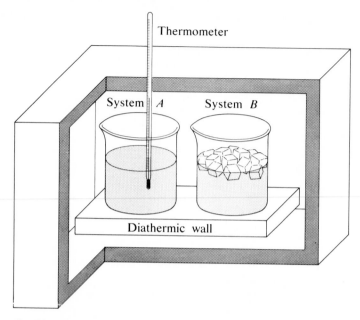

Fig. 5.3. Diathermic wall connecting two systems.

The heat associated with the melting of a known mass of ice is thus determined.

In modern practice, heats associated with phase changes are determined directly by means of electrical measurements or are calculated indirectly by means of appropriate equations, some of which are developed in this book.

5.5 HEAT CAPACITY

Equations (5.2) or (5.3) may be written in the form

$$C = \frac{Q}{\Delta T} \tag{5.7}$$

where ΔT equals $T_f - T_i$. The quantity C is called a heat capacity. The quantity so defined is actually an average heat capacity over the temperature interval ΔT and its value for any system would depend on the interval as well as the temperature itself. In order to overcome the dependence on the interval, the true heat capacity is defined as the limit of $Q/\Delta T$ as ΔT goes to zero and is written as dQ/dT so that

$$C = \lim_{\Delta T \to 0} \frac{Q}{\Delta T} = \frac{dQ}{dT} \tag{5.8}$$

The quantity of heat absorbed by a system for a given temperature change from T_i to T_f is then given by the integral

$$Q = \int dQ = \int_{T_i}^{T_f} C \, dT \tag{5.9}$$

The differential quantity dQ is inexact (Section 5.6) and consequently the integral may depend on the path of integration.

The units of heat capacity are generally cal deg^{-1}. The specific heat is the heat capacity per gram of substance; the units are calories per gram degree, or cal g^{-1} deg^{-1}. The molar heat capacity is the heat capacity per mole of substance; the units are calories per mole degree, or cal mole^{-1} deg^{-1}. The symbol used in this book for molar heat capacity is $\tilde{C}$.

The molar heat capacity at constant pressure for cyclohexane as a function of temperature is shown in Fig. 5.4. The discontinuities in the curves indicate

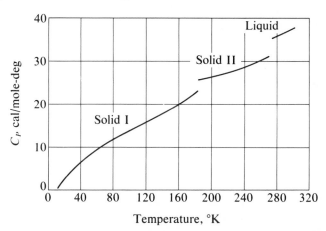

Fig. 5.4. The molar heat capacity of cyclohexane. (Aston et al., *J. Am. Chem. Soc.*, 65, 1135 (1943).) (*Reprinted by permission of the copyright owner—the American Chemical Society.*)

the presence of phase changes. In general the heat capacity of solids normally increases as the temperature increases; the heat capacity of liquids also increases in the same direction and the values are larger than those for solids; and for gases the heat capacity increases with increasing temperature, but near the normal boiling point the heat capacity of a gas is frequently lower than that for the liquid.

5.6 INEXACTNESS OF THE DIFFERENTIAL OF HEAT

In all the experiments discussed in previous sections, we have either ignored the pressure or volume of the systems or have suggested a pressure of 1 atm. In so doing we have not defined the state of a system completely. To do so for a closed system, we must use at least two independent variables. First, let us choose the temperature and volume and consider the differential quantity of heat associated with differential changes of both temperature and volume. For this dQ may be written as

$$dQ = M(T, V)\, dT + N(T, V)\, dV \tag{5.10}$$

where both $M(T, V)$ and $N(T, V)$ are functions of the temperature and volume. We find by experiment that $(\partial M/\partial V)_T$ does not equal $(\partial N/\partial T)_V$ and thus the differential dQ is inexact. This means, of course, that the heat absorbed by a system for any change of state depends upon the path along which the change of state occurs. (For example, a system may be changed isobarically from one state to another by a varying combination of heat and work effects; see Chapter 7.)

Similarly, when the temperature and pressure are taken as independent variables, we may write

$$dQ = X(T, P)\, dT + Y(T, P)\, dP \tag{5.11}$$

where $X(T, P)$ and $Y(T, P)$ are functions of the temperature and pressure. Again we find by experiment that $(\partial X/\partial P)_T$ does not equal $(\partial Y/\partial T)_P$ and therefore dQ is inexact.

Equations (5.10) and (5.11) can be related through the knowledge that the volume of a system is a function of its temperature and pressure; namely,

$$dV = \left(\frac{\partial V}{\partial T}\right)_P dT + \left(\frac{\partial V}{\partial P}\right)_T dP \tag{5.12}$$

When this expression is substituted for dV in Eq. (5.10) we obtain

$$dQ = \left[M(T, V) + N(T, V)\left(\frac{\partial V}{\partial T}\right)_P\right] dT + \left[N(T, V)\left(\frac{\partial V}{\partial P}\right)_T\right] dP \tag{5.13}$$

Comparison with Eq. (5.11) shows that

$$X(T, P) = M(T, V) + N(T, V)\left(\frac{\partial V}{\partial T}\right)_P \tag{5.14}$$

and

$$Y(T, P) = N(T, V)\left(\frac{\partial V}{\partial P}\right)_T \tag{5.15}$$

Heat capacities have been defined in a general way as

$$C = \frac{dQ}{dT}$$

According to Eq. (5.10) we find that $dQ = M(T, V) dT$ when the volume is constant, and consequently $M(T, V)$ represents the heat capacity of a system at constant volume, which is designated as C_V. Similarly the heat capacity of a system at constant pressure C_P is given as $X(T, P)$ in Eq. (5.11). The relation between the two heat capacities is given in a general form by Eq. (5.14). It will be shown in a later chapter that $N(T, V)$ equals $T(\partial P/\partial T)_V$. It must be emphasized that C_V for a closed system is in general a function of temperature and volume and that C_P for a closed system also is in general a function of the temperature and pressure. There are actually other useful heat capacities in addition to those at constant volume and constant pressure based on the general definition given in Eq. (5.8).

The concept that Q depends upon the path is illustrated in Fig. 5.5. Two states of a closed system are considered, the initial state at A where the initial temperature and volume are designated as T_1 and V_1, respectively, and the final state at B where the temperature and volume are T_2 and V_2. Three paths are indicated: ABC, ADC, and the diagonal AC. Along the path AB, dV is zero and $dQ = C_V(T, V)\,dV$ where C_V is evaluated at V_1. Along the path BC, dT is zero and $dQ = N(T, V)\,dV$ evaluated at T_2. The total heat absorbed by the system along the path ABC is

$$Q = \int_{T_1}^{T_2} C_V(T, V_1)\,dT + \int_{V_1}^{V_2} N(T_2, V)\,dV \qquad (5.16)$$

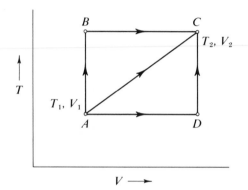

Fig. 5.5. Inexactness of the differential of heat.

Along the path AD, dT is zero and $dQ = N(T, V)\,dV$ evaluated at T_1 and along the path DC, dV is zero and $dQ = C_V(T, V)\,dT$ evaluated at V_2. The total heat absorbed by the system along ADC is then

$$Q = \int_{T_1}^{T_2} C_V(T, V_2)\,dT + \int_{V_1}^{V_2} N(T_1, V)\,dV \qquad (5.17)$$

These two heats are not equal. Along the diagonal path AC, either T or V must be eliminated from Eq. (5.10) by the use of the linear relationship

$$T = \frac{T_1 V_2 - T_2 V_1}{V_2 - V_1} + \frac{T_2 - V_1}{V_2 - V_1} V \qquad (5.18)$$

valid along the path AC. The integration would then be in terms of the remaining variable.

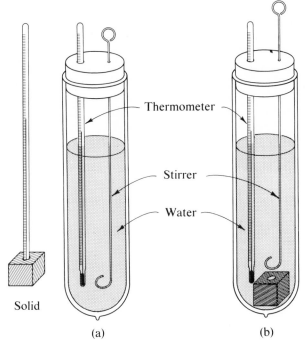

Thermometer

Stirrer

Water

Solid

(a)   (b)

Fig. 5.6. Simple Dewar calorimeter.

5.7 CALORIMETRY

Heat effects associated with processes are measured in devices called calorimeters. They can be used for the determination of heat capacity or for measuring heat changes found in chemical reactions. Since much of the edifice of thermodynamics rests on the foundation supplied by the precise measurement of heat effects, it is worthwhile to discuss how these effects are measured.

A simple way to determine the heat capacity of an insoluble solid is shown in Fig. 5.6. In (a) a Dewar flask contains a known weight of water, a thermometer, and a stirrer. The solid of known weight and temperature (which should be above or below the temperature of the water) is dropped into the Dewar, (Fig. 5.6 (b)). The water is stirred, and temperature readings are taken as a function of time until both solid and water are in thermal equilibrium.

From the temperature changes, the known weights, and the known heat capacity of water, the heat capacity of the solid may be calculated. As one case let us take the system as being comprised of several subsystems, which are the solid, the water, the stirrer, the thermometer, and the Dewar (including the cover). Because of the Dewar and its cap the system is essentially isolated from its surroundings. For the system isolated in this ideal way Q must be zero. The heat effects for the system can be summed up as

$$Q = 0 = C(\text{sol})\, \Delta T(\text{sol}) + C(\text{H}_2\text{O})\, \Delta T(\text{H}_2\text{O})$$
$$+ C(\text{therm})\, \Delta T(\text{therm}) + C(\text{stir})\, \Delta T(\text{stir})$$
$$+ C(\text{Dewar})\, \Delta T(\text{Dewar}) \tag{5.19}$$

In practice, there is some interaction between the system as defined above and its surroundings. The heat effects would be summed up as

$$Q = C\,(\text{surr})\, \Delta T(\text{surr}) = C(\text{sol})\, \Delta T(\text{sol})$$
$$+ C(\text{H}_2\text{O})\, \Delta T(\text{H}_2\text{O})$$
$$+ C(\text{therm})\, \Delta T(\text{therm})$$
$$+ C(\text{stir})\, \Delta T(\text{stir})$$
$$+ C(\text{Dewar})\, \Delta T(\text{Dewar}) \tag{5.20}$$

In precise calorimetric measurements great effort is expended in keeping the value of Q in Eq. (5.20) small or approximately zero. Separate experiments must be carried out to determine the heat capacity of the calorimeter (in the case above, this includes the Dewar, its cap, the thermometer, and the stirrer). For certain experiments the stirring must be vigorous, and the small amount of heat introduced in this way must be accounted for. When all quantities except $C(\text{sol})$ are known, the heat capacity of the solid may be calculated.

Figure 5.7 shows a schematic diagram of a more elaborate type of calorimeter used for measuring heat capacities. The central well A contains a platinum resistance thermometer and an electric heater. The sample is in B. The sample container is suspended inside the heated radiation shield C. By means of the thermocouple G and appropriate regulating circuits it is possible to maintain the temperature of C the same as that of the sample container. Since these two are at the same temperature there will be no heat exchange

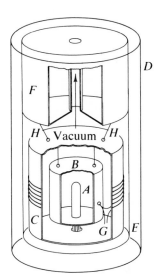

Fig. 5.7. Adiabatic calorimeter at low temperatures.

between them. The chambers inside C are evacuated to a low pressure and the space between C and D is evacuated to a very low pressure. For low-temperature measurements the reservoir F is filled with a liquefied gas such as nitrogen, hydrogen or helium, which maintains the temperature of the shield E close to the desired temperature. In a particular measurement, known quantities of heat are introduced electrically into the sample by the heater in A and temperature changes are recorded.†

5.8 CONCLUDING COMMENTS

The concept of heat has been elucidated by an operational approach in which two bodies having different temperatures are brought into thermal contact and the temperature changes noted. The quantitative measure of heat has been established in terms of a standard substance, water, although now the measure is usually in terms of electrical work. The symbol Q designates the heat absorbed by a system and the numerical value of Q is positive for

† See Chapter 10, "Calorimetry," by J. M. Sturtevant, in *Physical Methods of Organic Chemistry*, 3d ed. (A. Weissberger, ed.). New York: Wiley (Interscience), 1959. An excellent discussion of calorimetry.

heat absorbed and negative for heat evolved by a system. The differential dQ in general is inexact and the integration of dQ to obtain the total heat in going from one state to another must be taken along a designated path.

The heat capacity of a system is defined generally as $C = dQ/dT$. The two heat capacities most generally used are at constant volume and constant pressure.

Exercises

5.1 Discuss the operational definition of heat.

5.2 If you look carefully at the surface of a hot object you will notice that there is a shimmering in the air which appears to rise. Is this shimmering heat? Can you see heat flow? Discuss this phenomenon in terms of what you know about the nature of heat.

5.3 (a) How would you prove that the differential of heat is inexact?

(b) Does it make sense to talk about the ΔQ associated with a change in state?

(c) Are there processes for which the differential of heat is exact?

5.4 A certain quantity of ice at 263° K and 1 atm pressure is added adiabatically and at constant pressure to 100 g of water at 298° K and 1 atm. The specific heat of ice is 0.53 cal g^{-1} deg^{-1} and the specific heat of water is 1.00 cal g^{-1} deg^{-1} and both specific heats may be considered to be independent of the temperature. The heat of fusion of ice at 273° K and 1 atm is 80 cal g^{-1}. Find the final temperature and the quantity of ice at equilibrium when the quantity of ice added is 10 g, 100 g, 1000 g, and 3000 g.

5.5 The molar heat capacity of n-pentane in the gaseous state is represented by the following equation in the range 300–1500° K where T is in °K:

$$\tilde{C}_P = 5.91 + 88.4 \times 10^{-3}T - 274 \times 10^{-7}T^2$$

(a) Calculate the molar heat capacity at 300°, 500°, and 700° K.

(b) Calculate the average molar heat capacity at 400°, 500°, and 600° K by simply averaging the heat capacities calculated at temperatures 100° or 200° above and below 400°, 500° and 600° K.

(c) Compare the molar heat capacities at 500° calculated in (a) and (b) and comment on the difference. Which value is the "true" molar heat capacity?

5.6 A 100 g block of aluminum (specific heat of 0.217 cal g^{-1} deg^{-1}) initially at 373° K is added to 200 g of water at 298° K in a calorimeter. The final temperature of the water, the aluminum, and the calorimeter is 303° K. What is the quantity of heat absorbed by (a) the water, (b) the calorimeter?

5.7 The molar heat capacity of a gas at constant pressure may be represented by the equation $\tilde{C}_P = a + bT + cT^2$ or the equation $\tilde{C}_P = a' + b'T + (c'/T)$ where a, a', b, b', c, and c' are constants. For an isobaric process where the only effect is the heating of n moles of a gas from T_1 to T_2, what is the amount of heat transferred during the process? Use both equations to find general solutions.

5.8 An average man produces about 2500 kcal of heat each day through metabolic activity. If a man were a closed adiabatic system of mass 70kg with the heat capacity of water, what would be the temperature rise of a man in one day? Man is actually an open system and the main mechanism of heat loss is through the evaporation of water. How much water would a man need to evaporate in a day to maintain constant temperature? The heat of vaporization of water at 310° K is 575 cal g^{-1}.

5.9 Calculate Q for the change in state at constant pressure for 10 g of water as shown below:

$$H_2O(\text{sol}, 263° \text{ K}) \rightarrow H_2O(\text{gas}, 473° \text{ K})$$

The specific heat of ice is 0.53 cal g^{-1} deg^{-1}; for water, 1.00 cal g^{-1} deg^{-1}; and for steam, 0.44 cal g^{-1} deg^{-1}. The heat of fusion for water is 80 cal g^{-1} and the heat of vaporization is 540 cal g^{-1}.

5.10 Discuss the determination of the heat capacity of a solid (Fig. 5.6) when the solid and the water are taken as the system and the Dewar, stirrer, and thermometer are taken as the only surroundings of the system.

6 Work

Work is introduced in this chapter as another way in which a system may interact with its surroundings. The development of the concept of work begins with a discussion of mechanical work, particularly the work associated with the pressure and volume changes of a system and the movement of a mass in a gravitational field. At the end of the chapter the concept is generalized to include other types of interactions between a system and its surroundings which are also classified as work.

The concept of work itself may be relatively simple. However, when we apply it in thermodynamics, where we are concerned with both the system and its surroundings, we find that the development of a language required to describe interactions involving work can become a formidable problem. The difficulty arises with the varied types of systems considered, with our specific interest in the system and the surroundings, and with the type of process, whether it is unidirectional or cyclic. These difficulties are discussed in Section 6.3. By our studies we will develop an understanding of work, particularly in the simpler systems. Still we must completely define the system, its surroundings, and the boundary between them; we also must analyze the interaction between the system and its surroundings and be cognizant of our specific interest in the process, whether in the measurement of work or in the description of what has happened to the system or its surroundings or both. In short there is no simple answer in thermodynamics to the question "what is work?"

6.1 GENERAL CONCEPTS

We recognize from experience that when we wish to move an object possessing mass we must do something to the object which may be described as pushing it, pulling it, lifting it, or letting it drop. Such actions are generally described as exerting a force on the object. (When we allow a body to drop in the gravitational field of the earth we recognize that a force is acting on it.) Newton's second law of motion equates the force acting on a body to the time rate of change of momentum of the body. This relation affords a means of defining the unit of force and also a means of measuring the force. Thus the dyne is the force which imparts an acceleration of 1 cm sec^{-1} to a mass of 1 g. Also, if we can measure the acceleration of a body of known and constant mass, we can calculate the force acting on it. More frequently a force is measured by opposing it by known forces *under equilibrium conditions.*†

With the concept of force in hand we can proceed to develop the concept of mechanical work. We recognize that a body, having mass, can be moved by exerting a sufficiently large force on it. This operation is described in words as the performance or the doing of work. The precise definition of work in terms of a differential is based on the mathematical relation

$$dW = \mathbf{f} \cdot \mathbf{ds} \tag{6.1}$$

where dW is the differential quantity of work done by the force $\mathbf{f}$ when the displacement of the body on which the force is exerted is the differential $\mathbf{ds}$. Both the force and the displacement are vector quantities and work is defined in terms of the scalar or dot product of the two vectors. In scalar notation

$$dW = f \cos \alpha \, ds \tag{6.2}$$

where α is the angle between the direction of the force and that of the displacement. Equation (6.2) then states that the differential of the work is the product of the component of the force acting in the direction of the displacement and the differential of the displacement. We have noted by using the symbol dW that the differential of the work is an inexact differential. The implications of this are discussed in later sections.

† O. Redlich, *J. Phys. Chem.*, **66**, 585 (1962).

We see from its definition that work is not measured directly but is obtained by the integration of Eq. (6.1) or Eq. (6.2). The determination of work requires a knowledge of the force and its dependence on the displacement, if any. The unit of work is defined in terms of Eq. (6.1) or Eq. (6.2): If the force is expressed in dynes and the displacement in centimeters, the work is expressed in ergs. Many other units of work are used, but each depends upon the units used for the force and the displacement. With the determination of the relation between units of heat and units of work (Chapter 7), or the definition of the defined calorie, Eq. (5.5), work may be expressed in terms of units of heat, and vice versa.

6.2 WORK ASSOCIATED WITH PRESSURE-VOLUME CHANGES OF A SYSTEM

Our notions relating to work must be expanded for thermodynamic problems over what was discussed in the preceding section. For most problems we are concerned with the pressure-volume properties of a system and with the changes of these quantities for a given process accompanying a change of state. We therefore limit our attention in the next several sections to work associated with pressure-volume changes of a system; in Section 6.3

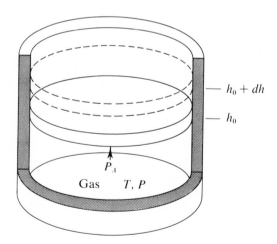

Fig. 6.1. Piston and cylinder arrangement.

we discuss several thought-type experiments in order to consolidate our ideas and to obtain an understanding of the term *work* as used in thermodynamics.

First let us consider a constant mass of gas confined in a piston and cylinder at a given temperature and pressure, as illustrated in Fig. 6.1. The gas is chosen to be the system and the piston and cylinder are chosen as the surroundings. The state of the system is defined by specifying the particular gas, the mass of the gas, its temperature, and its pressure. We assume for the present that the piston is stationary. If the area of the piston is represented by A, the force exerted by the gas on the lower face of the piston is PA, which is the product of the pressure and the area because pressure is defined as force per unit area. If now we allow the piston to move upward by some means through the differential distance dh, the differential amount of work done by the gas is

$$dW = PA \, dh \tag{6.3}$$

But $A \, dh$ is the differential of the volume dV and consequently

$$dW = P \, dV \tag{6.4}$$

Equation (6.4) is the basic equation used to calculate the work associated with pressure-volume changes of a system. While the equation has been developed for a gas as the system, it is equally applicable to all systems whether the substance is a gas, a liquid, a solid, or whether the system exists in two or more phases. It must be emphasized that the force used in Eq. (6.3) or the pressure used in Eq. (6.4) must be that force or pressure which the system exerts on the surroundings *at the boundary* between the system and the surroundings. For example, if we consider the piston to be part of the system rather than a part of the surroundings, the boundary between the system and the surroundings is the upper surface of the piston. Then, if the mass of the piston is m and if the movement of the piston is parallel to the direction of the gravitational field of the earth, the force which the system exerts on the boundary between the system and surroundings is $PA - mg$ and

$$dW = (PA - mg) \, dh \tag{6.5}$$

$$= P \, dV - mg \, dh \tag{6.6}$$

91

where g is the acceleration of gravity. We note here that the equations developed in this section do not give a complete description of the interaction of a system and its surroundings in terms of work. Additional concepts and equations are developed in the next section.

We could have considered a displacement in the downward direction just as easily. In so doing the gas would have been compressed. We describe such a process as one in which work is done on the system. Work can thus be done by the system or on the system and in dealing with numerical values we must be consistent in the sign. The symbols dW and W (the work associated with a finite process) are taken by convention to represent work done by the system. A positive numerical value of W indicates work done by the system and a negative numerical value indicates work done on the system.

Work has been defined in terms of a differential dW. We must integrate the differential in order to get the work done by the system, W, for a finite process. But the integration of Eqs. (6.4), (6.5), and (6.6), cannot be carried out directly. Further knowledge of the pressure is required. We assume for the present that the pressure exerted on the piston by the system is a property of the system. For a single-phase closed system the pressure is a function of the temperature and volume no matter whether the phase is solid, liquid, or gas, or whether it is a pure substance or a solution. For other closed systems the pressure may be a function of the temperature alone or it may be constant. Let us consider the most general case in which the pressure is taken to be a function of both temperature and volume, and make use of Eq. (6.4). The integral taken between limits V_1 and V_2 of the volume may be written as

$$W = \int dW = \int_{V_1}^{V_2} P(T, V)\, dV \tag{6.7}$$

where we emphasize that the pressure P is a function by using the symbol $P(T, V)$. The integrand is thus a function of two independent variables, but the integration is carried out with respect to only one of them. We cannot perform the integration until we know the temperature as a function of the volume. This problem is illustrated in Fig. 6.2, where we use the temperature and volume as the two coordinates and consider a change of state from an initial temperature T_1 and an initial volume V_1 to a final temperature T_2 and a final volume V_2. Three different paths are illustrated.

We may change the volume at a constant temperature T_1 (path a) and then change the temperature at constant volume V_2 (path b). We may change the temperature at constant volume V_1 (path c) and then change the volume at constant temperature T_2 (path d). Or we may follow path e which represents the condition that the temperature is changed as the volume is changed in such a manner that the temperature is a linear function of the volume.

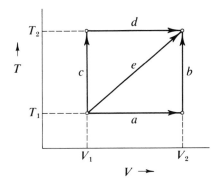

Fig. 6.2. Inexactness of the differential of work.

Actually we may choose to set the temperature as any arbitrary function of the volume; experimentally we would be required to control the temperature in some way so that the temperature of the system followed the arbitrary function as the volume is changed. We see that in choosing such a function we are defining a path along which the process must take place. There are an infinite number of such arbitrary functions and consequently there are an infinite number of such paths; Fig. 6.2 illustrates just three such paths. We find by calculation that the work done by the system along the different paths in going from the initial state (T_1, V_1) to the final state (T_2, V_2) depends upon the path. Therefore dW is an inexact differential and W is not a function. Indeed the work W is associated with a process and an interaction between a system and its surroundings. We cannot write $W = W(T, V)$, which would imply that for any set of values assigned to the temperature and volume there is at least one value of W. Similarly it is incorrect to write ΔW rather than W because ΔW implies a change in the value of a function. We emphasize not only that dW is an inexact differential but also, in any real problem in thermodynamics involving pressure-volume changes of a system, that we must determine or define how the temperature is changed.

93

Equation (6.4) apparently has little relationship to the form of the inexact differential expressions discussed in Chapter 2, Eq. (2.65). The relationship may be readily shown by considering the volume as a function of the temperature and pressure, so that

$$dV = \left(\frac{\partial V}{\partial T}\right)_P dT + \left(\frac{\partial V}{VP}\right)_T dP \tag{6.8}$$

The differential quantity of work may be written as

$$dW = P\left(\frac{\partial V}{\partial T}\right)_P dT + P\left(\frac{\partial V}{\partial P}\right)_T dP \tag{6.9}$$

when Eq. (6.8) is substituted into Eq. (6.4). The similarity of this equation to Eq. (2.65) is clear. Moreover it is readily shown that

$$\left[\frac{\partial [P(\partial V/\partial T)_P]}{\partial P}\right]_T \neq \left[\frac{\partial [P(\partial V/\partial P)_T]}{\partial T}\right]_P$$

6.3 ADDITIONAL CONCEPTS AND SEVERAL SIMPLIFIED EXPERIMENTS

In order to understand some of the problems associated with the meaning of the term *work* and the language used to describe interactions between a system and its surroundings involving work, it is necessary to consider several simplified experiments. First let us consider a given quantity of gas confined by a frictionless piston in a cylinder (Fig. 6.3). The gas is considered as the system and the initial state of the system is defined by the given mass, temperature, and pressure of the gas. The cylinder and piston are considered as part of the surroundings. The total mass of the piston is designated by m. There may be an atmosphere, external to the piston and cylinder, or some other part of the surroundings such as a spring which exerts a force F_e on the piston. The piston is held in place at the level h_0 by suitable lugs. Finally, the cylinder is placed on a rigid, massive base so that there is no movement of the cylinder because of reaction when the gas is allowed to expand. The boundary is the lower surface of the piston.

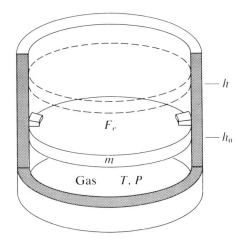

Fig. 6.3. Unlimited expansion of gas.

We now assume that the force exerted on the piston by the gas is greater than the force acting downward. The piston will then move upward and the gas will expand when the lugs are removed. We seek to describe what has happened when the lower surface of the piston attains the level designated as h. For the present purpose of developing the concepts associated with work, it is not necessary to describe the process more completely, for example, as an isothermal, adiabatic, or other process. However, it must be realized that the processes discussed below have not been defined completely. We will return to this problem in Chapter 10. During the actual expansion the state of the gas cannot be defined in terms of the temperature and pressure because turbulence will occur in the gas, and temperature and pressure gradients will develop. The force exerted by the gas during the expansion will be designated by F; this force will not be constant in general and may not be known. The net force acting upward on the lower surface of the piston is $F - mg - F_e$ and according to Newton's second law

$$m \frac{dv}{dt} = F - mg - F_e \qquad (6.10)$$

where v is the velocity of the piston and t the time. Now the differential of the velocity is

$$dv = \left(\frac{dv}{dt}\right) dt \tag{6.11}$$

and the differential of the displacement dh may be written as

$$dh = v \, dt \tag{6.12}$$

When Eqs. (6.10), (6.11), and (6.12) are combined, the equation

$$mv \, dv = (F - mg - F_e) \, dh \tag{6.13}$$

is obtained. This equation may be integrated between the limits 0 and v for the velocity and h_0 and h for the displacement. The result is

$$\tfrac{1}{2}mv^2 = \int_{h_0}^{h} F \, dh - mg(h - h_0) - \int_{h_0}^{h} F_e \, dh \tag{6.14}$$

For purposes of discussion we rewrite this equation as

$$\int_{h_0}^{h} F \, dh = mg(h - h_0) + \int_{h_0}^{h} F_e \, dh + \tfrac{1}{2}mv^2 \tag{6.15}$$

so that the term on the left-hand side of the equation pertains to the system and those on the right-hand side pertain to the surroundings. This equation expresses in mathematical terms the results of the interaction of the system and its surroundings. The force F is the force exerted by the system on the boundary between the system and the surroundings, and hence we can describe the term on the left-hand side of the equation as the work done by the system or, more specifically, the work associated with the force F. If this force is not known we have to devise the surroundings so that the three terms on the right-hand side of the equation can be evaluated. The mass of the piston presents no problem. The force F_e must be known or measurable, and some means of determining the velocity of the piston when its lower surface is at h must be devised. With this knowledge, the three terms can be evaluated and the sum equated to the work done by the system. In this context, each of the three terms has some connotation of work.

So far our interests have resided in the system and in measurement. When we turn our attention to the surroundings, our interpretation of Eq. (6.15) changes. Each of the first two terms involves a displacement and a force exerted by the surroundings on the boundary. We recognize these terms as work terms, each term being associated with a given force, and can say that the work done against the forces mg and F_e results in raising the piston in the gravitational field and in doing work against the force F_e. The last term is the kinetic energy which the piston has at the position h. (Here we accept the concept of kinetic energy defined as $(1/2)mv^2$, but in no way have we defined the concept of energy.) Certainly the kinetic energy of the piston is the result of the system doing work on the surroundings, but we cannot say that the kinetic energy term represents work. With this description of what has occurred in the surroundings we see that work is not conserved; the work done by the force F does not equal the work done against the forces mg and F_e. The difference is the kinetic energy. This difference becomes important when we consider cyclic processes in which an expansion is followed by a compression.

A variation of this experiment illustrates how the language we might use depends upon our interests. We insert lugs into the cylinder wall above the piston so that the piston cannot move beyond the point where its lower surface is at the position h (Fig. 6.4). We idealize the experiment in our

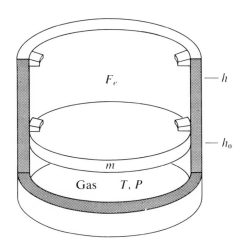

Fig. 6.4. Limited expansion of gas.

thoughts and assume that the piston is stopped instantaneously upon collision with the lugs and that no changes occur in the cylinder, piston, or the lugs as a result of the collision except a temperature change. We further assume that the gas or other device which exerts the force F_e on the upper surface of the piston is separated from the piston and cylinder by an adiabatic membrane and that temperature equilibrium is attained between the piston, cylinder, and the gas within the cylinder. We start the experiment with the gas confined by the piston, with the lower surface of the piston at h_0; then we remove the lower set of lugs and allow the gas to expand and the piston, to collide with the upper set. We observe that the temperature of the gas, the piston, and the cylinder at the end of the experiment is greater than that in the original experiment when the two initial states are the same; that is, the final states in the two experiments are not identical. We can change the temperature of the gas, the cylinder, and the piston to the final temperature in the original experiment by placing a thermal reservoir in contact with the cylinder and allowing heat to flow from the cylinder into the reservoir. (It is only in this sense that we can say anything about heat resulting from the performance of work.)

Equation (6.15) is applicable in this experiment up to the instant of collision, but after collision the kinetic energy of the piston is zero. We postulate that the heat transferred to the reservoir is equivalent to the kinetic energy and therefore write Eq. (6.15) as

$$\int_{h_0}^{h} F \, dh = mg(h - h_0) + \int_{h_0}^{h} F_e \, dh + Q_{res} \tag{6.16}$$

where Q_{res} represents the heat transferred to the reservoir. The analysis of this equation is the same as that for the previous one. The work done by the system and the force F is given by $\int_{h_0}^{h} F \, dh$. If we do not know the force, the value of the integral is determined as the sum of the three terms on the right-hand side of the equation. As before, two of these terms represent work terms associated with given forces and the heat term represents the result of the system doing work on the surroundings and of the collision, but the heat term itself cannot be considered as work. Thus, when we consider the surroundings and apply the word "work" to only those processes involving a force and a displacement, the work done against the forces exerted by the surroundings is the sum only of the first two terms on the right-hand side.

Work again is not conserved and the difference between the work done by the force F and that done against the forces mg and F_e is equal to the heat that has been transferred to the thermal reservoir.

Let us now consider the compression of a gas. The experimental apparatus is similar to that shown in Fig. 6.3 with the exception that the piston is held originally by lugs so that the lower surface of the piston is at the position h. The boundary between the system and the surroundings is again the lower surface of the piston. In order to compress the gas, $F_e' + mg$ must be greater than F', where the symbols have the same meaning as before. The primes are used to indicate that the values of the forces are different from those in the previous experiment; in general, F' will be larger than F and F_e' must be larger than F_e if the compression is to take place. When the lugs are removed, the piston moves downward and we seek to describe what has happened when the lower face of the piston reaches the position h_0. For convenience in this discussion we measure the movement of the piston positively in the downward direction. The equation for this process, similar to Eq. (6.15), is

$$\int_h^{h_0} F' \, dh = mg(h_0 - h) + \int_h^{h_0} F_e' \, dh - \tfrac{1}{2}mv^2 \qquad (6.17)$$

When we are concerned with the system itself the description and the use of Eq. (6.17) is the same as in the previous cases. The term on the left-hand side of the equation represents the work done on the system against the force F'. This work can be determined from the algebraic sum of the three terms on the right-hand side of the equation when F' is not known. However, when we consider the surroundings the situation is again different. The two terms $mg(h_0 - h)$ and $\int_h^{h_0} F_e' \, dh$ involve forces exerted by the surroundings, and thus these terms represent the work done by the two forces. In this context, work is not conserved and the work done against the force F' is less than the work done by the forces mg and F_e', the difference being the kinetic energy imparted to the piston. But the piston is part of the surroundings and the operation of the forces to impart kinetic energy to the piston has no part whatsoever in the interaction between the system and its surroundings. The work done by the surroundings on the system is simply $\int_h^{h_0} F' \, dh$.

Let us return to the expansion case which was first discussed but now we consider the piston to be part of the system. The boundary between the system and the surroundings is the upper surface of the piston, as indicated

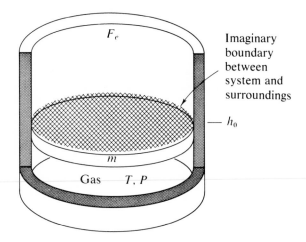

Fig. 6.5. Expansion of gas with piston as part of system.

in Fig. 6.5. The force acting on this boundary in the upward direction is $F - mg$ and that acting in the downward direction is F_e. Equation (6.14), which still applies in this case, becomes

$$\int_{h_0}^{h} F \, dh - mg(h - h_0) - \tfrac{1}{2}mv^2 = \int_{h_0}^{h} F_e \, dh \qquad (6.18)$$

when the terms pertaining to the system are placed on the left-hand side and those pertaining to the surroundings are placed on the right-hand side of the equation. We now have quite a different situation. The only effect of the interaction of the system with its surroundings is that an amount of work equal to $\int_{h_0}^{h} F_e \, dh$ has been done on the surroundings. The quantity is easily evaluated when F_e is known. The raising of the piston in the gravitational field and the imparting of kinetic energy to the piston have no part in the interaction between the system and its surroundings. Certainly, if we desired to evaluate $\int_{h_0}^{h} F \, dh$, we would use Eq. (6.15). However, that part of the work done by the force F in raising the piston and in imparting kinetic energy to it involves only the system itself.

The equation applicable to the process of compression when the piston is taken as part of the system is

$$\int_h^{h_0} F' \, dh - mg(h - h_0) + \tfrac{1}{2}mv^2 = \int_h^{h_0} F_e' \, dh \qquad (6.19)$$

The force exerted by the surroundings on the boundary between the system and surroundings is F_e' and the work associated with this force is $\int_h^{h_0} F_e' \, dh$. This quantity represents the only interaction between the system and its surroundings. The result of this interaction in the system is that a quantity of work $\int_h^{h_0} F' \, dh$ is done against the force F' and kinetic energy is imparted to the piston. The force mg aids in the compression but is not involved in the interaction between the system and its surroundings as measured by the right-hand side of the equation. Work again is not conserved in the sense that $\int_h^{h_0} F_e' \, dh$ is greater than $\int_h^{h_0} (F' - mg) \, dh$ by the kinetic energy of the piston.

We can now summarize the discussion and consolidate our ideas about the interaction of a system with its surroundings in terms of work. The equations applicable when the piston is considered as part of the surroundings are, Eq. (6.15)

$$\int_{h_0}^h F \, dh = \int_{h_0}^h F_e \, dh + mg(h - h_0) + \tfrac{1}{2}mv^2$$

and, Eq. (6.17),

$$\int_h^{h_0} F' \, dh = \int_h^{h_0} F_e' \, dh + mg(h - h_0) - \tfrac{1}{2}mv^2$$

where the first equation applies to the process of expansion and the second to the process of compression. The equations applicable when the piston is considered as part of the system are, Eq. (6.18),

$$\int_{h_0}^h F \, dh - mg(h - h_0) - \tfrac{1}{2}mv^2 = \int_{h_0}^h F_e \, dh$$

for the expansion process and, Eq. (6.19),

$$\int_{h}^{h_0} F' \, dh - mg(h - h_0) + \tfrac{1}{2}mv^2 = \int_{h}^{h_0} F_e' \, dh$$

for the compression process. In developing these equations we have made the measurements of the displacement positive in the direction of the movement of the piston and have determined the sum of the forces acting at the boundary between the system and the surrounding so that the net force acts in the direction of the motion of the piston.

We next consider unidirectional processes, that is, those of either expansion or compression. We observe from Eqs. (6.15) and (6.17) that the result of the interaction of the system and its surroundings in terms of work is given by either of the integrals

$$\int_{h_0}^{h} F \, dh \qquad \text{or} \qquad \int_{h}^{h_0} F' \, dh$$

as the case may be. The integrals are evaluated when necessary by means of the changes occurring in the surroundings as expressed by the terms on the right-hand side of the equations. When the piston is part of the system the result of the interaction of the system and its surroundings is most easily determined by either of the integrals

$$\int_{h_0}^{h} F_e \, dh \qquad \text{or} \qquad \int_{h}^{h_0} F_e' \, dh$$

according to Eq. (6.18) or Eq. (6.19). The appropriate integral measures the change which takes place in the surroundings for either one of the processes.

In cyclic processes we are interested in the difference between the work done on the surroundings in the expansion process and the work done by the surroundings in the compression process. The word "work" in this context refers to the work done on or by the surroundings as determined by the forces exerted by the surroundings on the boundary. According to Eqs. (6.15) and (6.17) the work terms of interest are those involving the forces F_e, F_e' and mg, whereas according to Eqs. (6.18) and (6.19) the terms are those involving F_e and F_e' only. The difference in the interpretation of Eqs. (6.15) and (6.17) between the unidirectional process and the cyclic process results from the kinetic energy of the piston. In the cyclic process, the piston must be stopped at the end of the expansion process and also at the end of the compression process. Although we do not specify here the particular method of stopping the piston, the results are an increase of temperature of some part of the system or the surroundings, or both, or in the transfer of heat to some thermal reservoir, as we discussed in the second experiment. (It is well to recall here that the processes and accompanying changes of state have not been completely defined; we have limited the discussion solely to the work concept.) There is no difficulty in the use of language in relation to the surroundings in cyclic processes when the piston is considered as part of the system because only the forces F_e and F_e' are concerned, according to Eqs. (6.18) and (6.19). The problem of the kinetic energy relates to the system rather than the surroundings, and this problem has already been discussed. In general, more work must be done by the surroundings in the compression process than is done on the surroundings in the expansion process because F_e' must be greater than F_e.

We have not introduced frictional effects in this discussion except possibly in the second experimental case in which the piston was stopped according to an idealized process and measurements were made in a specific manner. In general, when frictional effects are present, the mechanical and thermal interactions between a system and its surroundings become so involved that it is difficult to describe the effects of the interaction, as observed in either the system or surroundings, specifically in terms of heat and work. We might be able to define the boundary in such a way that all effects of friction are confined to the system so that the changes observed and measured in the surroundings could be described clearly in terms of heat and work. The simplification which may be achieved by an appropriate definition of the boundary is illustrated in the two sets of equations, Eqs. (6.15) and (6.17) and Eqs. (6.18) and (6.19). It is evident that the effect of the interaction on the surroundings may be clearly designated as work when the boundary is chosen to include the piston in the system. We must warn, however, that when we define the boundary, including not only its position but its properties, in order to simplify the analysis or description of the interactions, we may introduce a certain degree of artificiality or idealization into the process or into the system and its surroundings. But we try to make the effect of idealization as small as possible so that the results of the analysis and description may approximate the actual process or system and surroundings as closely as possible.

6.4 A LANGUAGE TO DESCRIBE WORK EFFECTS IN THERMODYNAMICS

We are now in a position to extend the meaning of the symbols dW and W beyond that given in Section 6.2. We are here concerned with the interaction between a system and its surroundings. Also, even though we are primarily interested in the system and the changes which take place within it, we find it convenient to arrange the surroundings so that these changes can be determined by changes which occur in the surroundings. We may state that dW for a differential process and W for a finite process, represent the work done by a system on the surroundings as measured by appropriate changes which take place in the surroundings. In simple cases the interpretation of this statement is clear, but if there is any doubt in any specific case it should be interpreted in terms of applicable equations similar to those developed in the preceding section. The statement is shortened usually to "work done by the system on the surroundings" but the meaning of this statement must be well understood. The sign of the values dW and W is always positive for work done by the system on the surroundings. If the value of dW or W is negative then work is actually done on the system by the surroundings, again measured by the changes which take place in the surroundings.†

If it is necessary or if we choose to consider work in any other context, we must clearly define the meaning of the words we use. For example, when we consider any single term in the equations used in the preceding section, we recommend the language of work associated with a specific force. The sign convention would be consistent with Eq. (6.1).

6.5 QUASI-STATIC PROCESSES— EXPANSION AND COMPRESSION

The processes discussed in Section 6.3 are somewhat related to actual experience, but in such processes the force exerted by the gas on the piston is not related directly to the equilibrium properties of the gas. Another

---

†Some authors use the opposite sign convention and care must be taken in studying any thermodynamics text to determine the convention which is used. We have adopted the convention used by most authors in the United States at the present time.

process, idealized to be sure, has been devised in which the force is related to the pressure of the gas. The work done by the system on the surroundings can then be calculated for such processes, which are called *quasi-static*. We choose a gas confined in a frictionless piston and cylinder to be the system, as in the previous examples. The piston is taken to be part of the surroundings so that the boundary is the lower surface of the piston. However, the surroundings are modified as shown in Fig. 6.6. A rod is attached rigidly to the piston; the mass of both the piston and the rod is designated by *m*. A stepped device is used to permit the expansion of the gas and the upward movement of the piston in a succession of incremental steps. The steps are sufficiently small so that the piston never acquires appreciable velocity in any single step. We assume that under such conditions the state of the gas can always be determined both during and after the expansion and that the pressure of

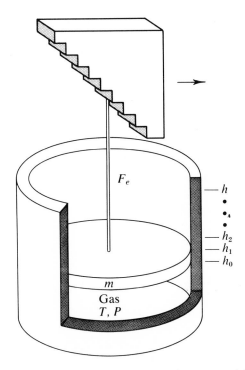

Fig. 6.6. Quasi-static expansion using a stepped device.

the gas can always be taken as a function of the temperature and volume. Then the force exerted by the gas on the lower side of the piston is always PA where P is the pressure of the gas. The force acting downward at the lower surface of the piston is $(F_e - mg)$. For an expansion, PA must be greater than $(F_e + mg)$.

Now consider the piston to be held so that its lower surface is at h_0. The stepped device is moved to the right to release the rod; the piston moves upward but is stopped by the next step so that the lower surface of the piston is at h_1. The collision process is assumed to be the same as that discussed in Section 6.3. Although the kinetic energy of the piston just before hitting the step is small, it will still be finite. At the time of the collision the kinetic energy becomes zero and a temperature increase of the gas, piston, cylinder, and stepped device is observed. The work done by the system on the surroundings is given by the equation

$$\int_{h_0}^{h_1} PA \, dh = mg(h_1 - h_0) + \int_{h_0}^{h_1} F_e \, dh + (\tfrac{1}{2}mv^2)_1 \tag{6.20}$$

or

$$\int_{V_0}^{V_1} P \, dV = mg(h_1 - h_0) + \int_{h_0}^{h_1} F_e \, dh + (\tfrac{1}{2}mv^2)_1 \tag{6.21}$$

according to Eq. (6.15). The kinetic energy term is included to account for all effects even though the kinetic energy appears as an equivalent quantity of heat in the sense defined in Section 6.3.

After the expansion the system and the surroundings are permitted to come to equilibrium. Then the device is again moved to the right and the whole process is repeated. The work done by the system on the surroundings is given by

$$\int_{V_1}^{V_2} P \, dV = mg(h_2 - h_1) + \int_{h_1}^{h_2} F_e \, dh + (\tfrac{1}{2}mv^2)_2 \tag{6.22}$$

Each step is repeated until the lower surface of the piston reaches the position h. The total work done by the system is given by the sum of Eqs. (6.21) and (6.22), etc., so that

$$\int_{V_0}^{V_h} P \, dV = mg(h - h_0) + \int_{h_0}^{h} F_e \, dh + \sum_i (\tfrac{1}{2}mv^2)_i \qquad (6.23)$$

where V_h is the volume of the gas when the piston is at h and the $\sum$ sign indicates the summation of all the kinetic energy effects. The total work done by the system on the surroundings, $\int_{V_0}^{V_h} P \, dV$, can be calculated and will be larger here than in the initial example. The work done against the forces mg and F_e, $mg(h - h_0) + \int_{h_0}^{h} F_e \, dh$, can also be calculated. The difference gives the total kinetic energy imparted to the piston, $\sum_i(\tfrac{1}{2}mv^2)_i$, the effects of which appear as an increase in temperature or as heat.

A quasi-static compression can be accomplished by the use of a similar stepped device when $F_e + mg$ is greater than PA. The concept of quasi-static processes can be expanded to many other processes. The important point is that the process is devised so that during the various steps of the process the forces operating are determinable from the equilibrium properties of the system and of the surroundings. In order to accomplish this the kinetic energy associated with any part of the system or surroundings in each step must be small.

6.6 REVERSIBLE PROCESSES—EXPANSION AND COMPRESSION

We considered an idealized process, which is a fair approximation to a real process (with the exception of frictional interactions), in Section 6.3. In Section 6.5, we considered a much more idealized process. For each process there is a limiting process called a *reversible* process. The concept of reversible processes is extremely important to the understanding of the second law of thermodynamics and to the concept of equilibrium in thermodynamics. In each of the previous sections, the net force $F - mg - F_e$ or $PA - mg - F_e$ was not zero. In the limiting case of the *reversible* process, the net force is zero; that is, the forces are balanced. Actually in such cases no movement of the piston can take place. We may, however, conceive of the difference between the forces as being infinitesimal and consider the limit as this difference goes to zero. A reversible process may be considered as one whose direction is reversed by an infinitesimal change in one of the forces. All other processes are called *irreversible* processes.

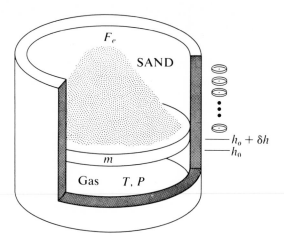

Fig. 6.7. Grains of sand are removed one at a time and placed in containers on right.

In a reversible process, the forces operating are determined by the equilibrium properties of the system and of the surroundings, just as in the case of a quasi-static process. A reversible process is quasi-static but a quasi-static process may or may not be reversible. As an example of a reversible process, let us consider that the lower surface of the piston is at h_0 and that PA equals $mg + F_e$, as shown in Fig. 6.7. A part of the mass of the piston is composed of extremely fine grains of sand. We remove one grain of sand, thus decreasing the mass of the piston by an infinitesimal amount, δm. The piston would move upward over an infinitesimal distance δh. Newton's second law gives the relation

$$(m - \delta m) \frac{dv}{dt} = g \, \delta m \tag{6.24}$$

which yields

$$\tfrac{1}{2}(m - \delta m)v^2 = g \, \delta m \, \delta h \tag{6.25}$$

for the kinetic energy of the piston when it reaches the position $h + \delta h$. The kinetic energy is thus proportional to the product of two infinitesimals and is extremely small. In the limit that δm goes to zero, the kinetic energy also goes to zero. The state of the gas after the infinitesimal expansion is easily defined in terms of its temperature and volume or pressure. Note that the gas could be compressed by replacing the one grain of sand.

We continue to remove one grain of sand at a time until the piston has reached the position h. At no time does the piston attain any sensible kinetic energy. In the limit that δm goes to zero, the work done by the system on the surroundings in such an expansion is

$$W = \int_{V_0}^{V} P(T, V)\, dV \tag{6.26}$$

This quantity of work is also equal to the work done against the forces mg and F_e so that

$$W = \int_{h_0}^{h} mg\, dh + \int_{h_0}^{h} F_e\, dh \tag{6.27}$$

We will be concerned with such processes throughout this book. While we have used a gas as the system, the concepts and equations which have been developed are equally applicable to any system, whether it is a gas, a liquid, or a solid, or whether it is composed of a single phase or several phases.

6.7   WORK EFFECTS AND IDEAL GASES

The work done by the gas on the surroundings in an expansion (or compression by choice of the limits) is

$$W = \int_{V_1}^{V_2} P(T, V)\, dV \tag{6.28}$$

for quasi-static or reversible processes when the gas is taken as the system and the force acting on the boundary results only from the pressure of the gas. To be able to evaluate the integral in Eq. (6.28) we must specify the path along which the process proceeds, by designating how the temperature of the gas is changed as the volume changes; that is, the temperature must be given as a function of the volume. The pressure is then determined by an appropriate equation of state. For an ideal gas, $P = nRT/V$ is the function of P to be used in Eq. (6.28).

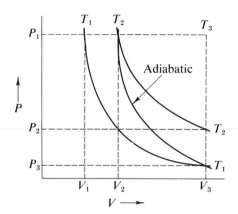

Fig. 6.8. Adiabatic and isothermal paths of integration.

1. First consider the case of the isobaric quasi-static expansion at P_1 from T_1 to T_2 (see Fig. 6.8). Since the pressure is constant it may be placed outside the integral sign in Eq. (6.28) to give

$$W = P_1 \int_{V_1}^{V_2} dV = P_1(V_2 - V_1) = nR(T_2 - T_1) \tag{6.29}$$

If the expansion were to T_3, then Eq. (6.29), would become

$$W = P_1 \int_{V_1}^{V_3} dV = P_1(V_3 - V_1) = nR(T_3 - T_1) \tag{6.30}$$

The units of work associated with Eq. (6.29) or Eq. (6.30) would be literatmospheres if P is in atmospheres and V is in liters or in the same units used for R.

One important special case of an isobaric expansion of a gas concerns the venting of gas from a cylinder or other container to the atmosphere, as is

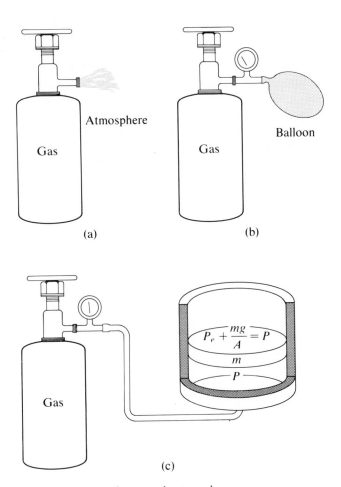

Fig. 6.9. Venting of a gas to the atmosphere.

shown in Fig. 6.9. There are a number of difficulties in obtaining the work done by the gas on the surroundings in Fig. 6.9(a):

(1) There is no boundary for the gas to expand against; (2) the gas and the surroundings mix, and in attempting to make the process reversible, it will be extremely difficult (if not impossible) to unmix the gas and the atmosphere; and (3) we cannot discuss work effects until the system, its surroundings, and

the nature of the boundary between them are carefully defined. One method of getting around these objections is illustrated in Fig. 6.9(b) where the gas expands into a balloon which is considered to be the boundary between the gas and the atmosphere.

The system is the gas and the surroundings are the cylinder, the valve, the balloon, and the atmosphere external to the balloon. We assume that the balloon has no tension. When the gas is allowed to pass through the valve into the balloon at a sufficiently slow rate the difference between the pressure of the gas in the balloon and the pressure exerted by the atmosphere P_e is very small. Then the work done by the gas on the surroundings when P_e is constant is

$$W = P(V_f - V_i) = P_e(V_f - V_i) \tag{6.31}$$

where V_f and V_i are respectively the final and initial volumes of the balloon. The change of pressure of the gas across the valve occurs within the system and enters in no way in the work done by the system on the surroundings. A more controlled way of carrying out this expansion is shown in Fig. 6.9(c) where the pressure of the gas is just balanced by the combined pressure exerted by the atmosphere and the frictionless piston of mass m. Thus $P = P_e + (mg/A)$. The process may be carried out quasi-statically by letting out gas from the cylinder at an infinitely slow rate. The work done by the gas is given by Eq. (6.31) where the volumes now refer to the piston and cylinder arrangement. In the process shown in Fig. 6.9(a) we can talk only about the gas doing work if we can place a suitable boundary, imaginary or otherwise, between the system and its surroundings. If this is not done the problem is indeterminate.

A second, somewhat similar, isobaric case is the evaporation of a liquid. This is illustrated in Fig. 6.10. In Fig. 6.10(a) the process is carried out under such conditions that $P = P_e + (mg/A)$ at all times while the pressure of the vapor is exerted on a boundary at the bottom surface of the piston. The work done by the gas on the surroundings is given by Eq. (6.31). If the vessel is open to the atmosphere and some liquid evaporates, the problem is once again indeterminate. We can talk of the system doing work in the case shown in Fig. 6.10(b) only if we imagine a massless boundary between the system and the atmosphere. It is only in this latter sense that the system is sufficiently defined and distinct so that we can talk about the system exerting a force on the boundary and doing work on the surroundings.

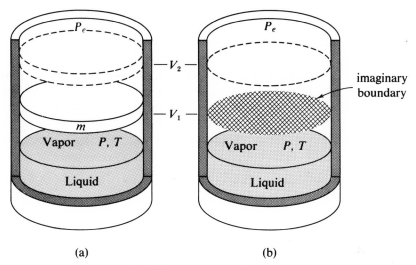

Fig. 6.10.   Evaporation of a liquid.

2. For an isochoric process the volume of the system is constant, dV is zero, and therefore W is zero. It is not possible for the system to do work in an isochoric process.

3. For the isothermal expansion at the temperature T_1 from the volume V_1 or the pressure P_1 to the volume V_3 or pressure P_3, the work done on the surroundings is

$$W = \int_{V_1}^{V_3} P(T, V)\, dV = nRT_1 \int_{V_1}^{V_3} \frac{dV}{V} = nRT_1 \ln \frac{V_3}{V_1} \qquad (6.32)$$

When the ideal gas equation of state is used to substitute pressures for the volumes this expression becomes

$$W = nRT_1 \ln \frac{P_1}{P_3} \qquad (6.33)$$

4. For the adiabatic expansion of a gas, $Q = 0$ and the temperature always

113

decreases. The adiabatic equation of state for an ideal gas is

$$PV^\gamma = k \qquad (6.34)$$

where $\gamma = C_P/C_V$. This ratio is independent of the temperature for an ideal monatomic gas. The constant k is determined for any initial state from the known values of P, V, and γ for that state. The work done by the system on the surroundings for a quasi-static or reversible adiabatic expansion of an ideal monatomic gas (see Fig. 6.8) is given by

$$W = \int_{V_2}^{V_3} P(T, V) \, dV = k \int_{V_2}^{V_3} \frac{dV}{V} = k \left(\frac{V^{-\gamma+1}}{-\gamma + 1} \right)\Big|_{V_2}^{V_3} \qquad (6.35)$$

or

$$W = \frac{k}{1 - \gamma} (V_3^{1-\gamma} - V_2^{1-\gamma}) \qquad (6.36)$$

6.8 OTHER TYPES OF WORK

So far in our discussion of work we have considered only two types: (1) P-V work and (2) work in a gravitational field for which $dW = \pm mg \, dh$. The $\pm$ sign is used in this last expression to emphasize the necessity of determining the appropriate sign for any system and process. We choose to make dh positive for an upward displacement in the earth's gravitational field. If now the system raises a mass which is part of the surroundings then work is done by the system on the surroundings and dW is positive. But if the system itself is raised in the gravitational field, work is done on the system by the surroundings and dW is negative.

There are other types of interaction between a system and its surroundings which are classified as work. In each case we find that an intensive quantity, which we come to recognize as a generalized force, is associated with the differential of a conjugate extensive quantity, which we recognize as a generalized displacement. We require further that any single generalized displacement be associated with only one mode of interaction between the system and the surroundings. The product of the dimensions of the two quantities must give the same dimensions as those obtained in mechanical work. From the operational point of view the concept of a generalized force can be developed only by observation and description of the appropriate phenomena coupled with the requirements stated above.

A galvanic cell or battery is considered as a system capable of doing *electrical* work on the surroundings. In this case the generalized force is the electromotive force (emf) of the cell and the generalized displacement is the quantity of electricity which passes through the cell. The expression for electrical work is then

$$dW = \mathscr{E} \, dc \tag{6.37}$$

where $\mathscr{E}$ is the emf of the cell and c is the quantity of electricity. When $\mathscr{E}$ is expressed in volts and c in coulombs, the unit of work is the joule. There is an arbitrariness in the sign of the emf or in the direction of flow of electricity. In chemical thermodynamics the signs of $\mathscr{E}$ and dc are chosen so that dW is positive for the case in which a cell does work on the surroundings. The maximum emf for a given cell is observed under reversible conditions in which the emf of the cell is opposed by an equal and opposite emf.

One or more surfaces are always present in a thermodynamic system. Such surfaces are the interfaces between the container and the system or between two or more phases in the system itself. Again we find from experience that a force, called surface tension, is associated with such surfaces and that work is associated with a change of the area of the surface. The differential of the work is then

$$dW = -\sigma \, dA \tag{6.38}$$

where σ is the surface tension and A the area of the surface. Here the negative sign is used because work is generally done on the system when the surface area is increased. Reversible conditions are obtained when the surface tension is opposed by an equal and opposite force. In most cases the values of the thermodynamic functions for the surface are so small compared with those for the bulk system that surface effects can be neglected. However, when the surface phenomenon is of special interest or when the effect of the surface is large, as in the case of a soap film or the rise of a liquid in a capillary tube, then we must be concerned with surface work as given in Eq. (6.38).

The stretching of a wire or rubber band also involves work. Here a force is exerted by the surroundings on the wire considered as the system. The displacement is the change of length l of the wire. The equation for such work is

$$dW = -F \, dl \tag{6.39}$$

where F is the force exerted on the wire and is called the tension.

Work is also associated with the magnetization of a system in a magnetic field and with the polarization of a system when placed in an electrostatic field. However, the concepts in these cases are somewhat more complicated than the other types of work which have been discussed, and consequently these are not considered further.

It is still important with these additional types of work to clearly define the system, the surroundings, and the boundary, and to be very careful in the language used in describing the interactions in terms of work.

6.9 CONCLUDING COMMENTS

The concept of work has been developed in this chapter by a study of the mechanical interactions which may take place between one particular system and its surroundings. Mechanical interactions between other types of systems and their surroundings may present problems similar to those discussed here. Problems can be simplified frequently by the judicious choice of the boundary between the system and its surroundings so that the effects which are observed in the surroundings can be clearly classified in terms of heat or work. Because of the variety of systems and various mechanical modes of interaction which may take place between them and their surroundings, a strict definition of work which is applicable in all cases is not easily obtained; rather ideas concerning work are developed by studying the interaction of many different systems with their specific surroundings. We have made one statement concerning the meaning of the symbols dW and W which we believe is adequate for the purposes of this book.

In general, work is defined in terms of a differential

$$dW = X \, dx \tag{6.40}$$

where X represents a generalized force and x the conjugate generalized displacement. The differential dW is inexact and no function W exists. The force depends upon the process, and under quasi-static or reversible conditions it is a function of the independent variables which must be used to define the state of the system. The signs are chosen so that dW and consequently W are positive for work done by the system.

Three types of processes have been discussed, an approximation to a real process, a quasi-static process, and a reversible process. A reversible process is one which takes place under the condition that the forces are balanced or one in which the direction of the process can be reversed by an infinitesimal change of one of the forces. In both the reversible and quasi-static processes, the forces are determined from the equilibrium properties of the system and of the surroundings. In these two processes no part of the system or surroundings can acquire any sensible amount of kinetic energy.

Exercises

6.1 Design a device for the quasi-static compression of a gas and discuss the factors which must be considered for the device to work properly.

6.2 One mole of gas is confined in a frictionless piston and cylinder. Obtain expressions for the work done by the gas for the isothermal quasi-static expansion of the gas from a volume V_1 to a volume V_2 when the equation of state is (a) $PV = RT$, (b) $PV = RT + B/V$, (c) $PV = RT + B'P + C'P^2$, where B, B', and C' are constants.

6.3 The adiabatic equation of state for one mole of an ideal gas is $PV^\gamma = k$, where $\gamma = C_P/C_V$ and k is a quantity which is constant for any given adiabatic change of state but whose value is dependent upon the initial conditions. For a monatomic ideal gas $C_P = (5/2)R$ and $C_V = (3/2)R$. Calculate the work done by the gas when one mole of a monatomic ideal gas is expanded (1 dm $=$ 10 cm) (a) from 1 dm^3 to 100 dm^3, starting at 298° K; (b) from 100 atm to 1 atm, starting at 298° K.

6.4 A system is composed of liquid water and water vapor at equilibrium at 373° K and 1 atm. Calculate the work done by the system when 2 moles of water are evaporated quasi-statically at 373° K.

6.5 A piece of apparatus is composed of two rigid flasks connected together by a stopcock. One flask contains a gas at a given temperature and pressure and the other flask is evacuated. Consider the gas to be the system and the flasks to be the boundary separating the system from the surroundings. How much work is done by the system when the stopcock is opened?

6.6 A cylinder with a movable piston contains n moles of an ideal gas. Consider a path indicated in Fig. 6.11.

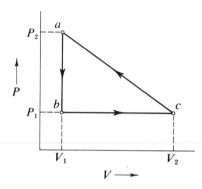

Fig. 6.11.

(a) Develop an expression in terms of P_1, V_1, P_2, and V_2 for the amount of work done quasi-statically on the surroundings for the cyclic path or process going from a to b to c and back to a.

(b) What relation does the area of the triangle have to this work?

6.7 The equation of state for one mole of a certain gas is given by

$$PV = RT\left(1 + \frac{B}{V}\right)$$

where $B = (-11{,}000 + 20T)$ cm^3 mole^{-1}. The gas is confined in a piston and cylinder. Calculate the work done by the gas quasi-statically on the surroundings along each of the two paths:

(a) $A(g, 20{,}000$ cm^3, $300°$ K$) \rightarrow A(g, 60{,}000$ cm^3, $300°$ K$)$
    $A(g, 60{,}000$ cm^3, $300°$ K$) \rightarrow A(g, 60{,}000$ cm^3, $500°$ K$)$

(b) $A(g, 20{,}000$ cm^3, $300°$ K$) \rightarrow A(g, 20{,}000$ cm^3, $500°$ K$)$
    $A(g, 20{,}000$ cm^3, $500°$ K$) \rightarrow A(g, 60{,}000$ cm^3, $500°$ K$)$

6.8 One mole of an ideal gas at 10 atm pressure and $244°$ K is contained in a rigid cylinder. The cylinder is connected through a valve to a piston and cylinder arrangement. The rigid cylinder and the piston and cylinder are contained in a thermostat at $244°$ K. The volume between the valve and the face of the piston is negligible. The valve is now just opened and the gas leaks slowly through and pushes the piston against a constant pressure of 1 atm until the pressure of the entire gas becomes 1 atm. The temperature is kept constant at 244° K. Calculate the work done quasi-statically by the gas on the surroundings.

6.9 One mole of a liquid is confined in a piston and cylinder at 1 atm pressure. The coefficient of expansion of the liquid is 10^{-3} deg^{-1}. Calculate the work done when the temperature is raised from 300° K to 500° K. The pressure is kept constant and no liquid evaporates. The molar volume of the liquid at 0° C is 100 cm^3 mole^{-1}.

6.10 Discuss the relationships involving work when a gas contained in a cylinder is allowed to pass through a valve into a balloon which has tension. Refer to Fig. 6.9(b).

6.11 Show that Eq. (6.36) can be written as

$$W = \frac{nR}{1 - \gamma}(T_1 - T_2)$$

7 The First Law of Thermodynamics— The Energy Function

We have developed the concepts of heat and work separately and have discussed the measurement of these quantities for the simpler cases. In considering the first law of thermodynamics we are concerned with the combined effects of these interactions on the system. It is the *system* with which we are concerned. Our studies lead to the first law of thermodynamics and the definition of the energy function. This function is a function of the independent variables which are used to define the state of a system. We are able, then, to calculate the difference between the values of the energy function for a given change of state without experimentally determining the values of Q and W for a process associated with the change of state. Conversely, with a knowledge of the change of the values of the energy function for a given change of state the values of Q and W for a process associated with the change of state may be calculated. The use of the first law is illustrated by applying it to gases, particularly to ideal gases.

7.1 RELATIONSHIP BETWEEN HEAT AND WORK

Our ideas of heat and work have been developed in terms of two independent and quite different operations. In order to study the combined effects on a system of the transference of heat and the performance of work, a relation between heat and work must be determined. A significant contribution was made by Count Rumford in 1798 as he observed thermal effects

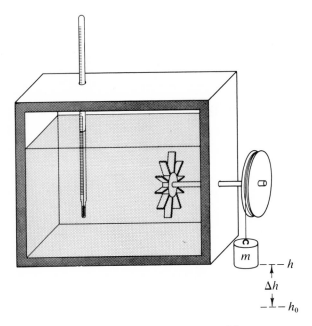

Fig. 7.1. Paddle-wheel movement caused by falling mass

in the boring of cannon. Probably the most crucial experiments were performed by Joule in the years 1840–1850. We discuss only one such experiment here.

We consider a specified amount of water in a container surrounded by an adiabatic, rigid wall as shown in Fig. 7.1. A rigid shaft passes through this wall into the water and paddle blades are attached to this end of the shaft. A device is constructed at the other end of the shaft so that the shaft is rotated solely by the lowering of a mass in the earth's gravitational field. We define the system as the water, the container, the paddle blades, the shaft, and the device, and the surroundings as the mass in the gravitational field. It is observed by means of a thermometer that the temperature of the system, increases when the shaft is rotated. All possible precautions are taken so that the only effect in the system is the increase in temperature and the only effect in the surroundings is the lowering of the mass. At the start of the experiment the initial temperature of the system is measured and the position of the mass is determined. Then the mass is allowed to move downward a specified

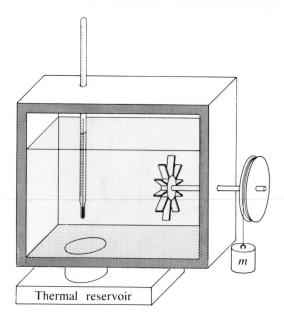

Fig. 7.2. Thermal reservoir in contact with stirred bath.

distance. The final temperature of the system is determined after temperature equilibrium is attained. The work done by the surroundings on the system is $mg\ \Delta h$, where m is the mass and Δh is the distance through which the mass is moved. The same change of state which has occurred in the system (the increase of temperature) is also accomplished by placing a thermal reservoir consisting of the standard thermometric substance in thermal contact with the system as shown in Fig. 7.2. Thus the quantity of heat required to raise the temperature of the system over the same interval is measured. These experiments determine the quantity of heat which must be transferred to the system to accomplish the same temperature change in the system as that observed when a known quantity of work is done on the same system. Joule determined that one 15-deg calorie was equivalent to 4.155 joules. The present relation, Eq. (5.5), is that one defined calorie is equivalent to 4.1840 joules. This last value is based on many refined and precise experiments.

A variation of this experiment is to remove heat from the system after the work has been done on it so that the system is brought to its original state.

This is a cyclic process and the result is that the amount of heat removed from the system is equal to the work done on the system when the same units are used for heat and work. All of the experiments which have been performed to determine the relation between the units of heat and those of work can be considered as cyclic processes, and the results are always the same. Many other cyclic processes of a different nature may be considered but processes in which measurements of heat and work are made always yield the same result. The conclusion obtained from these experiments leads to the first law of thermodynamics.

7.2 THE FIRST LAW OF THERMODYNAMICS— THE ENERGY FUNCTION

All experience has shown that for a closed system the cyclic integral of the quantity $(dQ - dW)$ is zero, independent of the process, or

$$\oint (dQ - dW) = 0 \tag{7.1}$$

This equation is a mathematical expression of the first law of thermodynamics. The law results from experience and there is no other proof. We note that the system is closed and that the interactions between the system and its surroundings are those which can be definitely classified in terms of heat and work.

The fact that the cyclic integral expressed in Eq. (7.1) is zero for all cyclic processes indicates that $(dQ - dW)$ is an exact differential and therefore is the differential of a function. We call this function the energy function and use the symbol E to represent the function. Then the differential of the energy is given by†

$$dE = dQ - dW \tag{7.2}$$

This equation is another mathematical statement of the first law.

The energy function is a function of the state variables which are used to

---

† The sign convention is consistent with the definition of dQ and dW. The value of the energy function increases when heat is transferred to the system and decreases when the system performs work on the surroundings.

define the state of the system; the value of the energy function for a given state is determined by the values assigned to the state variables. The function is defined only in terms of its differential, and the absolute value of the energy function for any given state of a system is not known. However, the difference between the values of the energy function in two states is determinable and is obtained by integration. Because dE is an exact differential, the difference is independent of the path followed in going from one state to the other. Thus, for the change of state represented as

State $A \rightarrow$ State B

we have

$$\int_A^B dE = E_B - E_A = \Delta E \tag{7.3}$$

The value of ΔE is independent of the path followed in going from state A to state B. For any change of state the symbol ΔE always refers, by convention, to the difference between the value of the energy function for the final state and that for the initial state. Also we obtain

$$\Delta E = Q - W \tag{7.4}$$

from Eq. (7.2) on integration. We observe that for any specific finite change of state the values of both Q and W depend upon the process used in going from the initial state to the final state, but the difference does not. In a cyclic process for which the initial and final states are identical, ΔE is, of course, zero.

When a system is isolated so that no interactions can take place between the system and the surroundings, both Q and W are zero and the value of ΔE must be zero. We therefore conclude that *the value of the energy function of an isolated system is constant*. This is another statement of the first law and is *the law of the conservation of energy*. No matter what changes of state may occur in an isolated system the value of the energy function is always a constant.

All machines which perform work on the surroundings can be devised to operate in cycles. If we take the machine as the system the value of the energy function returns to its original value at the end of any cycle. Then ΔE equals zero and Q equals W; that is, the work done by the system on the surroundings in the cyclic operation must equal the heat absorbed by the system. A perpetual motion machine of the first kind is one which would do work on the surroundings without absorbing an equivalent amount of heat. The first law denies the possibility of such a machine, and the fact that no such machine has yet been devised is further confirmation of the validity of the law.

The changes of the value of the energy function for a given change of state can be divided into several classifications and these classifications depend upon the effects of the interactions between the system and its surroundings on the system itself. If the interactions result in imparting kinetic energy to the overall system or changing its kinetic energy or, more exactly, if the interactions cause the center of mass of the system to move through space with a finite velocity or results in a change of the velocity of the center of mass, we can consider the change of the value of the energy function as a change of the kinetic energy of the system. If the change of the value of the energy function depends upon a change of the position of the system in some field, such as a change of the position of the center of mass in the gravitational field of the earth, the change may be described as a change in the potential energy of the system. Other interactions such as the addition or removal of heat result in effects within the system; here we may speak of changes in the value of the internal energy of the system. If we choose to designate the energy function, defined by Eq. (7.2) as the total energy function, the change of the value of the total energy function may be written as

$$\Delta E = \Delta U + \Delta E_k + \Delta E_p \tag{7.5}$$

where ΔU is the change in the internal energy; ΔE_k, the change in the kinetic energy; and ΔE_p, the change in the potential energy of the system. In many applications of thermodynamics, particularly those of an engineering nature, the classification indicated in Eq. (7.5) may be conveniently used. In many other applications the system has no kinetic energy as defined in this paragraph and the interactions cause no change in the potential energy, so that there is no distinction between the changes of the total energy function and those of the internal energy function. For every specific problem those variables must be determined which define the state of the system and whose values are changed by the interactions. The change of the values of these variables determines the change of the value of the energy function. There may be other state variables whose values are not changed and therefore do not influence the change of the value of the energy function. We can say that the energy function is not a function of these latter variables for the specific problem. The variables which must be used in the specific problem will largely determine whether it is convenient to classify the change of the value of the energy function as shown in Eq. (7.5). In any case the choice must be clearly indicated and the symbols defined. In this book we use the symbol E to designate the energy function as defined by Eq. (7.2) and make no distinction between the total energy and the internal energy. In essentially all cases, ΔE_k and ΔE_p are zero.

Throughout this section we have used the expressions "energy function" and "the change of the value of the energy function" in order to emphasize that the energy is a function. We shorten these expressions for convenience and by convention in the remainder of the book to "the energy" and "the change of energy."

7.3   OTHER TYPES OF INTERACTION AND THE FIRST LAW OF THERMODYNAMICS

The development of the concepts of heat and work, the determination of the relationship between heat and work, and the formulation of the first law and its gradual acceptance took place over a period of many years. As the years passed, interactions which could not be classified easily as heat or work were investigated; one such interaction is that between electromagnetic radiation and a system. With each new interaction the validity of the first law with respect to that interaction must be examined. It must be determined that the change of the energy of a system for a change of state involving the interaction is dependent only on the initial and final states and is independent of the path, or in other words that the energy of any isolated system is still constant. In carrying out the necessary experimental studies we obtain more and more accurate concepts of the phenomenon being studied; we learn how to define the system, the surroundings, and the boundary so that an analysis of the effects of the interactions may be made; and finally we develop the mathematical relationships required to define the energy function with respect to the new interaction. No exception to the first law has been found yet. With the general acceptance of the first law and with confidence in its validity, we become more concerned with the energy function and its properties in relation to all types of interactions and we are less concerned, at least from a scientific point of view, with the specific relation of the concepts of heat and work to the energy function. This is not to say that the concepts of heat and work are no longer important; we continue to consider these interactions in the development of thermodynamics in this book.

7.4   SOME GENERAL RELATIONS INVOLVING THE ENERGY FUNCTION

The differential of work in Eq. (7.2) includes all possible forms of work which can be performed on or by a system. If the work is restricted to pressure-volume work in quasi-static processes, and all other forms of work are excluded by keeping the appropriate state variables constant, the differential of the work will be given by $P\,dV$, and dE is given by

$$dE = dQ - P\,dV \tag{7.6}$$

For an adiabatic process, $dQ = 0$ and $dE = -P\,dV$, and for this condition the differential of work is exact. For a process at constant volume, $dW = P\,dV = 0$ and $dE = dQ$, or for this condition the differential of heat is exact.

Experience has shown that the energy for a closed system (that is, constant n) can be written as a function of the temperature and volume, $E = E(T, V)$, and therefore

$$dE = \left(\frac{\partial E}{\partial T}\right)_V dT + \left(\frac{\partial E}{\partial V}\right)_T dV \tag{7.7}$$

For an isochoric process, $dV = 0$ and $dE = (\partial E/\partial T)_V\, dT$. Also for an isochoric process, $dE = dQ = dQ$. From Eq. (5.8), it is seen that $dQ = C_V\,dT$ where C_V is the heat capacity at constant volume. By comparing this equation for dQ with the one for dE at constant volume we observe that

$$C_V = \left(\frac{\partial E}{\partial T}\right)_V \tag{7.8}$$

This relation is the definition of the heat capacity at constant volume in terms of a partial derivative of the energy function. For an isothermal process, $dT = 0$ and Eq. (7.7) becomes

$$dE = \left(\frac{\partial E}{\partial V}\right)_T dV \tag{7.9}$$

It is shown in Chapter 11 that

$$\left(\frac{\partial E}{\partial V}\right)_T = T\left(\frac{\partial P}{\partial T}\right)_V - P \tag{7.10}$$

This expression must be accepted here without proof. (Its proof requires the second law of thermodynamics.)

The combination of Eqs. (7.7), (7.8), and (7.10) gives

$$dE = C_V\, dT + \left[T\left(\frac{\partial P}{\partial T}\right)_V - P \right] dV \tag{7.11}$$

This equation affords the means of calculating the change of energy of a

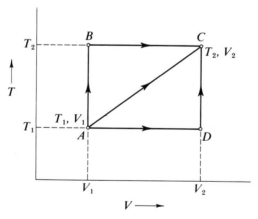

Fig. 7.3

closed system for a change of temperature, a change of volume, or a combination of a change of both temperature and volume from known properties of the system. In order to evaluate the coefficients of Eq. (7.11) as a function of the volume and temperature an equation of state for the system is necessary. These considerations are illustrated in Fig. 7.3. We consider a closed system whose initial state is at A, where the initial temperature and volume are designated as T_1 and V_1. The values of the independent variables in the final state are designated as T_2 and V_2 at C. Three paths ABC, ADC, and the diagonal AC are illustrated. The difference in the values of the energy function at C and A can be calculated by the equation

$$\Delta E = E_C - E_A = \int_{T_1}^{T_2} (C_V)_{V_1} \, dT + \int_{V_1}^{V_2} \left[T \left(\frac{\partial P}{\partial T} \right)_V - P \right]_{T_2} dV \quad (7.12)$$

along the path ABC. In this equation C_V is a function of the temperature but is evaluated at V_1 and $[T(\partial P/\partial T)_V - P]$ is a function of the volume evaluated at T_2. Along the path ADC the change of energy is

$$\Delta E = \int_{T_1}^{T_2} (C_V)_{V_2} \, dT + \int_{V_1}^{V_2} \left[T \left(\frac{\partial P}{\partial T} \right)_V - P \right]_{T_1} dV \quad (7.13)$$

where now C_V is evaluated at V_2 and $[T(\partial P/\partial T)_V - P]$ is evaluated at T_1. Along the path AC, one variable would have to be eliminated in Eq. (7.12) by means of a linear relation between the temperature and volume determined by the line AC.

The energy could be given as a function of the temperature and pressure but the resulting equations are somewhat more complicated. Thus we may give $E = E(T, P)$ for which

$$dE = \left(\frac{\partial E}{\partial T} \right)_P dT + \left(\frac{\partial E}{\partial P} \right)_T dP \quad (7.14)$$

The two derivatives are expressed (without proof) as

$$\left(\frac{\partial E}{\partial T} \right)_P = C_P - P \left(\frac{\partial V}{\partial T} \right)_P \quad (7.15)$$

129

and

$$\left(\frac{\partial E}{\partial P}\right)_T = -\left[T\left(\frac{\partial V}{\partial T}\right)_P + P\left(\frac{\partial V}{\partial P}\right)_T\right] \tag{7.16}$$

in terms of experimentally determinable quantities.

7.5 FREE EXPANSION OF A GAS AND THE JOULE EXPERIMENT

The process of expanding a gas into a vacuum is called a free expansion. Consider an isolated system (Fig. 7.4) which is divided into two parts A and B by a diathermic wall containing a stopcock. Side B is evacuated so that the pressure is zero. Side A contains a fixed quantity of gas at a pressure P_1 and a temperature T_1. The system is the gas but the volume of the system is determined by the rigid walls of the adiabatic envelope separating the system from the surroundings. Thus the volume of the system is constant and is the total volume of sides A and B. After an initial state of equilibrium is attained the stopcock is opened and gas is allowed to expand into side B. The question is "what is the temperature change of the gas?"

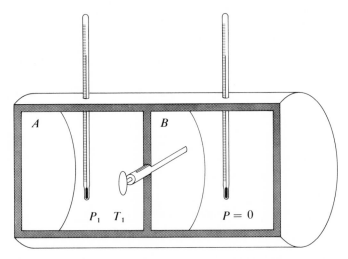

Fig. 7.4. The Joule experiment.

The energy is taken as a function of the temperature and volume so that

$$dE = \left(\frac{\partial E}{\partial T}\right)_V dT + \left(\frac{\partial E}{\partial V}\right)_T dV \tag{7.17}$$

The system is isolated and consequently $dE = 0$. With this condition Eq. (7.17) may be written as

$$\left(\frac{\partial T}{\partial V}\right)_E = -\frac{(\partial E/\partial V)_T}{(\partial E/\partial T)_V} \tag{7.18}$$

The derivative $(\partial E/\partial T)_V$ is the heat capacity of the gas at constant volume, which is always positive. Therefore the sign of the temperature change of the gas on the expansion depends upon the sign of $(\partial E/\partial V)_T$. The proof of the relation given in Eq. (7.10) requires a knowledge of the second law of thermodynamics. At this point we consider only the direct experimental determination of the temperature change.

The Joule experiment (*ca.* 1843) was designed to detect the temperature effect. The apparatus is depicted schematically in Fig. 7.5. Two bulbs submerged in a water bath are connected by a stopcock. B is evacuated and A contains the gas (air at a high pressure). The stopcock is opened and the temperature is recorded. Joule found that there was no detectable change in the temperature of the water bath. On further reflection this result for these

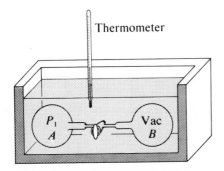

Fig. 7.5. The Joule experiment.

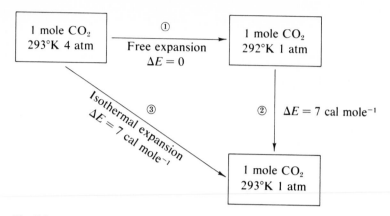

Fig. 7.6

experimental conditions should not be surprising. The heat capacity of the bath was very much greater than the heat capacity of the gas. As a matter of fact the temperature of the gas must have changed by several degrees. But the effect is generally small.†

For an ideal gas $(\partial E/\partial V)_T$ is defined to be zero. This definition is based on the observations that the temperature effects are small for real gases and that the effect decreases as the original pressure is decreased. The definition simply states that the energy of a constant mass of an ideal gas is not a function of the volume and is a function of the temperature alone. It is left as an exercise to show that $(\partial E/\partial P)_T$ also equals zero when $(\partial E/\partial V)_T$ equals zero.

For real gases it is found by precise experiments that the values of the partial derivatives $(\partial E/\partial V)_T$ and $(\partial E/\partial P)_T$ depend upon the temperature and on the volume or the pressure. For air at $301°$ K the value of $(\partial E/\partial P)_T$ is -1.45 cal mole^{-1} atm^{-1} and is essentially constant up to 45 atm. The free expansion of one mole of carbon dioxide at $293°$ K from 4 atm to 1 atm results in a temperature decrease of 1 deg. To illustrate that ΔE is independent of the path we consider the two paths shown in Fig. 7.6. For the free expansion (step 1) just described, $\Delta E = Q = W = 0$. For increasing the temperature from $292°$ to $293°$ K, ΔE equals 7 cal mole^{-1} (step 2). For the isothermal expansion

† See M. W. Zemansky, *Heat and Thermodynamics*, 4th ed. (New York: McGraw-Hill, 1957, pp. 116–118). This book discusses some of the experimental studies which have been made of the Joule experiment.

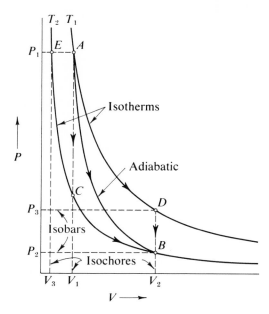

Fig. 7.7. Isothermal, isochoric, isobaric, and adiabatic processes.

at 293° K from 4 atm to 1 atm (step 3), ΔE is also 7 cal mole^{-1}. The change of energy along either path is the same.

7.6   APPLICATION OF THE FIRST LAW TO GASES

We now apply the first law of thermodynamics to both ideal and real gases and discuss the determination of the heat absorbed and the work done by the gas for four different processes and the change of energy for the corresponding change of state. The four processes are isothermal, isochoric, isobaric, and adiabatic. In all cases the system is taken as a fixed quantity of n moles of gas. The surroundings may be taken in general to be a piston and cylinder together with an adiabatic wall or any required body for adding heat to or removing heat from the system. All processes are quasi-static so that an equation of state may be used to determine the force acting on the piston.

Figure 7.7 illustrates the four processes. In this figure the pressure is the

133

ordinate and the volume the abscissa. The curves AD and EB represent two isotherms at the temperatures T_1 and T_2. The vertical dashed lines at V_1, V_2, and V_3 represent isochores. The horizontal dashed lines at P_1, P_2, P_3 are isobars. The curve AB represents the adiabatic which passes through point A.

(a) Isothermal expansion

We consider the isothermal expansion of the gas along AD so that the initial state is at A with temperature T_1 and volume V_1, and the final state is at D with temperature T_1 and volume V_2. The pressure of the gas follows the curve AD as the gas is expanded. For an ideal gas, dE is zero for the expansion because dT and $(\partial E/\partial V)_T$ are both zero, Eq. (7.7). Therefore

$$Q = W \tag{7.19}$$

and

$$W = \int_{V_1}^{V_2} P\, dV = nRT \ln \frac{V_2}{V_1} \tag{7.20}$$

For real gases P is expressed as a function of the temperature and pressure by the use of a suitable equation of state, and the work done by the gas on the surroundings is determined by the integration of $\int_{V_1}^{V_2} P\, dV$. The change in energy is calculated by the integration of Eq. (7.10) after the quantity $[T(\partial P/\partial T) - P]$ has been expressed in terms of T and V by the use of the equation of state. Finally, Q equals $\Delta E + W$.

For the isothermal expansion, work is done by the system on the surroundings and heat is absorbed by the system. The change of energy is zero for an ideal gas and may be positive or negative for a real gas.

(b) Isochoric Process

Along the path from D to B for the isochoric process at the volume V_2, the work done by the system is zero for both ideal and real gases because the volume is constant. Therefore

$$\Delta E = Q = \int_{T_1}^{T_2} C_V \, dT \tag{7.21}$$

For an ideal gas C_V is a function of the temperature only whereas for a real gas the function of T and V for C_V would have to be evaluated at V_2. Because T_2 is less than T_1 both ΔE and Q would be negative.

(c) Isobaric process

For an isobaric process we consider the path from E to A at the constant pressure P_1. The initial state is at T_2 and V_3 and the final state is at T_1 and V_1. The work done by the system is

$$W = P_1(V_1 - V_3) \tag{7.22}$$

because the pressure is constant. The change in energy for an ideal gas is given by the equation

$$\Delta E = \int_{T_2}^{T_1} C_V \, dT \tag{7.23}$$

because the energy of an ideal gas is independent of the volume. For a real gas one might suppose that Eq. (7.7) or Eq. (7.11) might be integrated to obtain the change of energy. However, this cannot be done easily because both C_V and $(\partial E / \partial V)_T$ are functions of the temperature and volume and the variables generally are not separable. But the change of energy is independent of the path and a path such as ECA can be used to calculate the change of energy in going from E to A. The path EC is an isothermal process and the path CA is an isochoric process. The sum of the two changes of energy from E to C and from C to A gives the change in energy from E to A. The heat absorbed by the gas can be obtained from $Q = \Delta E + W$ for both ideal and real gases. For the overall isobaric process discussed, Q and W are always positive and ΔE is generally positive.

(d) Adiabatic process

The calculations for an adiabatic process are somewhat more complicated. In establishing the adiabatic line AB we have stated that, starting at A, the temperature of the gas becomes T_2 when the volume becomes V_2. However, only three of the four variables T_1, V_1, T_2, and V_2 are independent for an adiabatic change of state. Thus, if T_1, V_1, and V_2 are chosen as independent, T_2 is dependent. The problem is the determination of the final temperature either by calculation or by experimental measurement. The calculations are relatively simple for an ideal gas but are generally very complicated for real gases. Therefore only ideal gases are discussed in this section.

For an adiabatic process the heat absorbed by the gas is zero, and therefore

$$dE = -dW \tag{7.24}$$

or

$$\Delta E = -W \tag{7.25}$$

If W is expressed as $\int_{V_1}^{V_2} P \, dV$, the integration cannot be performed directly because P is a function of both T and V and both variables are changing in the adiabatic expansion. However, for an ideal gas, $dE = C_V \, dT$, and with Eq. (7.24),

$$dE = C_V \, dT = -P \, dV \tag{7.26}$$

The equation

$$\frac{C_V}{T} \, dT = -\frac{nR}{V} \, dV \tag{7.27}$$

is obtained when the ideal gas equation of state is substituted for P. The heat capacity C_V is a function of the temperature alone, and consequently an integration can be carried out. Thus

$$\int_{T_1}^{T_2} \frac{C_V}{T} \, dT = -\int_{V_1}^{V_2} \frac{nR}{V} \, dV \tag{7.28}$$

or

$$\int_{V_1}^{T_2} \frac{C_V}{T}\, dT = -nR \ln \frac{V_2}{V_1} = nR \ln \frac{V_1}{V_2} \tag{7.29}$$

Equation (7.29) permits the calculation of T_2 when T_1, V_1, and V_2 are known. Then ΔE can be obtained by integration of Eq. (7.26) and the work done is also obtained by Eq. (7.25). For an adiabatic expansion the work is positive, ΔE is negative, and the temperature decreases.

7.7 CONCLUDING COMMENTS

All experience shows that $\oint (dQ - dW)$ is zero for any closed system. The quantity $(dQ - dW)$ is therefore an exact differential and represents the differential of some function of the variables which define the state of the system. This function is called the energy function E. The differential dE is exact and the change of the value of the energy function, ΔE, in going from some initial state to some final state is dependent only on the two states and not at all upon the path. The change of energy for some change of state may be expressed as $\Delta E = Q - W$. Therefore the value of the energy is constant for an isolated system.

When the energy is expressed as a function of the temperature and volume, the differential of the energy is given as $dE = C_V\, dT + [T(\partial P/\partial T)_V - P]\, dV$. The application of this differential expression to gases for various processes has been discussed.

An ideal gas has been defined as one for which $PV = nRT$ and $(\partial E/\partial V)_T = 0$.

Exercises

7.1 The equation of state for one mole of a certain gas is

$$PV = RT\left(1 + \frac{B}{V}\right)$$

where $B = -11{,}000 + 20T$ cm^3 mole^{-1}. Given the following steps:

(1) $A(g, 20{,}000 \text{ cm}^3, 300° \text{ K}) \rightarrow A(g, 60{,}000 \text{ cm}^3, 300° \text{ K})$;

(2) $A(g, 60{,}000 \text{ cm}^3, 300° \text{ K}) \rightarrow A(g, 60{,}000 \text{ cm}^3, 500° \text{ K})$;

(3) $A(g, 20{,}000 \text{ cm}^3, 300° \text{ K}) \rightarrow A(g, 20{,}000 \text{ cm}^3, 500° \text{ K})$;

(4) $A(g, 20{,}000 \text{ cm}^3, 500° \text{ K}) \rightarrow A(g, 60{,}000 \text{ cm}^3, 500° \text{ K})$.

(a) Calculate Q and W for the isothermal quasi-static expansion of the gas and ΔE for the change of state represented by (1) and (4).

(b) Calculate Q and W for the isochoric quasi-static process and ΔE for change of state represented by (2) and (3).

(c) What is the total heat absorbed and the total work done by the system, and ΔE for the system for the sum of the two steps (1) and (2)? for (3) and (4)?

(d) If the direction of the two steps (1) and (2) are reversed so that the combination of the four steps results in a cycle, calculate Q and W for the cycle for the processes given in (a) and (b). What is ΔE for the cycle?

Data for this problem:

$$\tilde{C}_V = 3.0 + 2.5 \times 10^{-3}T \quad \text{cal deg}^{-1} \text{ mole}^{-1} \text{ at } 20{,}000 \text{ cm}^3 \text{ mole}^{-1}$$

$$\tilde{C}_V = 3.0 + 5.2 \times 10^{-3}T \quad \text{cal deg}^{-1} \text{ mole}^{-1} \text{ at } 60{,}000 \text{ cm}^3 \text{ mole}^{-1}$$

7.2 Discuss the same steps, processes, and cycle for an ideal gas for which $PV = nRT$, $(\partial E/\partial V)_T = 0$, and C_V is a function of the temperature alone for the conditions in Exercise 1.

7.3 Derive the relationship between P and V for an ideal gas in an adiabatic expansion. (You may assume that $\tilde{C}_P = \tilde{C}_V + R$.) The expression may be simplified by using the relation that $\gamma = C_P/C_V$ where γ is just the ratio of the heat capacities.

7.4 Four moles of a certain ideal gas expand adiabatically from an initial temperature of $400°$ K and an initial pressure of 10 atm to a final pressure of 1 atm. Consider the gas as the system and calculate the final temperature and volume of the gas, and ΔE for the change of state, and Q and W for the process. Take $\tilde{C}_P = 9$ and $\tilde{C}_V = 7$ cal mole^{-1}. (*Hints*: By using the relation derived in Exercise 7.3 this problem may be simplified.)

7.5 One mole of ideal gas initially at 50 atm pressure and $300°$ K undergoes an isothermal free expansion for which the final volume is ten times the initial volume. (a) What is the final temperature, pressure, and volume of the gas? (b) Calculate Q and W for the gas for this process and ΔE for the change of state.

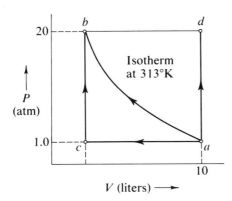

Fig. 7.8

7.6 With reference to Fig. 7.8 and assuming ideal gas behavior:
(a) Determine the number of moles of gas present and the volume at the final state b.
(b) What is the work done on the gas in going from a to b along the isotherm in a quasi-static process?
(c) Calculate the work done on the gas along the path acb and along the path adb.
(d) Which path represents the minimum work that is done on the gas in compressing it from a to b?
(e) If $\tilde{C}_V$ for this gas is 5.0 cal mole^{-1} deg^{-1}, calculate Q and ΔE for each of the three paths indicated above.

7.7 One-tenth of a mole of an ideal gas ($\tilde{C}_V = 3$ cal mole^{-1} deg^{-1}) is heated from T_1 to T_2 along a path governed by the equation $V = ae^{bT}$ in which a and b are constants (e is the base of natural logarithms).
(a) Derive expressions for the quasi-static heat and work effects attending this process.
(b) If T_1 is 300° K and T_2 is 400° K, and b is 0.01 deg^{-1}, calculate Q, W for this process, and ΔE for the change of state.

7.8 Show that the work done by an ideal monatomic gas during a quasi-static adiabatic expansion is equal to

(a) $W = C_V(T_i - T_f)$;

(b) $W = \dfrac{P_i V_i - P_f V_f}{\gamma - 1}$;

(c) $W = \dfrac{P_i V_i}{\gamma - 1}\left[1 - \left(\dfrac{P_f}{P_i}\right)^{(\gamma - 1)/\gamma}\right]$.

Note. $\gamma = C_P/C_V$.

7.9 For a quasi-static adiabatic process for an ideal gas, derive the following expression (assuming γ to be constant): $T/P^{(\gamma - 1)/\gamma} = $ const.
(a) One mole of neon ($\gamma = 5/3$) at 400° K and 1 atm pressure is compressed adiabatically and quasi-statically to a pressure of 10 atm. Considering neon to be an ideal gas, determine the final temperature and volume.
(b) If one mole of neon is compressed isothermally and quasi-statically from 1 atm and 400° K to 10 atm, what is the final volume? And what are Q and W for this process and ΔE for the change of state?

7.10 Remembering that dE is an exact differential, show that for an ideal gas

$$\left(\frac{\partial C_V}{\partial V}\right)_T = 0 \quad \text{and} \quad \left(\frac{\partial C_P}{\partial P}\right)_T = 0$$

7.11 Remembering the definitions of the coefficient of thermal expression, α, and isothermal compressibility, β, show that $(\partial E/\partial P)_V = \beta C_V/\alpha$.

7.12 Prove that $(\partial E/\partial P)_T$ equals zero for an ideal gas, starting from the fact that $(\partial E/\partial V)_T$ is zero for an ideal gas.

8 The Enthalpy Function and Thermochemistry

For practically all processes which take place in the laboratory or in industry, the pressure is more easily controlled than the volume. If a process takes place in a vessel open to the atmosphere, the pressure usually may be considered constant. The equations relating the energy to the pressure as an independent variable are somewhat more complicated than those relating the energy to the volume as an independent variable. It is therefore convenient to define a new function for which the pressure is a more suitable independent variable. In the first part of this chapter, the enthalpy function is defined and its properties are developed. The enthalpy function is related to the heat capacity at constant pressure, the relationship between the heat capacity at constant pressure and that at constant volume is derived, and the equations giving the dependence of the enthalpy on the temperature and pressure as independent variables are applied to processes involving gases.

The subject of thermochemistry, the study of the relations of heat to changes of phase and processes involving chemical reactions, is related to the enthalpy function. The last part of the chapter is devoted to thermochemistry.

8.1 THE ENTHALPY FUNCTION

The differential of the energy for a closed system for the process in which the only work done by the system on the surroundings is the work of expansion or compression performed quasi-statically is

$$dE = dQ - P\,dV \tag{8.1}$$

where P is the pressure of the system and is a function of the temperature and volume. The form of Eq. (8.1) indicates that the volume rather than the pressure is the more convenient variable. In order to define the new function the variable is changed from the volume to the pressure.

The change of variable is accomplished by considering the differential of the pressure-volume product of a system, $d(PV)$. This product is itself a function of the variables used to define the state of the system. The differential $d(PV)$ can be written as

$$d(PV) = P\,dV + V\,dP \tag{8.2}$$

By adding Eqs. (8.1) and (8.2) we obtain

$$d(E + PV) = dQ + V(T, P)dP \tag{8.3}$$

The symbol $V(T, P)$ is used to emphasize that V is a function of the temperature and pressure. The quantity $d(E + PV)$ is the differential of the new function H, which is called the enthalpy, so that

$$dH = d(E + PV) \tag{8.4}$$

When we integrate this expression, we obtain

$$H = E + PV + \text{const} \tag{8.5}$$

The absolute value of E is not known and thus the absolute value of H cannot be known. We are interested in the changes of the enthalpy for various changes of state just as we are for the energy, and in such changes the value of the constant in Eq. (8.5) cancels. ΔH is then independent of the value of the constant. As we are defining the new function, we can assign any value we please to the constant, and the most convenient value is zero. We therefore define the enthalpy function as

$$H = E + PV \tag{8.6}$$

This definition is independent of the fact that other work terms have been omitted in Eqs. (8.1) and (8.3); we are concerned only with the $P\,dV$ term in Eq. (8.1) and the change of variable. The enthalpy is a thermodynamic function of the variables which we use to define the state of a system; for a closed system these variables are usually the temperature and pressure and the appropriate variables for other work terms whenever necessary. The change of enthalpy for a given change of state is independent of the path and the change of enthalpy of a system for any cyclic path is zero.

From Eqs. (8.3) and (8.4), we have

$$dH = dQ + V\,dP \tag{8.7}$$

This equation is the basic equation used to develop the relations of the enthalpy with heat and with the independent variables, temperature and pressure.

8.2 HEAT CAPACITY AT CONSTANT PRESSURE

If the enthalpy of a closed system is taken as a function of the temperature and pressure alone, the differential of the enthalpy is given by

$$dH = \left(\frac{\partial H}{\partial T}\right)_P dT + \left(\frac{\partial H}{\partial P}\right)_T dP \tag{8.8}$$

At constant pressure

$$[dH]_P = [dQ]_P = \left(\frac{\partial H}{\partial T}\right)_P dT \quad (\text{const } P) \tag{8.9}$$

from Eqs. (8.7) and (8.8). From the general definition of heat capacity we have

$$[dQ]_P = C_P\,dT \quad (\text{const } P) \tag{8.10}$$

The substitution of Eq. (8.10) into Eq. (8.9) yields

$$\left(\frac{\partial H}{\partial T}\right)_P = C_P(T, P) \tag{8.11}$$

which relates the temperature dependence of the enthalpy at constant pressure to the heat capacity at constant pressure. Here we emphasize that the heat capacity is a function at the temperature and pressure in general, just as the heat capacity of a system at constant volume is a function of the temperature and volume.

As an example consider the change of state

$$A(g, P, 300° K) = A(g, P, 350° K)$$

where A represents any substance and the states are given in the parentheses, and let the heat capacity at constant pressure be given as

$$\tilde{C}_P = a + bT + cT^2 \tag{8.12}$$

In this equation the coefficients are functions of the pressure but may be considered as known at the pressure specified in the change of state. By

Table 8.1   Heat Capacities at Constant Pressure[a,b]

Substance	Temp. Range, °K	a	$b \times 10^3$	$c \times 10^7$
Hydrogen (g)	300–1500	6.9469	−0.1999	4.808
Oxygen (g)	300–1500	6.148	3.102	−9.23
Nitrogen (g)	300–1500	6.524	1.250	−0.01
Carbon dioxide (g)	300–1500	6.214	10.396	−35.45
Carbon monoxide (g)	300–1500	6.420	1.665	−1.96
Chlorine (g)	300–1500	7.5755	2.4244	−9.650
Bromine (g)	300–1500	8.4228	0.9739	−3.555
Water (g)	300–1500	7.256	2.298	2.83
Hydrogen chloride (g)	300–1500	6.7319	0.4325	3.697
Sulfur trioxide (g)	300–1200	6.077	23.537	−96.87
Methane (g)	300–1500	3.381	18.044	−43.00
Ethane (g)	300–1500	2.247	38.201	−110.49
Propane (g)	300–1500	2.410	57.195	−175.33
Benzene (g)	300–1500	−0.409	77.621	−264.29
Chlorine (l)	172– 239	14.850	15.5	−500.
Carbon disulfide (l)	161– 319	18.47	−4.95	123.

[a] H. M. Spencer *et al.*, *J. Am. Chem. Soc.*, **56**, 2311 (1934); *ibid.*, **64**, 2511 (1942); *ibid.*, **67**, 1859 (1945); *Ind. Eng. Chem.*, **40**, 2152 (1948).
[b] C_P in cal mole^{-1} deg^{-1}.

integration of Eq. (8.11) the change of enthalpy is given by

$$\Delta \tilde{H} = \int_{300}^{350} \tilde{C}_p \, dT \tag{8.13}$$

and

$$\Delta \tilde{H} = \int_{300}^{350} (a + bT + cT^2) \, dT \tag{8.14}$$

The heat capacity at a constant pressure of one atmosphere for a number of substances is given in Table 8.1 for Eq. (8.12).

8.3 THE RELATION BETWEEN HEAT CAPACITY AT CONSTANT PRESSURE AND HEAT CAPACITY AT CONSTANT VOLUME

The heat capacity at constant pressure is equal to $(\partial H / \partial T)_P$ from Eq. (8.11) and this can be written as

$$\left(\frac{\partial H}{\partial T} \right)_P = C_P = \left(\frac{\partial (E + PV)}{\partial T} \right)_P \tag{8.15}$$

from the definition of the enthalpy, or

$$C_P = \left(\frac{\partial E}{\partial T} \right)_P + P \left(\frac{\partial V}{\partial T} \right)_P \tag{8.16}$$

The differential of the energy as a function of the temperature and volume is

$$dE = \left(\frac{\partial E}{\partial T} \right)_V dT + \left(\frac{\partial E}{\partial V} \right)_T dV \tag{8.17}$$

which may be transformed to

$$\left(\frac{\partial E}{\partial T} \right)_P = \left(\frac{\partial E}{\partial T} \right)_V + \left(\frac{\partial E}{\partial V} \right)_T \left(\frac{\partial V}{\partial T} \right)_P \tag{8.18}$$

145

when the energy is taken as a function of the temperature and pressure. The substitution of Eq. (8.18) into Eq. (8.16) gives

$$C_P = C_V + \left[P + \left(\frac{\partial E}{\partial V}\right)_T\right]\left(\frac{\partial V}{\partial T}\right)_P \tag{8.19}$$

as a relation between C_P and C_V when Eq. (7.8) is used. The substitution of $[T(\partial P/\partial T)_V - P]$ for $(\partial E/\partial V)_T$ in Eq. (8.19) gives

$$C_P = C_V + T\left(\frac{\partial P}{\partial T}\right)_V\left(\frac{\partial V}{\partial T}\right)_P \tag{8.20}$$

In Eq. (8.20) the first partial derivative is the thermal pressure coefficient γ, and the second partial derivative is $V\alpha$ where α is the isobaric coefficient of expansion. With these substitutions Eq. (8.20) becomes

$$C_P = C_V + TV\alpha\gamma \tag{8.21}$$

The relation $\gamma = \alpha/\beta$ gives

$$C_P = C_V + \frac{TV\alpha^2}{\beta} \tag{8.22}$$

or

$$C_P = C_V - T\left(\frac{\partial V}{\partial T}\right)_P^2\left(\frac{\partial V}{\partial P}\right)_T^{-1} = C_V - T\left(\frac{\partial P}{\partial T}\right)_V^2\left(\frac{\partial P}{\partial V}\right)_T^{-1} \tag{8.23}$$

Equations (8.20) to (8.23) give various forms for relating C_P and C_V through derivatives and coefficients, which can be evaluated from P-V-T data or from equations of state.

For an ideal gas, $(\partial E/\partial V)_T = 0$ and Eq. (8.19) reduces to

$$C_P = C_V + nR \tag{8.24}$$

for n moles of gas, or on a molar basis,

$$\tilde{C}_P = \tilde{C}_V + R \tag{8.25}$$

Equation (8.25) approximates with reasonable agreement the difference between $\tilde{C}_P$ and $\tilde{C}_V$ for many real gases, as is shown in Table (8.2).

Table 8.2 Molar Heat Capacities (cal mole^{-1} deg^{-1}) of Gases and Differences between Them at 298° K

Gas	$\tilde{C}_P$	$\tilde{C}_V$	$\tilde{C}_P - \tilde{C}_V$
Acetylene	10.499	8.508	1.991
Argon	4.968	2.981	1.987
Benzene	19.52	17.54	1.98
Carbon Dioxide	8.874	6.890	1.984
Ethane	12.585	10.593	1.992
Ethylene	10.41	8.42	1.99
Hydrogen	6.892	4.905	1.987
Methane	8.536	6.546	1.990
Oxygen	7.017	5.027	1.990

8.4 SOME GENERAL RELATIONS INVOLVING THE ENTHALPY

The differential of the enthalpy of a closed system is

$$dH = \left(\frac{\partial H}{\partial T}\right)_P dT + \left(\frac{\partial H}{\partial P}\right)_T dP \tag{8.26}$$

when the enthalpy is taken as a function of the temperature and the pressure. We know from Eq. (8.11) that $(\partial H/\partial T)_P$ equals C_P. We will show when we have developed the second law of thermodynamics that

$$\left(\frac{\partial H}{\partial P}\right)_T = V - T\left(\frac{\partial V}{\partial T}\right)_P \tag{8.27}$$

With these two relations the differential of the enthalpy of a closed system can be written as

$$dH = C_P dT + \left[V - T\left(\frac{\partial V}{\partial T}\right)_P\right] dP \tag{8.28}$$

147

This equation makes it possible to calculate the change of enthalpy of a closed system consisting of a single phase for a change of temperature at constant pressure, a change of pressure at constant temperature, or a combination of a change of both temperature and pressure. In order to perform the calculations, the heat capacity at constant pressure must be known as a function of the temperature at one pressure and an appropriate equation of state must be used.

As an example, consider the change of state

$$A(T_1, P_1) \rightarrow A(T_2, P_2)$$

where A represents any substance and the states are given in the parentheses. The phase is unimportant here except that we permit no phase change to take place between the two states. In general, Eq. (8.28) cannot be integrated directly because the variables do not separate. However, the value of the change of enthalpy does not depend upon the path and we can choose either of two paths, given by the changes of state

$$A(T_1, P_1) \rightarrow A(T_1, P_2)$$

$$A(T_1, P_2) \rightarrow A(T_2, P_2)$$

or

$$A(T_1, P_1) \rightarrow A(T_2, P_1)$$

$$A(T_2, P_1) \rightarrow A(T_2, P_2)$$

Along the first path the pressure is changed at the constant temperature T_1 and the temperature is then changed at the constant pressure P_2. For this path ΔH is given by

$$\Delta H = \int_{T_1}^{T_2} [C_P]_{P_2} \, dT + \int_{P_1}^{P_2} \left[V - T\left(\frac{\partial V}{\partial T}\right)_P \right]_{T_1} dT \qquad (8.29)$$

where C_P is evaluated at P_2 and $[V - T(\partial V/\partial T)_P]$ is evaluated at T_1. Along the second path the temperature is changed at the constant pressure P_1 and then the pressure is changed at the constant temperature T_2. For this path ΔH is given by

$$\Delta H = \int_{T_1}^{T_2} [C_P]_{P_1} \, dT + \int_{P_1}^{P_2} \left[V - T\left(\frac{\partial V}{\partial T}\right)_P \right]_{T_2} dP \qquad (8.30)$$

where C_P is evaluated now at P_1 and $[V - T(\partial V/\partial T)_P]$ is evaluated at T_2. The two values of ΔH *must* be equal.

An equation directly relating dQ to differentials of the temperature and pressure is of interest. When we equate Eqs. (8.7) and (8.28), we obtain

$$dQ = C_P \, dT - T\left(\frac{\partial V}{\partial T}\right)_P dP \qquad (8.31)$$

That dQ is an inexact differential is easily shown from the fact that $(\partial C_P/\partial P)_T$ does not equal $-\{\partial[T(\partial V/\partial T)_P]/\partial T\}_P$. Equation (8.31) affords a method, alternative to the use of Eqs. (8.7) and (8.28) separately, of calculating the heat absorbed by a system for a change of temperature and pressure. For some processes which take place at constant temperature and pressure, heat is absorbed by the system. Neither Eq. (8.28) or Eq. (8.31) is valid for these processes. Equation (8.7) is still valid and hence is the more fundamental equation.

8.5   APPLICATION OF THE ENTHALPY TO GASES

In this section we consider the determination of the change of the enthalpy for isothermal, isobaric, isochoric, and adiabatic changes of state. The basic equation is Eq. (8.28). For ideal gases $(\partial H/\partial P)_T$ is zero because $(\partial E/\partial V)_T$ is zero (the proof is left as an exercise); then Eq. (8.28) becomes

$$dH = C_p \, dT \qquad (8.32)$$

for ideal gases. For real gases, an appropriate equation of state must be used to evaluate $(\partial H/\partial P)_T$ and to determine the dependence of C_P on the pressure. Actually Eq. (8.28) is applicable also to liquids and solids but no suitable equation of state has yet been developed.

For isothermal changes of state

$$dH = \left[V - T\left(\frac{\partial V}{\partial T}\right)_P \right] dP \tag{8.33}$$

for real gases and

$$dH = 0 \tag{8.34}$$

for ideal gases.

For isobaric changes of state

$$dH = C_P \, dT \tag{8.35}$$

for both real and ideal gases. For ideal gases, C_P is independent of the pressure while for real gases C_P must be evaluated at the particular pressure of interest.

Two methods are possible to determine ΔH for isochoric changes of states. For such changes of state the pressure is a function of the temperature alone or the temperature is a function of the pressure alone, so that we have either

$$dP = \left(\frac{\partial P}{\partial T}\right)_V dT \tag{8.36}$$

or

$$dT = \left(\frac{\partial T}{\partial P}\right)_V dP \tag{8.37}$$

When Eq. (8.36) is used to eliminate dP from Eq. (8.28), the result is

$$dH = \left\{ C_P + \left[V - T\left(\frac{\partial V}{\partial T}\right)_P \right]\left(\frac{\partial P}{\partial T}\right)_V \right\} dT \tag{8.38}$$

$$dH = \left[C_V + V\left(\frac{\partial P}{\partial T}\right)_V \right] dT \tag{8.39}$$

When Eq. (8.37) is used to eliminate dT from Eq. (8.28) the result is

$$dH = \left\{ C_P \left(\frac{\partial T}{\partial P} \right)_V + \left[V - T \left(\frac{\partial V}{\partial T} \right)_P \right] \right\} dP \tag{8.40}$$

For an ideal gas, Eq. (8.38) becomes

$$dH = C_P \, dT \tag{8.41}$$

and Eq. (8.39) becomes

$$dH = \frac{C_P V}{nR} \, dP \tag{8.42}$$

The alternative method is to calculate ΔE for the isochoric change of state by the use of Eq. (7.8) and then from that calculate ΔH by the relation Eq. (8.6),

$$\Delta H = \Delta E + V(P_2 - P_1) \tag{8.43}$$

where P_1 and P_2 are the initial and final pressures, respectively.

The problems concerning adiabatic changes of state are similar to those discussed in Section 7.6(d). An adiabatic change of state is determined by fixing the initial temperature and initial pressure and either the final temperature or the final pressure, but the complete final state is not known. We must determine the final pressure or the final temperature, as the case may be, either by experimental measurement or by calculation. The calculations are generally not possible for real gases and we limit the discussion to ideal gases.

For ideal gases the enthalpy is a function of temperature alone and consequently Eq. (8.32) applies to adiabatic changes of state. From Eq. (8.7) we also have

$$dH = V \, dP \tag{8.44}$$

so that

$$C_P \, dT = V \, dP \tag{8.45}$$

Upon substitution of the ideal gas law into Eq. (8.45) and integration between the limits of T_1 and T_2 and of P_1 and P_2, we obtain

$$\int_{T1}^{T_2} C_P \, dT = nR \ln \frac{P_2}{P_1} \tag{8.46}$$

With a knowledge of C_P as a function of the temperature, we can calculate T_2 when T_1, P_1, and P_2 are known or P_2 where T_1, P_1, and T_2 are known. ΔH for the change of state is calculated by integration of Eq. (8.32). The adiabatic equation of state, $PV^\gamma = k$, might be used to integrate Eq. (8.44). Except for monatomic ideal gases, the ratio γ of C_P to C_V is not strictly a constant. However, for most gases its value varies very slowly with temperature and can be used as a constant with only a small error resulting in the calculations.

8.6 THERMOCHEMISTRY

Thermochemistry primarily refers to the transfer of heat between a chemical system and its surroundings when a change of phase or a chemical reaction takes place within the system. The quantities of heat which are transferred are related to changes of both the energy and the enthalpy for the changes of state which occur in the system. However, because the pressure is the more convenient variable than volume, we are more concerned with changes of the enthalpy than with changes of the energy. Moreover the concept of thermochemistry is expanded to include changes of enthalpy for various changes of state without reference to the transfer of heat for various processes. In this discussion of thermochemistry we briefly develop the relations of enthalpy changes with heat for certain processes and changes of state. We will then enlarge the concepts to discuss changes of enthalpy for changes of state involving phase changes and chemical reactions.

(a) Constant-Pressure Calorimetry

The differential of the enthalpy is given by Eq. (8.7). From this equation we see that

$$dH = dQ_P \tag{8.47}$$

for differential changes of state at constant pressure and consequently

$$\Delta H = Q \tag{8.48}$$

for a finite change of state at constant pressure. This equation tells us that the change of enthalpy for a change of state which takes place in a constant-pressure calorimeter is equal to the heat absorbed by the system in such a calorimeter. The simple Dewar calorimeter shown in Fig. 5.6 is a constant-pressure calorimeter because the system is open to the atmosphere. The heat effects discussed in Section 5.7 are examples of constant-pressure calorimetry.

(b) Constant-Volume Calorimetry

The differential of the energy is given by

$$dE = dQ_V \tag{8.49}$$

for changes of state at constant volume and consequently

$$\Delta E = Q_V \tag{8.50}$$

for finite changes of state at constant volume. Thus we see that the change of energy for a change of state which takes place in a constant volume calorimeter is equal to the heat absorbed by the system in such a calorimeter. A constant-volume calorimeter consists partially of a sturdy steel vessel called a bomb, and this type of calorimetry is usually referred to as bomb calorimetry. The reacting substances are placed inside the bomb which is immersed in a thermostat. The reaction is initiated usually by electrical means and appropriate measurements are made so that the heat absorbed by the system can be determined.

Equations (8.48) and (8.50) are the basic equations used for all calorimeter measurements under conditions of constant pressure or constant volume. The change of state which takes place within the calorimeter must be experimentally determined or known. Once the change of state is known, the heat absorbed by the system in the calorimeter must be equal to ΔH or ΔE, as the case may be, for that change of state. In all cases it is extremely important to define the system completely.

8.7 CHANGE OF ENTHALPY FOR A CHANGE OF PHASE OF A PURE SUBSTANCE

We are interested in determining the change of enthalpy when a known quantity of substance is transferred from one phase to another under equilibrium conditions. We find from experiment that when two such phases of a pure substance are in equilibrium with each other, the pressure of the two-phase system is a function of the temperature alone or, conversely, the temperature is a function of the pressure alone (see Chapter 16). Thus, when the temperature of such a two-phase system is fixed, the pressure is fixed, or when the pressure is fixed so is the temperature. We also find by experiment that when two phases are at equilibrium, we may change the amount of the substance in either phase by the addition or removal of heat to the substance considered as a system at constant temperature and pressure. Consider, as an example, a liquid and its vapor confined in a piston and cylinder arrangement at a fixed temperature. The piston and cylinder are placed in a constant temperature thermostat which is at the desired temperature. The liquid and vapor are taken as the system. The piston, cylinder, and thermostat are considered as the surroundings. The boundary is chosen to be the surface of the piston adjacent to the vapor. Now, when a small amount of heat is added to the system, some of the liquid evaporates and the piston moves upward under equilibrium conditions while the pressure and temperature remain constant. Such a change of state may be written as

$$n A(l, T, P) = n A(g, T, P)$$

when n moles are evaporated. This change of state is at constant pressure and therefore ΔH for the change of state is equal to Q or the amount of heat added to the system. Thus, by measuring Q, we determine ΔH. Such quantities are called the change of enthalpy for evaporation, sublimation, condensation, melting, or freezing, depending on the type of phase change.

8.8 CHANGES OF ENTHALPY FOR CHANGES OF STATE INVOLVING CHEMICAL REACTIONS

The changes of enthalpy for changes of state in which chemical reactions are involved are quite important in thermodynamics; they may be related, though indirectly in most cases, to the heat absorbed by a system when chemical reactions take place within the system; they are related to the variation of the equilibrium constant of a chemical reaction with the temperature; and they afford means of compiling a large amount of data in a concise manner.

Before discussing the changes of enthalpy for changes of state which involve chemical reactions, we must clearly distinguish between changes of state for which no real processes are conceived and those changes of state which are associated with a process. If we are concerned solely in the change of enthalpy for a given change of state, only the initial and final states are important. The initial state of the system is many times the pure reactants, unmixed, in arbitrarily defined states and the final state is usually the pure products, also unmixed, in arbitrarily defined states. We are not concerned with a process by which the change of state can be accomplished, and in many cases the change of state cannot be easily or directly carried out in practice. In such cases, while the change of enthalpy has a definite value for the particular change of state, no notion of heat can be considered because the process has not been defined. When we are interested in the heat absorbed by a system in which a chemical reaction takes place, the process must be defined. A change of state is associated with the process and the initial and final states must be known. There may be some freedom in the choice of these states, but the complete definition of them is influenced or dictated by the chosen process. In many cases, the reactants may be mixed, and although we may choose a temperature the partial pressures of gases or the concentrations of the reactants in a liquid solution may be dictated by the process. Similarly, in the final state, the products may be mixed and the phases present and the relative quantities of products may depend upon the chosen process. For the particular change of state associated with the process, there is a definite value of the change of enthalpy and this change of enthalpy is related to the heat absorbed by the system according to the given process.

These distinctions are illustrated by the following example. Let us imagine that we want to determine the change of enthalpy for the change of state

$$CH_4(g, 1 \text{ atm}, 298° \text{ K}) + 2O_2(g, 1 \text{ atm}, 298° \text{ K})$$
$$= CO_2(g, 1 \text{ atm}, 298 °\text{K}) + 2H_2O(l, 1 \text{ atm}, 298 °\text{K})C \tag{8.51}$$

From experience we know that the combustion of methane in oxygen can be studied in a bomb calorimeter, so we choose to use such a calorimeter. The process then is one at constant volume. We also know from experience that

155

an excess of oxygen must be used to ensure complete combustion to form carbon dioxide with no carbon monoxide or carbon. Let us choose a 20 : 1 mole ratio of oxygen to methane. We place a certain number of moles of this gas mixture into the bomb and adjust the temperature to 298° K. The initial state then is this number of moles of gas mixture at 298° K in the volume of the bomb. The total pressure is determined by the volume and the number of moles. The ratio of the partial pressures of oxygen and methane is 20 : 1. The reacting substances and the products of the reaction are chosen to be the system. The mixture is ignited electrically and the temperature of the system is brought back to 298° K. The final state is a gas mixture of oxygen, carbon dioxide, and water vapor, and a liquid phase consisting of a dilute solution of carbon dioxide in water at 298° K in the same volume as that of the initial state. The partial pressures of carbon dioxide and oxygen would be determined by the number of moles of each substance in the gas phase and the partial pressure of the water vapor would be approximately the vapor pressure of pure water at 298° K. It is apparent that the two changes of state represented by Eq. (8.51) and the laboratory experiment are quite different. In the experiment the heat absorbed by the system is determined and this heat is equal to the change of energy of the system for the change of state which has taken place in the calorimeter. The change of enthalpy for this same change of state can be calculated by use of the relation $\Delta H = \Delta E + \Delta(PV)$, with the knowledge of the PV product of the initial and final states of the system. As the final step we must devise a path connecting the two changes of state by means of which we can calculate the difference between the two changes of enthalpy and thus obtain the change of enthalpy for the change of state given in Eq. (8.51). We associate no process with this change of state and consequently can impart no notion of heat to the value of the change of enthalpy.

The inverse problem is also of interest. Assume that we know the change of enthalpy for the change of state given in Eq. (8.51). Now we desire to burn methane in oxygen in some type of gas burner or torch open to the atmosphere and we need to know the quantity of heat absorbed by the system, the reactants, and products, when a fixed number of moles of methane are burned. To do so we must determine by experiment or otherwise the actual change of state which is associated with the burning process. When this is known we have to devise a path connecting the two changes of state by means of which we can calculate the difference between the changes of enthalpy for the changes of state. We thus can calculate the change of enthalpy for the change of state associated with the process and this quantity is equal to the heat absorbed by the system for the constant-pressure process.

We now return to the discussion of the change of enthalpy for changes of state which involve chemical reactions.

The number of possible reactions between all chemical substances is enormous. If we add to this the very many different states determined by possible variations of the pressure, temperature, and concentration (in solution), the possibilities multiply. A method is sought, therefore, by which the change of enthalpy for changes of state involving chemical reactions can be calculated from a minimum amount of data without the necessity of experimentally determining the change of enthalpy for each possible change of state.

For the present we center our attention on the change of state given in Eq. (8.51). The change of enthalpy is always the difference between the enthalpy of the final state and that of the initial state. We can write the change of enthalpy for Eq. (8.51) as

$$\Delta H = H_f - H_i = \tilde{H}_{CO_2}[g, 1 \text{ atm}, 298°] + 2\tilde{H}_{H_2O}[l, 1 \text{ atm}, 298°]$$

$$- \tilde{H}_{CH_4}[g, 1 \text{ atm}, 298°] - 2\tilde{H}_{O_2}[g, 1 \text{ atm}, 298°] \qquad (8.52)$$

Here the subscripts represent the substances and the quantities in the brackets define the state of each substance. Equation (8.52) implies a knowledge of the absolute values of the enthalpies of the substances taking part in the change of state, but unfortunately such values are not known. However, we know that the enthalpy of the system is a function of the variables which we use to define the state of the system and consequently that the change of enthalpy is independent of the path. We then seek a path along which we can determine changes of enthalpy and which will result in the same change of state. Because of the mass balance requirement of all chemical reactions, any reaction may be written as a sum of reactions, all of which express the formation of a compound from the elements. In thermodynamics, we must include the definition of the state. Thus, for Eq. (8.51), we can write the changes of state as

$$C(s, 1 \text{ atm}, 298°) + 2H_2(g, 1 \text{ atm}, 298°) = CH_4(g, 1 \text{ atm}, 298°) \quad (8.53)$$

$$C(g, 1 \text{ atm}, 298°) + O_2(g, 1 \text{ atm}, 298°) = CO_2(g, 1 \text{ atm}, 298°) \quad (8.54)$$

157

$$H_2(g, 1 \text{ atm}, 298°) + 1/2O_2(g, 1 \text{ atm}, 298°) = H_2O(l, 1 \text{ atm}, 298°)$$
$$(8.55)$$

Equation (8.51) can now be obtained by adding two times (8.55) and (8.54) and subtracting (8.53). The corresponding changes of enthalpy are

$$\Delta \tilde{H}_{f,CH_4} = \tilde{H}_{CH_4}(g, 1 \text{ atm}, 298°) - \tilde{H}_C(s, 1 \text{ atm}, 298°)$$
$$- 2\tilde{H}_{H_2}(g, 1 \text{ atm}, 298°) \quad (8.56)$$

$$\Delta \tilde{H}_{f,CO_2} = \tilde{H}_{CO_2}(g, 1 \text{ atm}, 298°) - \tilde{H}_C(s, 1 \text{ atm}, 298°)$$
$$- \tilde{H}_{O_2}(g, 1 \text{ atm}, 298°) \quad (8.57)$$

and

$$\Delta \tilde{H}_{f,H_2O} = \tilde{H}_{H_2O}(l, 1 \text{ atm}, 298°) - \tilde{H}_{H_2}(g, 1 \text{ atm}, 298°)$$
$$- \tfrac{1}{2}\tilde{H}_{O_2}(g, 1 \text{ atm}, 298°) \quad (8.58)$$

When the molar enthalpies for CH_4, CO_2 and H_2O are eliminated in Eq. (8.52) by the use of Eqs. (8.53), (8.54), and (8.55), the result is

$$\Delta H = \Delta \tilde{H}_{f,CO_2} + 2\Delta \tilde{H}_{f,H_2O} - \Delta \tilde{H}_{f,CH_4} \quad (8.59)$$

It must be emphasized here that in canceling the enthalpies of compounds the states must be the same; otherwise the values of the enthalpies do not cancel. Each of the changes of enthalpy expressed in Eqs. (8.53), (8.54), and (8.55) is called the change of enthalpy on the formation of the compound from the elements, or briefly, the enthalpy of formation. Equation (8.59) expresses the change of enthalpy for the change in state expressed in Eq. (8.51) as the algebraic sum of the molar enthalpies of formation of the compounds taking part in the change of state.

In this discussion emphasis has been made on the change of enthalpy on the formation of the compound from the elements. An equivalent concept is to define the enthalpy of the elements in the states given here as zero. Then the change of enthalpy on formation may be considered as the value of the enthalpy of the component relative to that of the elements. The net result is the same, but the idea of the *change of enthalpy on formation* appears to be more fundamental.

We have discussed only one chemical reaction, but the treatment given for this reaction is general. We may consider a generalized change of state as

$$a\,A(g, P, T) + b\,B(l, P, T) = m\,M(s, P, T) + n\,N(l, P, T) \qquad (8.60)$$

where the small letters represent the moles of a substance expressed by the capital letters. The state of aggregation may be gas, liquid, or solid (or even in solution). For the present, however, we require the pressure and temperature of each substance to be the same. By the same arguments used previously, the change of enthalpy for this change of state may be written as a sum of the changes of enthalpy on the formation of the compound from the elements, all at the same pressure and temperature, the elements being in their naturally occurring state of aggregation at this pressure and temperature; thus

$$\Delta H = m\Delta \tilde{H}_{f,M}(s, P, T) + n\,\Delta \tilde{H}_{f,N}(l, P, T)$$
$$- a\,\Delta \tilde{H}_{f,A}(g, P, T) - b\,\Delta \tilde{H}_{f,B}(l, P, T) \qquad (8.61)$$

Equation (8.61) can be used in either of two ways. It is an equation relating five quantities; a knowledge of any four permits the calculation of the fifth. Thus, if all four changes of enthalpy for formation are known, ΔH can be calculated. If ΔH is known from experimental measurement and three of the enthalpy changes on formation are known, the fourth may be calculated.

8.9 STANDARD STATES

We have indicated that the change of enthalpy for a change of state involving a chemical reaction is dependent upon the temperature and pressure of each substance involved. The compilation of data for each possible pressure and temperature becomes an imposing task. However, as we shall see, it is possible to determine the differences between such enthalpy changes at different temperatures and pressures as well as different states of aggregation. It is convenient, then, to agree by convention that certain states shall be chosen as *standard* states and to compile data in terms of these states. Any differences in the enthalpies at different temperatures, pressures, and states of aggregation can be calculated. The standard states so chosen for all elements and compounds are the naturally occurring states of aggregation at 298.15° K and 1-atm pressure. A *superscript zero* is used to designate all enthalpies and enthalpy changes for the standard states. Thus the changes of state expressed in Eq. (8.51) and the changes of enthalpy expressed in Eqs. (8.52), (8.53), (8.54), (8.55), and (8.59) are all standard. (The standard state for gases is taken as the ideal gas rather than the real gas. At low pressures the difference between the real gas and ideal gas are very small, and for this

Table 8.3 Standard Molar Changes of Enthalpy of Formation at 298° K[a]

Substance	ΔH_f^0 kcal mole^{-1}	Substance	ΔH_f^0 kcal mole^{-1}
H (g)	52.089	C (g)	171.698
O (g)	59.159	C (diamond)	0.4532
F (g)	18.3	C (graphite)	0.
Cl (g)	29.012	O_2 (g)	0.
Br (g)	26.71	CO (g)	−26.4157
Br_2 (g)	7.34	CO_2 (g)	−94.0518
I (g)	25.482	Methane(g)	−17.889
I_2 (g)	14.876	Ethane (g)	−20.236
H_2O (g)	−57.7979	Propane (g)	−24.820
H_2O (l)	−68.3174	*n*-Butane (g)	−30.15
HF (g)	−64.2	Acetylene (g)	54.194
HCl (g)	−22.063	Benzene (g)	19.820
HBr (g)	−8.66	Methanol (g)	−48.08
HI (g)	6.20	Methanol (l)	−57.02
N (g)	85.565	Ethanol (g)	−56.24
NO (g)	21.600	CCl_4 (g)	−25.5
NO_2 (g)	8.091	CCl_4 (l)	−33.3

[a] From "Selected Values of Chemical Thermodynamic Properties," Natl. Bur. Standards (U.S.), Circ. No. 500, (1952), and "Selected Values of Physical and Thermodynamic Properties of Hydrocarbons," API Project 44 (1953).

reason we shall assume in this text that all gases are ideal for purposes of calculations except in problems where real gases are introduced.) Table 8.3 contains values of the standard change of enthalpy of formation for a variety of substances.

8.10 THE DEPENDENCE OF CHANGES OF ENTHALPY ON TEMPERATURE

Let us assume that we know $\Delta H°$ for the change of state

$$a\text{A}(g, 1 \text{ atm}, 298°) + b\text{B}(l, 1 \text{ atm}, 298°) = m\text{M}(s, 1 \text{ atm}, 298°)$$
$$+ n\text{N}(l, 1 \text{ atm}, 298°)$$
$$(8.62)$$

and desire ΔH for the change of state

$$a\,\text{A}(g, 1 \text{ atm}, T_\text{A}) + b\text{B}(l, 1 \text{ atm}, T_\text{B}) = m\text{M}(s, 1 \text{ atm}, T_\text{M})$$
$$+ n\text{N}(l, 1 \text{ atm}, T_\text{N}) \qquad (8.63)$$

The second change of state can be obtained from the first by adding the following changes of state to the first:

$$a\,\text{A}(g, 1 \text{ atm}, T_\text{A}) = a\,\text{A}(g, 1 \text{ atm}, 298°) \qquad (8.64)$$

$$b\text{B}(l, 1 \text{ atm}, T_\text{B}) = b\text{B}(l, 1 \text{ atm}, 298°) \qquad (8.65)$$

$$m\text{M}(s, 1 \text{ atm}, 298°) = m\text{M}(s, 1 \text{ atm}, T_\text{M}) \qquad (8.66)$$

$$n\text{N}(l, 1 \text{ atm}, 298°) = n\text{N}(l, 1 \text{ atm}, T_\text{N}) \qquad (8.67)$$

The change of state for these four equations concerns only a change of temperature at constant pressure. We know that $(\partial H/\partial T)_P = C_P$ and that the change of enthalpy is the integral of this expression between the appropriate limits. On performing the additions in terms of enthalpies we find that

$$\Delta H = \Delta H° + m \int_{298}^{T_\text{M}} \tilde{C}_{P,\text{M}}\, dT + n \int_{298}^{T_\text{N}} \tilde{C}_{P,\text{N}}\, dT + a \int_{T_\text{A}}^{298} \tilde{C}_{P,\text{A}}\, dT$$
$$+ b \int_{T_\text{B}}^{298} \tilde{C}_{P,\text{B}}\, dT \qquad (8.68)$$

In the *special case* that the limits of integration are the same, Eq. (8.68) may be written as

$$\Delta H = \Delta H^\circ + \int_{298}^{T} (m\tilde{C}_{P,M} + n\tilde{C}_{P,N} - a\tilde{C}_{P,A} - b\tilde{C}_{P,B})\, dT \qquad (8.69)$$

$$\Delta H = \Delta H^\circ + \int_{298}^{T} \Delta C_P\, dT \qquad (8.70)$$

Here ΔC_P is defined as $m\tilde{C}_{P,M} + n\tilde{C}_{P,N} - a\tilde{C}_{P,A} - b\tilde{C}_{P,B}$, and is the change of the heat capacity for the given change of state when *all temperatures are the same*. When Eq. (8.70) is differentiated we obtain

$$\left(\frac{\partial \Delta H}{\partial T}\right)_P = \Delta C_P \qquad (8.71)$$

But in the use of this equation it must be remembered that the change of state is isothermal. Moreover the concept of constant pressure is that the pressure of each substance is kept constant with the change of temperature; it does not imply, in the general case, a process at constant pressure.

When a change of phase occurs in the course of a change of temperature, the change of enthalpy for the change of state of aggregation must be included. Consider again the change of state expressed in Eq. (8.51) where standard states are used. We desire to obtain the change of enthalpy for the change of state

$$CH_4(g,\ 1\ atm,\ 500^\circ) + 2O_2(g,\ 1\ atm,\ 500^\circ) = CO_2(g,\ 1\ atm,\ 500^\circ)$$
$$+ 2H_2O(g,\ 1\ atm,\ 500^\circ) \qquad (8.72)$$

This additional complication requires a determination of ΔH for

$$H_2O(l,\ 1\ atm,\ 298^\circ) = H_2O(g,\ 1\ atm,\ 500^\circ) \qquad (8.73)$$

But this change of state can be considered as the sum of three changes of state:

$$H_2O(l,\ 1\ atm,\ 298^\circ) = H_2O(l,\ 1\ atm,\ 373^\circ) \qquad (8.74)$$

$$H_2O(l, 1 \text{ atm}, 373°) = H_2O(g, 1 \text{ atm}, 373°) \tag{8.75}$$

$$H_2O(g, 1 \text{ atm}, 373°) = H_2O(g, 1 \text{ atm}, 500°) \tag{8.76}$$

The required ΔH is thus the sum of the change of enthalpy for the three steps indicated above.

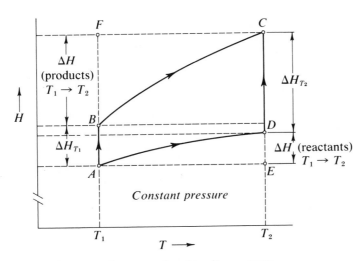

Fig. 8.1. Enthalpy changes as a function of temperature.

Figure 8.1 gives a representation of enthalpy changes as a function of temperature. Starting with all reactants at T_1, the isothermal enthalpy of reaction is given by $\Delta H_{T_1} = H_B - H_A$. If the reactants were at T_2 they would have to be heated at constant pressure from A to D and the increase in enthalpy to get the reactants from T_1 to T_2 would be

$$\Delta H(T_1 \rightarrow T_2) = H_D - H_A = \int_{T_1}^{T_2} \sum_i n_i \tilde{C}_{P_i} \, dT \quad \text{(reactants)} \tag{8.77}$$

where $\Sigma_i n_i \tilde{C}_{P_i}$ is for the heat capacities of the reactants. For the reaction taking place at T_2 the enthalpy change is $\Delta H_{T_2} = H_C - H_D$. The products at B and T_1 could be heated to T_2 and state C along the path BC and the enthalpy change for this process would be

163

$$\Delta H(T_1 \rightarrow T_2) = H_C - H_B = \int_{T_1}^{T_2} \sum_i n_i \tilde{C}_{P_i} \, dT \qquad \text{(products)} \qquad (8.78)$$

It is evident that the enthalpy change for the change of state from A to C is independent of the path. The availability of heat capacity data as a function of temperature may decide which path to follow in any given calculation.

8.11 DEPENDENCE OF CHANGES OF ENTHALPY ON PRESSURES AND ON CONCENTRATION IN SOLUTION

In all the examples discussed in Sections 8.6 through 8.10, the pressure of each substance in the change of state was 1 atm. When it is necessary to change the pressure, the same methods as those discussed in Section 8.10 would be used with Eq. (8.27) as the basic equation. For ideal gases the enthalpy is independent of the pressure; for real gases at low pressure and for liquids and solids the enthalpy changes very slowly with pressure. Consequently the effect of a change of pressure on the change of enthalpy is usually small and can be neglected in many cases. For precise work, corrections for pressure must be made.

Changes of enthalpy for changes of state involving solutions are beyond the scope of this book and are omitted.

8.12 CONCLUDING COMMENTS

The enthalpy is a thermodynamic function defined by the relation $H = E + PV$, and it was developed so that the pressure becomes a convenient variable for a state function. The heat capacity at constant pressure is related to the enthalpy. Relationships between C_P and C_V were developed and discussed.

The general dependence of the enthalpy on the temperature and pressure is discussed and the derived relationships are applied to changes of state involving gases. To evaluate enthalpy changes as the temperature changes, it is necessary to know the temperature dependence of the heat capacity. The enthalpy changes associated with phase transitions may be calculated and are important for many engineering applications.

Changes of state involving chemical reactions are of great interest to chemists and engineers, and in the last part of this chapter the relationships for enthalpy changes for these reactions were developed. This required the definition of standard states and the idea of standard changes of enthalpy on the formation of a compound. From tables of $\Delta H_f{}^\circ$ and the dependence of C_P on temperature, enthalpy changes may be calculated for a very large number of chemical reactions under a variety of conditions.

Exercises

8.1 Is the definition of the enthalpy an operational one or not. If your answer is "yes," go over the steps. If "no," what type of definition was used for the enthalpy?

8.2 Starting with Eq. (8.26), derive a relationship between C_P and C_V for (a) a real gas, and (b) an ideal gas.

8.3 Show that both $(\partial H/\partial P)_T$ and $(\partial H/\partial V)_T$ are zero for an ideal gas, starting with the condition that $(\partial E/\partial V)_T$ is zero.

8.4 Calculate ΔH for each of the following changes of state:

(a) $H_2O(l, 1 \text{ atm}, 300^\circ \text{ K}) = H_2O(l, 1 \text{ atm}, 350^\circ \text{ K})$.

(b) $3H_2O(s, 1 \text{ atm}, 263^\circ \text{ K}) = 3H_2O(g, 1 \text{ atm}, 500^\circ \text{ K})$.

(c) $H_2O(s, 1 \text{ atm}, 263^\circ \text{ K}) = H_2O(l, 1 \text{ atm}, 263^\circ \text{ K})$.

Data: For water substance, all at 1 atm pressure:

$\Delta \tilde{H}_{\text{fusion}} = 1440 \text{ cal mole}^{-1}$ at 273° K

$\Delta \tilde{H}_{\text{evap}} = 9700 \text{ cal mole}^{-1}$ at 373° K

$\tilde{C}_P(s) = 9.5 \text{ cal deg}^{-1} \text{ mole}^{-1}$

$\tilde{C}_P(l) = 18 \text{ cal deg}^{-1} \text{ mole}^{-1}$

$\tilde{C}_P(g) = 7.44 + 0.002T$

8.5 (a) The molar heat capacity in cal mole^{-1} deg^{-1} of an ideal gas is given by the relation $\tilde{C}_P = 6.00 + 0.001T$. Calculate ΔE and ΔH for the change of state A(g, 300° K, 1 atm) = A(g, 500° K, 100 atm) where A represents the ideal gas.

(b) For the same change of state, calculate Q and W for each of the following paths, assuming each to be quasi-static. (i) The gas is first heated at 1 atm pressure from 300° to 500° K and then is compressed from 1 atm pressure to 100 atm. (ii) The gas is first compressed from 1 atm pressure to 100 atm at 300° K and then heated from 300° to 500° K at 100 atm. (iii) The pressure is changed simultaneously with the temperature under such conditions that the pressure is a linear function of the Kelvin temperature.

8.6 When one mole of water is evaporated at 373° K and 1 atm pressure 9700 cal of heat are absorbed by the water substance. Two vessels, one having a volume of 100 ml and the other having a volume of 1000 ml are sealed together by means of a stopcock. The smaller vessel is filled with water and the larger vessel is evacuated. The entire assembly is placed in a thermostat at 373° K. The quantity of water in the smaller vessel is such that it just fills the vessel to the stopcock at this temperature and 1 atm pressure. After temperature equilibrium has been obtained the stopcock is opened and some of the water evaporates. Calculate ΔE and ΔH for the change of state that takes place and also Q and W for the process.

8.7 Given the following data: (a) standard molar changes of enthalpy of formation at 298° K and 1 atm pressure:

C_2H_5OH (l)	-66.36 kcal mole^{-1}
CO_2 (g)	-94.05 kcal mole^{-1}
H_2O (l)	-68.32 kcal mole^{-1}
CO (g)	-26.42 kcal mole^{-1}
ZnO (s)	-83.17 kcal mole^{-1}

(b) Molar changes of enthalpy on changes of state of aggregation:
Evaporation of H_2O at 373° K and 1 atm, 9.7 kcal mole^{-1}
Melting of Zn at 692° K and 1 atm, 1.57 kcal mole^{-1}
Evaporation of Zn at 1180° K and 1 atm, 30.5 kcal mole^{-1}

(c) Molar heat capacities at constant pressure in cal deg^{-1} mole^{-1}:

H_2O (l)	18
H_2O (g)	$7.187 + 0.00237T - 0.208 \times 10^{-6}\, T^2$

Zn (s)	6
Zn (l)	8
Zn (g)	5
ZnO (s)	10
CO (g)	$6.5 + 0.001T$
CO$_2$ (g)	$8.0 + 0.004T$

(1) Calculate ΔH^0 for the change of state

$$C_2H_5OH(l, 298°, 1 \text{ atm}) + 3\tfrac{1}{2}O_2(g, 298°, 1 \text{ atm})$$
$$= 2CO_2(g, 298°, 1 \text{ atm}) + 3H_2O(l, 298°, 1 \text{ atm})$$

(2) The change of enthalpy for the change of state

$$C_6H_6(l, 298°, 1 \text{ atm}) + 7\tfrac{1}{2}O_2(g, 298°, 1 \text{ atm})$$
$$= 6CO_2(g, 298°, 1 \text{ atm}) + 3H_2O(l, 298°, 1 \text{ atm})$$

is -781.0 kcal. Calculate $\Delta \tilde{H}_f{}^0$ for liquid benzene (C_6H_6)

(3) Calculate the change of enthalpy for the change of state

$$C_{12}H_{22}O_{11}(s, 298°, 1 \text{ atm}) + H_2O(l, 298°, 1 \text{ atm})$$
$$= 4C_2H_5OH(l, 298°, 1 \text{ atm}) + 4CO_2(g, 298°, 1 \text{ atm})$$

The change of enthalpy for the change of state

$$C_{12}H_{22}O_{11}(s, 298°, 1 \text{ atm}) + 12O_2(g, 298°, 1 \text{ atm})$$
$$= 12CO_2(g, 298°, 1 \text{ atm}) + 11H_2O(l, 298°, 1 \text{ atm})$$

is -1349.6 kcal.

(4) Calculate $\Delta \tilde{H}_f{}^0$ for water in the hypothetical state of H_2O (g, 298°, 1 atm)

(5) Calculate ΔH for each of the following changes of state:

(a) $ZnO(s, 298°, 1 \text{ atm}) + CO(g, 298°, 1 \text{ atm})$
$$= Zn(s, 298°, 1 \text{ atm}) + CO_2(g, 298°, 1 \text{ atm})$$

(b) ZnO(s, 298°, 1 atm) + CO(g, 298°, 1 atm)

$\qquad$ = Zn(l, 692°, 1 atm) + CO$_2$(g, 692°, 1 atm)

(c) ZnO(s, 298°, 1 atm) + CO(g, 298°, 1 atm)

$\qquad$ = Zn(g, 1180°, 1 atm) + CO$_2$(g, 1180°, 1 atm)

(d) ZnO(s, 1300°, 1 atm) + CO(g, 1300°, 1 atm)

$\qquad$ = Zn(g, 1300°, 1 atm) + CO$_2$(g, 1300°, 1 atm)

8.8 Three moles of an ideal gas at 1 atm pressure and 20° C are heated at constant pressure until the final temperature is 80° C. For this gas $\tilde{C}_V = 7.50 + 3.2 \times 10^{-3}T$ cal mole^{-1} deg^{-1}. Calculate ΔE and ΔH for the change of state and Q and W for the process.

8.9 Two liters of N$_2$ at 0° C and 5 atm pressure are expanded isothermally and quasi-statically until the pressure of the gas is 1 atm. Assuming the gas to be ideal, what are the values of ΔE and ΔH for the change of state and Q and W for the process?

8.10 Calculate the work done by 5 moles of an ideal gas during expansion from 5 atm at 25° C to 2 atm at 50° C. The quasi-static path followed is in two steps: an isochoric decrease in pressure to 2 atm, followed by an isobaric expansion with the gas pressure held constant at 2 atm. If, for this gas, $\tilde{C}_P = 5.0$ cal mole^{-1} deg^{-1}, find ΔE, ΔH, and Q for the process.

8.11 One mole of an ideal gas (not necessarily monatomic) is subjected to the following sequence of steps:

(a) It is heated isochorically from 25° to 100° C.

(b) It is expanded freely into a vacuum (Joule type of experiment) to double its volume.

(c) It is cooled quasi-statically along an isobar to 25° C.

Calculate (in calories and joules) ΔE, ΔH, Q, and W for the overall process (a) + (b) + (c). Note that it is not necessary to know the heat capacity of the gas, and explain why this is so. Represent (a), (b), and (c) on a PV diagram.

8.12 One mole of an ideal gas ($\tilde{C}_V = (3/2) R$) is subjected to the following sequence of steps:

(a) The gas is heated quasi-statically and isobarically ($P = 1$ atm) from 25° to 100° C.

(b) Next the gas is expanded quasi-statically and isothermally to double its volume.

(c) Finally the gas is cooled adiabatically and quasi-statically to 35° C. Calculate ΔE, ΔH, Q, and W for the overall process (a) + (b) + (c). Represent the changes of state on a PV diagram.

8.13 For a certain gas which can be assumed to behave ideally, $\tilde{C}_P = 8.58$ cal mole^{-1} deg^{-1}. What will be the final volume and temperature when 2 moles of the gas at 20° C and 15 atm are allowed to expand adiabatically and quasi-statically to 5-atm pressure? Find W, Q, ΔE, and ΔH for the process.

8.14 When one mole of liquid water is evaporated at 100° C and 1-atm pressure, 9700 cal of heat are absorbed. Calculate W for the evaporation of one mole of water at a constant pressure of 1 atm and ΔH and ΔE for the change of state. The density of liquid water may be taken as 1 g cc^{-1} and the ideal gas equation may be used for water vapor.

8.15 Show that

$$\left(\frac{\partial C_V}{\partial V}\right)_T = T\left(\frac{\partial^2 P}{\partial T^2}\right)_V \quad \text{and} \quad \left(\frac{\partial C_P}{\partial P}\right)_T = -T\left(\frac{\partial^2 V}{\partial T^2}\right)_P$$

9 The Joule-Thomson Experiment

In previous chapters we have applied the first law to processes involving primarily ideal gases. The behavior of real gases as interpreted through the first law is the subject of this chapter. The Joule-Thomson experiment is discussed for ideal gases and for real gases. The important area of gas liquefaction is then considered. The use of equations of state applicable to real gases is discussed in the last part of this chapter.

9.1 THE JOULE-THOMSON EXPERIMENT†

The Joule experiment involves the expansion of a gas into a vacuum. The Joule-Thomson experiment (carried out originally by Joule and Thomson between 1852 and 1862) involves the expansion of a gas from one fixed pressure to another under adiabatic conditions. The apparatus for the Joule-Thomson experiment is shown schematically in Fig. 9.1.

It consists of a cylinder divided into two parts by a porous plug, a needle valve, or other throttling device. A fixed quantity of gas is confined in the cylinder by frictionless pistons placed on either side of the porous plug. The entire piston and cylinder arrangement is surrounded by an adiabatic wall. The gas is the system and the movable boundaries between the system and the surroundings are the surfaces of the pistons adjacent to the gas. The gas

†This is sometimes called the Joule-Kelvin experiment, since William Thomson was also Lord Kelvin. It is also referred to as the "porous plug experiment."

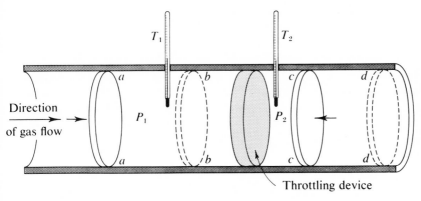

Fig. 9.1. Apparatus for the Joule-Thomson experiment.

to the left of the porous plug is at a pressure P_1 and that to the right of the plug is at a lower pressure P_2. The left-hand piston is moved to the right quasi-statically and under such conditions that the pressure P_1 is kept constant. The gas flows through the porous plug, causing the piston on the right to move to the right quasi-statically so that the pressure of the gas on the right remains constant. Under these conditions the kinetic energy associated with the flow of the gas through the plug is negligible. The process is continued until the change of volume of the part of the system on the left is V_1 and the corresponding change of volume of that part of the system on the right is V_2.

The work done by the system on the surroundings is

$$W = P_2 V_2 - P_1 V_1 \tag{9.1}$$

Because the process is adiabatic,

$$\Delta E = -W \tag{9.2}$$

and therefore

$$\Delta E = E_2 - E_1 = P_1 V_1 - P_2 V_2 \tag{9.3}$$

From this equation we obtain

$$E_2 + P_2 V_2 = E_1 + P_1 V_1 \tag{9.4}$$

and from the definition of the enthalpy we can write

$$H_2 = H_1 \tag{9.5}$$

We thus conclude that the enthalpy of the gas which has moved across the porous plug is the same on either side of the plug and that the process is one which takes place at constant enthalpy; that is, it is an *isenthalpic* process.

We consider the enthalpy to be a function of the temperature and the pressure, so that

$$dH = \left(\frac{\partial H}{\partial T}\right)_P dT + \left(\frac{\partial H}{\partial P}\right)_T dP \tag{9.6}$$

For isenthalpic changes of state this equation may be written as

$$\left(\frac{\partial T}{\partial P}\right)_H = -\frac{(\partial H/\partial P)_T}{(\partial H/\partial T)_P} \tag{9.7}$$

The partial derivative $(\partial T/\partial P)_H$ is called the Joule-Thomson coefficient and is given the symbol μ_{JT},† so that

$$\mu_{JT} = \left(\frac{\partial T}{\partial P}\right)_H \tag{9.8}$$

This derivative relates the change of temperature of the gas with the change of pressure in the Joule-Thomson experiment.

Several relations involving the Joule-Thomson coefficient can be written immediately, based on Eq. (9.7). First, from Eq. (9.8),

$$\mu_{JT} = -\frac{1}{C_P}\left(\frac{\partial H}{\partial P}\right)_T \tag{9.9}$$

and from Eq. (8.27),

$$\mu_{JT} = \frac{T(\partial V/\partial T)_P - V}{C_P} \tag{9.10}$$

---

† The subscript JT will be used throughout to specify the Joule-Thomson coefficient, since the symbol μ will be given another significance later in this book.

Also, from the definition of the enthalpy,

$$\mu_{JT} = -\frac{1}{C_P}\left[\left(\frac{\partial E}{\partial P}\right)_T + \left(\frac{\partial(PV)}{\partial P}\right)_T\right] \tag{9.11}$$

$$\mu_{JT} = -\frac{1}{C_P}\left[\left(\frac{\partial E}{\partial V}\right)_T\left(\frac{\partial V}{\partial P}\right)_T + \left(\frac{\partial(PV)}{\partial P}\right)_T\right] \tag{9.12}$$

The sign of the Joule-Thomson coefficient is determined by the sign of the numerator in Eq. (9.10) because the heat capacity at constant pressure is positive. For ideal gases the numerator is always zero; the Joule-Thomson coefficient is thus zero and the temperature of an ideal gas does not change in the experiment. For real gases the numerator (and thus the Joule-Thomson coefficient) may be positive, negative, or zero, depending upon the temperature and pressure of the gas. The change of pressure, dP, is always negative, so that when the coefficient is positive, dT is negative and when the coefficient is negative, dT is positive. These effects are summarized in Table 9.1.

Table 9.1 The Joule-Thomson Coefficient and Temperature Changes

Experimental Result	μ_{JT}	$\left(\frac{\partial H}{\partial P}\right)_T$	Comment
$T_2 < T_1$	$(+)$	$(-)$	Most gases. H_2 and He at low temperatures
$T_2 = T_1$	Zero	Zero	Ideal gas. Real gas at inversion temperature
$T_2 > T_1$	$(-)$	$(+)$	Most gases at high temperature. H_2 and He at ordinary temperature

The Joule-Thomson experiment has been used in many studies of the properties of real gases. The advantage is that the Joule-Thomson coefficient is zero for ideal gases, and consequently the value of the coefficient is directly related to the deviations from ideal gas behavior. The derivative $(\partial H/\partial P)_T$ is evaluated easily from the Joule-Thomson coefficient and the heat capacity at constant pressure.

Table 9.2 gives values of the Joule-Thomson coefficient and heat capacities for helium, nitrogen, and carbon dioxide as functions of temperature.

Table 9.2   Joule-Thomson Coefficients and Heat Capacities at I Atm for He, N_2, and CO_2

$t°$ C	Helium[a] C_P cal g^{-1} deg^{-1}	μ_{JT} deg atm^{-1}	Nitrogen[b] C_P	μ_{JT}	Carbon Dioxide[c] C_P	μ_{JT}
300	1.271	−0.0597	0.2501	0.0139	0.2501	0.2650
200	1.264	−0.0641	0.2490	0.0558	0.2349	0.3770
100	1.257	−0.0638	0.2476	0.1291	0.2181	0.6490
25	1.252	−0.0624	0.2467	0.2216	0.2045	1.0658
0	1.250	−0.0616	0.2466	0.2655	0.1997	1.2900
−100	1.243	−0.0584	0.2473	0.6487	—	—
−180	1.237	−0.0412	0.2480	2.391	—	—

[a] Roebuck and Osterberg, *Phys. Rev.*, **43**, 60 (1933); *ibid.*, **45**, 332 (1934).
[b] Roebuck and Osterberg, *ibid.*, **48**, 450 (1935).
[c] Roebuck, *et al.*, *J. Am. Chem. Soc.*, **64**, 400 (1942).

Table 9.3 gives values of the coefficient for nitrogen as a function of both temperature and pressure. The coefficient is a function of both the temperature and the pressure and, of course, the nature of the gas. An approximate value

Table 9.3   Joule-Thomson Coefficients for Nitrogen[a]

Pressure atm	μ_{JT} (deg atm^{-1}) 0° C	25° C	50° C	100° C	200° C
1	0.2656	0.214	0.179	0.1292	0.0540
20	0.2494	0.200	0.166	0.1173	0.0460
60	0.2088	0.169	0.141	0.0975	0.0365
100	0.1679	0.138	0.115	0.0768	0.0260
200	0.0891	0.078	0.066	0.0419	0.0075

[a] Roebuck and Osterberg, *Phys. Rev.*, **48**, 450 (1935).

of the coefficient can be calculated from the van der Waals equation of state (see Section 9.2) but precise values ordinarily are obtained experimentally.

The Joule-Thomson experiment is an example of a "steady state" process in which measurements are made under conditions of continuous flow. Although there is a continuous transport of matter through the throttling device under steady-state conditions there will be a pressure and a temperature which can be measured and assigned to each side and which does not vary as long as the system is well behaved. As another example of the steady state, we can measure the temperature of a flowing river at one point and if the temperature is constant for a period of time we can then specify the temperature of the river for that point and that particular steady state. In the case of the Joule-Thomson experiment the pressure and temperature gradients are confined to the throttling device. The steady state arises, then, when these gradients are constant in time.

9.2 THE JOULE-THOMSON COEFFICIENT AND THE VAN DER WAALS EQUATION OF STATE

The van der Waals equation of state for one mole of gas may be rearranged to give

$$PV = RT - \frac{a}{V} + bP + \frac{ab}{V^2} \tag{9.13}$$

If the pressure is not too large, the last term in Eq. (9.13), ab/V^2, is essentially negligible. Also, in the second term, V may be replaced by RT/P without much error. This gives

$$PV = RT - \frac{aP}{RT} + bP \tag{9.14}$$

Division by P gives

$$V = \frac{RT}{P} - \frac{a}{RT} + b \tag{9.15}$$

and differentiation with respect to T at constant P gives

$$\left(\frac{\partial V}{\partial T}\right)_P = \frac{R}{P} + \frac{a}{RT^2} \tag{9.16}$$

Equation (9.14) may be arranged to give

$$\frac{R}{P} = \frac{V - b}{T} + \frac{a}{RT^2} \tag{9.17}$$

which, on substitution into Eq. (9.16), yields

$$\left(\frac{\partial V}{\partial T}\right)_P = \frac{V - b}{T} + \frac{2a}{RT^2} \tag{9.18}$$

Equation (9.18) can be rearranged to

$$T\left(\frac{\partial V}{\partial T}\right)_P - V = \frac{2a}{RT} - b \tag{9.19}$$

Thus the Joule-Thomson coefficient for a van der Waals gas is approximately given by

$$\mu_{JT} = \frac{1}{C_P}\left(\frac{2a}{RT} - b\right) \tag{9.20}$$

Table 9.4 shows some values of μ_{JT} calculated from Eq. (9.20) for three gases. The agreement between the observed and calculated values is reasonable, considering the assumptions made in the derivation of Eq. (9.20) and the applicability of the van der Waals equation.

Table 9.4   The Joule-Thomson Coefficient for Three Gases Calculated from the van der Waals a and b†

Gas	a liter^2 atm mole^{-2}	b liters mole^{-1}	$\tilde{C}_P$ liter atm deg^{-1} mole^{-1}	μ_{JT} Calc	Obs
Hydrogen	0.254	2.67×10^{-2}	0.29	−0.017	−0.03
Oxygen	1.32	3.12	0.30	0.29	0.31
Carbon Dioxide	3.60	4.28	0.38	0.73	1.30

† From S. Glasstone, *Textbook of Physical Chemistry* 3rd ed. New York: D. Van Nostrand, 1950, p.293.

The inversion temperature T_i is defined as the temperature where $\mu_{JT} = 0$. From Eq. (9.20) the inversion temperature is given by

$$T_i = \frac{2a}{Rb} \qquad (9.21)$$

A more rigorous solution for the van der Waals gas yields the following relation:

$$\frac{2a}{RT_i} - \frac{3abP}{R^2T_i^2} - b = 0 \qquad (9.22)$$

which implies that there are actually two inversion temperatures at each pressure. That this is indeed the case is shown in Fig. 9.2 where the experimental inversion temperature is plotted as a function of the pressure for

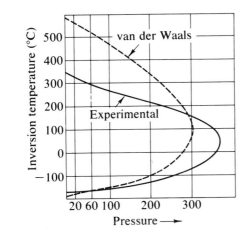

Fig. 9.2. Joule-Thomson inversion curve for nitrogen.

nitrogen. Also plotted in Fig. 9.2 are the inversion temperatures for nitrogen calculated from the van der Waals equation according to Eq. (9.22). The maximum pressure at which the inversion temperature occurs is at 376 atm and 313° K. The Joule-Thomson coefficient is positive to the left of the curve and negative to the right of it. Table 9.5 lists the upper and lower inversion temperatures (experimental) for nitrogen.

Table 9.5 Joule-Thomson Inversion Temperatures for Nitrogen

Pressure atm	Inversion Temperature °C Upper	Lower
1	348.	—
20	330.0	−167.0
60	299.6	−162.4
100	277.2	−156.5
180	235.0	−134.7
220	212.5	−117.2
300	158.7	−68.7
376	40	

9.3 LIQUEFACTION OF GASES BY USE OF THE JOULE-THOMSON EFFECT

The throttling process, in which a gas expands to a lower pressure, can result in lowering the temperature of the gas considerably under appropriate conditions. Let us take the case of adiabatic expansion by the throttling process for one mole of nitrogen initially at 100° C and 200 atm to 1 atm. Using the average value of μ_{JT} at 100° between 200 atm and 1 atm we find $\mu_{JT} = 0.0856$ deg atm^{-1}. For a change of 200 atm the temperature change is 200×0.0856, or about -17 deg. From Table 9.3 we note that the average decrease in μ_{JT} in the range 0° to 100° C is 0.0918×10^{-2} deg atm^{-1}, from which we can deduce a better average value of μ_{JT} for this expansion of 0.1012 deg atm^{-1}. This gives a temperature decrease of 20 deg or a final temperature of 80° C. In this case the Joule-Thomson expansion results in an appreciable decrease in the temperature.

Advantage of the effect is used in the liquefaction of a gas. The apparatus is shown schematically in Fig. 9.3. The direction of gas flow is indicated by the arrows. The compressed high-pressure gas is cooled first in a cooling section. Then it passes through a countercurrent heat exchanger to the throttling valve. At this point the gas expands and cools and flows back through the heat exchanger, cooling the high-pressure gas. After repeated

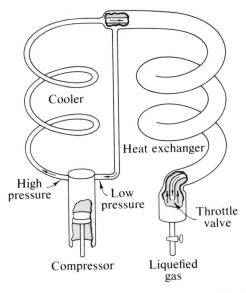

Fig. 9.3.   Liquefaction of a gas by use of the Joule-Thomson effect.

cycles the temperature of the expanded gas is sufficiently low for some of it to condense. In practice, these units operate continuously with a constant flow of liquefied gas. Modern gas liquefiers also use adiabatic work to cool the gas down to the point where it liquefies or to the point at which the gas may be used for cooling by the Joule-Thomson effect.

In the design of gas liquefiers close attention must be paid to the operating pressures and temperatures. The initial temperature and pressure before expansion must be in the region of positive values of μ_{JT}. For example, to use hydrogen, the initial temperature must be below 200° K. This can be accomplished by using liquid nitrogen to cool the hydrogen below its inversion temperature. Then the liquid hydrogen may be used to cool helium below its inversion temperature.

9.4   THE APPLICATION OF THE FIRST LAW TO REAL GASES

So far the first law has been applied mainly to changes of state for ideal gases, but many of the relations which have been developed are equally applicable to real gases. It is at the point where an equation of state is necessary that the difference between real and ideal gases becomes important. Also, for processes involving ideal gases $(\partial E/\partial V)_T = (\partial E/\partial P)_T = (\partial H/\partial V)_T = (\partial H/\partial P)_T = 0$, but for real gases these partial derivatives must be evaluated, usually from an equation of state or P-V-T data for real gases. The two important relations which we use here are

$$\left(\frac{\partial E}{\partial V}\right)_T = T\left(\frac{\partial P}{\partial T}\right)_V - P \tag{9.23}$$

$$\left(\frac{\partial H}{\partial P}\right)_T = V - T\left(\frac{\partial V}{\partial T}\right)_P \tag{9.24}$$

Let us consider the isothermal quasi-static expansion of a gas whose equation of state is $PV = RT + BP$ where B is assumed to be independent of the temperature. For this equation of state $(\partial E/\partial V)_T$ equals zero and thus ΔE must also be zero for the isothermal expansion. Then the heat absorbed by the gas must equal the work done by the gas, so that

$$Q = W = \int P\, dV = \int \left(\frac{RT}{V - B}\right) dV = RT \int \frac{dV}{V - B} \tag{9.25}$$

Integration of Eq. (9.25) between the limits V_1 and V_2 (at constant T) gives

$$Q = W = RT \ln\left(\frac{V_2 - B}{V_1 - B}\right) \tag{9.26}$$

For this same equation of state

$$\left(\frac{\partial H}{\partial P}\right)_T = V - T\left(\frac{\partial V}{\partial T}\right)_P = V - \left(\frac{RT}{P}\right) = B \tag{9.27}$$

Thus

$$dH = B\, dP \tag{9.28}$$

and

$$\Delta H = B \int_{P_1}^{P_2} dP = B(P_2 - P_1) \qquad (9.29)$$

Although $dE = 0$ for an isothermal process for a gas whose equation of state is $PV = RT + BP$, the work done by the gas, the heat absorbed by the gas, and the change in the enthalpy are not those obtained in the case of an ideal gas.

It was assumed in this development that B was a constant, independent of the temperature. Let us now assume that B depends on the temperature according to the equation

$$B = B_1 + \frac{B_2}{T^2} \qquad (9.30)$$

where B_1 and B_2 are constants. The equation of state then is

$$PV = RT + B_1 P + \frac{B_2 P}{T^2} \qquad (9.31)$$

Solving (9.31) for P gives

$$P = \frac{RT}{V - B_1 - B_2 T^{-2}} \qquad (9.32)$$

It is readily seen that evaluating $(\partial P/\partial T)_V$ from Eq. (9.32) will result in some involved relationships. However, $(\partial P/\partial T)_V$ may be evaluated indirectly by the identity (proof left to the reader)

$$\left(\frac{\partial P}{\partial T}\right)_V \doteq -\frac{(\partial V/\partial T)_P}{(\partial V/\partial P)_T} \qquad (9.33)$$

The two partial derivatives on the right-hand side are

$$\left(\frac{\partial V}{\partial T}\right)_P = \frac{R}{P} - \frac{2B_2}{T^3} \quad \text{and} \quad \left(\frac{\partial V}{\partial P}\right)_T = -\frac{RT}{P^2} \qquad (9.34)$$

181

For the partial derivative $(\partial E/\partial V)_T$ this gives

$$\left(\frac{\partial E}{\partial V}\right)_T = -\frac{2B_2P^2}{RT^3} \tag{9.35}$$

The total differential of the energy function $E(T, V)$ is

$$dE = C_V\,dT - \frac{2B_2P^2}{RT}\,dV \tag{9.36}$$

from which it is evident that $dE \neq 0$ for an isothermal expansion for this gas when $B = B(T)$.

9.5 CONCLUDING COMMENTS

The Joule-Thomson coefficient μ_{JT} is defined as $(\partial T/\partial P)_H$, and in a Joule-Thomson expansion it is positive for a temperature decrease and negative for an increase in temperature. For an ideal gas, μ_{JT} equals zero, but for a real gas it may be positive, negative, or zero. Gases have two inversion temperatures (where $\mu_{JT} = 0$), and the inversion temperature is a function of the pressure and the nature of the gas. The Joule-Thomson effect is useful for evaluating partial derivatives such as $(\partial E/\partial T)_V$ and $(\partial H/\partial P)_T$. The effect is also the basis of a process for the liquefaction of gases. Some applications of the first law to real gases have been presented.

Exercises

9.1 The equation of state for one mole of a gas is $PV = RT + BP$ where B is a constant independent of the temperature. Starting with one mole of the gas at 300° K and a pressure of 10 atm, consider the following quasi-static processes:
(a) an adiabatic expansion to 20 liters.
(b) an isobaric expansion to 20 liters.
(c) an isothermal expansion to 20 liters.
(d) an isochoric decrease in pressure to 1 atm.
If the value of B is 1.5 liters and $\tilde{C}_P$ is 7 cal mole^{-1} deg^{-1} and $\tilde{C}_V$ is

5 cal mole^{-1} deg^{-1} for this gas, find
  (i) Relations for calculating Q, W, ΔE, and ΔH for each of the above processes.
  (ii) Q, W, ΔE, and ΔH for each of the above processes.

9.2 The van der Waals constants for helium are $a = 0.0341$ liters^2 atm mole^{-2} and $b = 23.7$ cc mole^{-1}. Using Eqs. (9.21) and (9.22), calculate the inversion temperature for helium at 1, 10, 50, and 100 atm. What is the approximate maximum temperature at which helium could be used for cooling in a Joule-Thomson expansion?

9.3 For nitrogen, the van der Waals constants are $a = 1.39$ liters^2 atm mole^{-2} and $b = 39.1$ cc mole^{-1}; $\tilde{C}_P = 6.91$ cal mole^{-1} deg^{-1} and can be considered to be independent of the temperature. Calculate the Joule-Thomson coefficient for 298° K and 1 atm and compare this value with the one in Table 9.2. Also use the μ_{JT} in Table 9.2 at 298° K to calculate $(\partial\tilde{H}/\partial P)_T$ for nitrogen at 1 atm.

9.4 Using the information in Table 9.3 for nitrogen, calculate what the temperature decrease would be for a Joule-Thomson expansion starting at (a) 473° K and 200 atm, and (b) 473° K and 100 atm, and ending at 1 atm.

9.5 (a) Derive the relationship

$$\left(\frac{\partial C_P}{\partial P}\right)_T = -\mu_{JT}\left(\frac{\partial C_P}{\partial T}\right)_P - C_P\left(\frac{\partial\mu_{JT}}{\partial T}\right)_P$$

(b) For nitrogen $\tilde{C}_P = 6.45 + 1.41 \times 10^{-3}T - 0.81 \times 10^{-7}T^2$. Calculate the value of $(\partial\tilde{C}_P/\partial P)_T$ for nitrogen at 300° K, making appropriate approximations. What is the value of $(\partial\tilde{C}_P/\partial P)_T$ for an ideal gas?

9.6 You can assume that $(\partial E/\partial V)_T$ for a van der Waals gas is equal to a/V^2. Show that the change in the energy function for an isothermal expansion of one mole of the gas from a volume V_1 to a volume V_2 is given by

$$\Delta E = a\left(\frac{1}{V_1} - \frac{1}{V_2}\right)$$

9.7 Calculate μ_{JT} for CO at 298° K and 400 atm pressure, given that $(T/V)(\partial V/\partial T)_P$ is 0.984, the molar volume is 76.25 cc mole^{-1}, and

$\tilde{C}_P$ is 8.91 cal mole^{-1} deg^{-1}. Determine μ_{JT} for these conditions, but assume CO to behave as a van der Waals gas.

9.8 For a gas whose equation of state for one mole is $P\tilde{V} = RT + (B'/\tilde{V})$ where $B' = 37$ liters^2 atm mole^{-1} and B' is independent of the temperature, carry out the steps requested in Exercise 9.1 for the conditions stated in that exercise.

9.9 (a) If a gas obeys the equation of state $PV(1 - \beta P) = RT$, show that for an isothermal quasi-static expansion the work will be

$$W = \frac{RT}{1 - \beta P_2} - \frac{RT}{1 - \beta P_1} + RT \ln \frac{P_1(1 - \beta P_2)}{P_2(1 - \beta P_1)}$$

$$= P_2 V_2 - P_1 V_1 + RT \ln \frac{P_1{}^2 V_1}{P_2{}^2 V_2}$$

(*Hint:* Integrate by parts to evaluate $\int_{V_1}^{V_2} P\, dV$.)

(b) If the gas is heated at constant pressure, show that

$$W = \frac{R}{1 - \beta P}(T_2 - T_1)$$

9.10 Make a chart showing the change in ΔE, ΔH, ΔT, and the sign of Q and W for the following processes for an ideal gas:
(a) Adiabatic expansion.
(b) Adiabatic compression.
(c) Adiabatic free expansion.
(d) Isothermal expansion.
(e) Isothermal compression.
(f) Isochoric increase in temperature.
(g) Isobaric decrease in temperature.

9.11 Represent each of the processes in Exercise 9.10 on a PV diagram.

10 The Second Law of Thermodynamics

The first law of thermodynamics requires that for any system operating in cycles the work done by the system must equal the heat absorbed by the system. However, the first law gives no information concerning any limitations on the relationship between the work done in a cycle and the total amount of heat which must be absorbed by the system, nor does it give information on the conditions which must be satisfied for the system to do work while it is operating in cycles. The province of the second law of thermodynamics is the study of the limitations under which a thermodynamic system must operate in order to do work in a cycle.

Closely associated with these questions is the one concerning the direction of a process. We have observed water flowing downhill, but we have never observed water flowing uphill of its own accord. We know from experience that when we place two gases in a vessel, each gas becomes uniformly distributed in the vessel, but we have never observed a mixture of gases to separate into the pure gases of their own accord in the same vessel. We know that a certain chemical reaction takes place when two or more specified chemicals are mixed, but we do not expect the products of the reaction to react to form the initial reagents spontaneously. We are quite accustomed to such unidirectional processes and we describe such processes by saying that the systems associated with the processes are moving to states of equilibrium. Experience has shown that all processes which take place naturally in an isolated system are those which produce a state of equilibrium in the system. The study of the thermodynamic properties of systems at equilibrium is also a province of the second law of thermodynamics.

Before we make any statement of the second law of thermodynamics, several pertinent topics which lead to an understanding of the second law are discussed. First, we establish more rigorously the ideas of reversible and irreversible processes and the net result when such processes take place in isolated systems. We consider an idealized cycle, called the Carnot cycle, from which the definition of the efficiency of a heat engine operating in cycles is established. We then turn to the definition of the thermodynamic temperature scale. With this preparation, we establish the statements of the second law of thermodynamics made by Kelvin and Planck and by Clausius.

10.1   REVERSIBLE TRANSFER OF HEAT

In Chapter 6 we established the condition of doing work reversibly, but we need to develop the operation required for the reversible transfer of heat between two bodies. Let us consider a quantity of water in a beaker at 298° K and 1 atm pressure and a piece of copper at 348° K and 1 atm pressure as shown in Fig. 10.1. The water and copper comprise the system. When we place the copper in the water, keeping the pressure at 1 atm, we observe convection currents in the water, developed because the water near the surface of the copper becomes warmer and hence less dense than the rest of the water. We then can no longer speak of the temperature of the water. Similarly, while

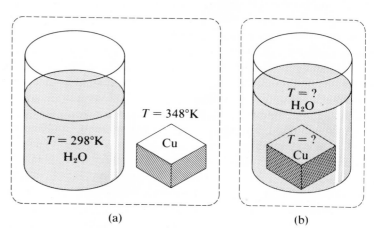

(a)   (b)

Fig. 10.1. Irreversible transfer of heat.

no convection currents as such can be established in the copper, we know that the surface of the copper is cooler than the interior of the copper. Again we can no longer speak of the temperature of the copper. Consequently there is no direct way of determining the heat absorbed by the water or the heat given off by the copper at any given time. However, if we wait long enough for temperature equilibrium to be established, we can measure the final temperature T of both the water and the copper. We can now calculate the heat absorbed by the water and given up by the copper by the two equations

$$Q_{H_2O} = \int_{298}^{T} (C_P)_{H_2O}\, dT \tag{10.1}$$

and

$$Q_{Cu} = \int_{348}^{T} (C_P)_{Cu}\, dT \tag{10.2}$$

(It is assumed that the heat capacities are known as a function of the temperature.) But we recognize that the value of the integral is the limit of a sum of terms $\sum C_P \,\Delta T$ as ΔT goes to zero. This calculation implies that we have knowledge of the temperature at every infinitesimal step.

These considerations indicate how the reversible transfer of heat may be carried out in "thought" processes. If we desire to change the temperature of a body from T_1 to T_2, we must have an infinite number of thermal reservoirs covering the whole range of temperatures from T_1 to T_2 with infinitesimal differences δT; that is, the temperature of one reservoir is T_1, that of the next reservoir is $T_1 + \delta T$, that of the third reservoir $T_1 + 2\delta T$, and so forth, and the temperature of the last reservoir is T_2. This is illustrated in Fig. 10.2. We can now place the body in thermal contact with the first reservoir at T_1 and allow temperature equilibrium to be attained. Then we place the body in contact with the next reservoir at $T_1 + \delta T$ and obtain thermal equilibrium. This process is repeated until the temperature T_2 is reached. In these processes, then, heat is transferred under conditions of approximate thermal equilibrium. In the limit as δT goes to zero, heat is transferred under equilibrium conditions. This limiting process constitutes reversible transfer of heat. The requirement that the process takes place under equilibrium conditions, in the limit, is the same requirement as that developed for the reversible expansion or compression of a fluid discussed in Chapter 6.

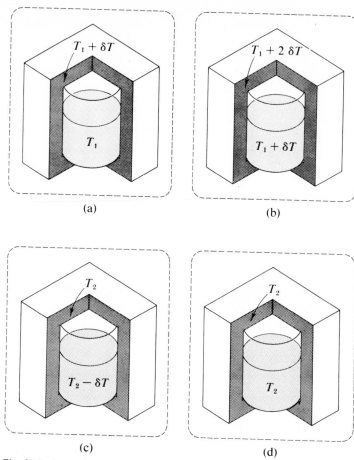

Fig. 10.2. Reversible transfer of heat.

10.2   CYCLIC IRREVERSIBLE AND REVERSIBLE PROCESSES

One particular cyclic process is considered in detail in order to obtain a comparison of the net results when the process is carried out irreversibly and reversibly.

We consider the quasi-static process discussed in Section 6.5, but now we imagine that the entire apparatus is placed in a thermostat so that the temperatures of the gas, piston, and the cylinder are kept constant. The system is defined as a definite quantity of a gas; the piston, cylinder, thermostat, and any masses which may be required are all parts of the surroundings; and the boundary is the lower surface of the piston. The change of state of the gas which takes place on expansion is

$$nA(g, T, V_0) \rightarrow nA(g, T, V)$$

where n represents the number of moles of the gas A. The reverse change of state takes place on compression.

The equation applicable for this process of expansion is Eq. (6.23) which may be written more generally as

$$\int_{V_0}^{V} P \, dV = \int_{ho}^{h} (F_e + mg) \, dh + \sum_{i} (\tfrac{1}{2}mv^2)_i \tag{10.3}$$

This form of the equation is used because we may make the mass of the piston variable. The term $\int_{V_0}^{V_h} P \, dV$ is the work done by the system as measured by changes in the surroundings, and the term $\int_{ho}^{h} (F_e + mg) \, dh$ is the work done against the forces F_e and mg. The sum $\sum_{i} (\tfrac{1}{2}mv^2)_i$ represents the total kinetic energy which has been associated with the piston in all the quasi-static steps. For this isothermal process a quantity of heat equivalent to this sum is transferred to the thermostat when the collision process is idealized, as was done in Section 6.3. For expansion, PA must be greater than $(F_e + mg)$, so the $\int_{V_0}^{V} P \, dV$ is greater than $\int_{ho}^{h} (F_e + mg) \, dh$.

Once the gas has been expanded we must return the gas to its original state by compression. The equation applicable for this step is similar to Eq. (10.3) and is

$$\int_{V}^{V_0} P \, dV = \int_{h}^{ho} (F_e' + m'g) \, dh + \sum_{j} (\tfrac{1}{2}m'v^2)_j \tag{10.4}$$

For compression, PA must always be less than $(F_e' + m'g)$ and therefore $(F_e' + m'g)$ must be greater than $(F_e + mg)$. Again $\int_{V}^{V_0} P \, dV$ represents the work done by the system as measured by the effects in the surroundings; but this quantity is negative and work is actually done on the system. The integral $\int_h^{h_0} (F_e' + m'g)$ represents the work done by the forces $(F_e' + m'g)$ and this quantity is also negative. Again the term $\sum_j (\frac{1}{2}m'v^2)_j$ represents the total kinetic energy which has been associated with the piston in all steps in the quasi-static process. A quantity of heat equivalent to the value of this sum is transferred to the thermostat when the collision process is idealized.

The net result in terms of work for the cyclic process is that

$$\int_{h_0}^{h} (F_e' + m'g)\, dh > \int_{h_0}^{h} (F_e + mg)\, dh \tag{10.5}$$

that is, the work done by the forces associated with the surroundings on compression is greater than the similar work done on expansion. If F_e' equals F_e, this difference is indicated by the result that certain masses used to change the mass of the piston have been lowered in the gravitational field of the earth.

We also consider the net amount of heat which has been transferred to the thermostat in the cyclic process. We have already indicated that some heat is added to the thermostat on both the expansion and compression processes, so that

$$Q = \sum_i (\frac{1}{2}mv^2)_i + \sum_j (\frac{1}{2}m'v^2)_j \tag{10.6}$$

But we must consider any heat which the gas has absorbed or given off in the cyclic process. At the end of the cycle the gas is in its original state so that the change of energy of the gas is zero. Thus the heat absorbed by the gas in the cycle equals the work done by the gas. But the work done by the gas on expansion is $\int_{V_0}^{V} P\, dV$ and the work done by the gas on compression is $\int_{V}^{V_0} P\, dV$ and consequently the net work done by the gas in the cycle is zero. Therefore the heat absorbed by the gas is zero; the same quantity of heat is transferred to the gas on expansion as is transferred from the gas on compression.

For the total cycle, then, a quantity of work W equal to

$$W = -\int_{h_0}^{h} (F_e' + m'g)\, dh + \int_{h_0}^{h} (F_e + mg)\, dh \tag{10.7}$$

has been done by the system against these forces and a quantity of heat Q equal to

$$Q = \sum_i (\tfrac{1}{2} m v^2)_i + \sum_j (\tfrac{1}{2} m' v^2)_j \qquad (10.8)$$

has been added to the thermostat. If we consider the gas, piston, and cylinder, the masses, the thermostat, and the device which exerts the forces F_e and F_e' all as constituting one isolated system, we observe that while the gas has been brought back to its original state the isolated system is *not* in its original state. Some work has been done by a part of the isolated system and some heat has been added to the thermostat. The question then arises whether we can bring the entire *isolated* system back to its original state by removing the added heat from the thermostat and using it to restore to its original state that part of the system which has done work. *All experience has shown that this is not possible.*

The initial and final states for the expansion and compression processes are illustrated in Figs. 10.3 and 10.4. In these illustrations F_e is assumed to be the same for both expansion and compression. The net result of the cyclic process is that a mass Δm has been lowered over the distance $(h - h_0)$. Also,

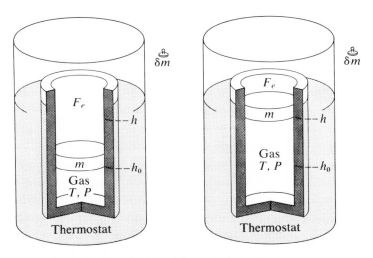

Fig. 10.3. Initial and final states of the expansion process.

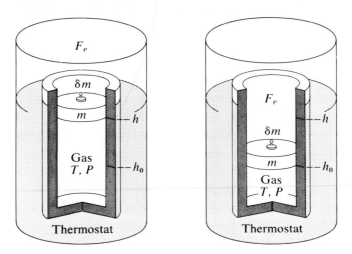

Fig. 10.4.   Initial and final states of the compression process.

a quantity of heat has been added to the heat reservoir (thermostat) at the constant temperature T.

When the expansion is carried out reversibly, the work done by the system equals that done on the surroundings. The piston does not acquire kinetic energy and no heat would be given to the thermostat as a consequence of stopping the motion of the piston. The same conclusions are obtained when the compression is also carried out reversibly. Therefore, no net work is done by the system (Eq. (10.7)) in the reversible cycle and no heat is added to the thermostat (Eq. (10.8)). In this case the *isolated* system has been brought back to its original state.

The results are illustrated graphically in Fig. 10.5. The curve drawn with a solid line represents the isotherm of the gas at a given temperature T. The initial state of the gas is at point a where its pressure and volume are P_1 and V_1 and the final state of the gas is at point h, pressure and volume of P_2 and V_2. We consider various quasi-static processes for expansion. In one case let us assume that $(F_e + mg)$ equals the final pressure P_2 and is held constant during the expansion. Then the work done by the system against the pressure P_2 is $\int_{V_1}^{V_2} P_2 \, dV$, which is represented by the area ‿ ᵢd. The heat absorbed by the gas from the thermostat, Eqs. (7.6) and (7.11), is $\int_{V_1}^{V_2} T(\partial P/\partial T)_V \, dV$ and the heat given to the thermostat because of the stopping of the piston is given by

$$Q' = \sum_i (\tfrac{1}{2}mv^2)_i = \int_{V_1}^{V_2} P \, dV - \int_{V_1}^{V_2} P_2 \, dV \tag{10.9}$$

The net heat removed from the thermostat is then

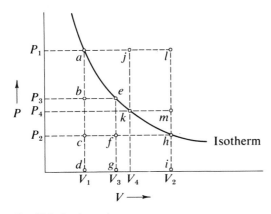

Fig. 10.5. Isothermal process.

$$Q'' = \int_{V_1}^{V_2} P_2 \, dV + \int_{V_1}^{V_2} \left(T \left(\frac{\partial P}{\partial T} \right)_V - P \right) dV \tag{10.10}$$

The first integral is the work done by the system against the pressure P_2 and the second integral is the heat absorbed by the gas resulting from the non-ideality of the gas. For an ideal gas the second integral is zero and in such a case the heat removed from the reservoir would also equal the area *chid*. For a real gas the second integral is usually small with respect to the first integral and consequently the heat removed from the thermostat approximates the area *chid*.

The expansion could be carried out in two steps rather than one. We could first make $(F_e + mg)$ equal to P_3 and allow the expansion to take place to the volume V_3, stopping the piston at that point. We could then change either F_e, m, or both, so that $(F_e + mg)$ is equal to P_2, and complete the expansion to the final volume V_2. By the same arguments used before, the work done on the surroundings would now be represented by the area *befhid*. For an ideal gas the heat removed from the thermostat would also be represented by this area, and for a real gas at low pressures it would approximate this area.

By increasing the number of steps taken to effect the expansion, the amount of work done by the system against the forces exerted by the surroundings and the heat removed from the thermostat is increased. In the limit, the work done by the system approaches the maximum value, the area under the curve *aeh*. The heat removed from the thermostat would also be a maximum.

Now consider the compression of the gas to return it to its original state. In a one-step compression $(F_e' + m'g)$ would have to be equal to or greater than P_1. We find by the use of arguments similar to those used for the expansion that the work done by the forces exerted by the surroundings is represented by the area *alid* and that the heat added to the thermostat is represented approximately by the same area when $(F_e' + m'g)$ equals P_1. The compression can be carried out in two steps; first under the condition that $(F_e' + m'g)$ is equal to P_4 and then under the condition that it is equal to P_1. In this case the work done by the forces $(F_e' + m'g)$ and the approximate heat added to the thermostat is represented by the area *ajkmid*. These amounts of work and heat are obviously less than those in the one-step process. As the number of steps are increased the amount of work done by the external forces and the amount of heat added to the thermostat decrease until, in the limit, the amounts of work and heat are represented again by the area under the curve *aeh*.

For the complete cycle it is evident, except for the case in which both the expansion and compression are carried out reversibly, that more work is done by the forces $(F_e' + m'g)$ on compression than is done against the similar forces on expansion; also, more heat is added to the thermostat for the compression process than is removed from the thermostat for the expansion process. We then have to determine whether it is possible to remove the net heat which has been added to the thermostat and to use it in some way to restore to their original state the systems which have done work, thus restoring all systems which were used in the cyclic process to their original states without causing changes in *other* systems. Experience has shown that this is not possible. Only in the limit of the reversible process are the two quantities of work and the two quantities of heat equal. In this limit not only is the gas returned to its initial state but so are the thermostat and whatever masses and other systems which were used to fix F_e and m.

If we consider the gas, the piston and cylinder, the masses, and the other systems all as an isolated system, then we can state that for any cyclic process except for the limiting reversible cycle of expansion and compression, the isolated system cannot be returned to its original state; only in the limiting reversible cycle can this be done.

Only one specific example of a cyclic process has been discussed. We could discuss many other cycles, such as the raising and lowering of masses in a gravitational field or the charging and discharging of a galvanic cell. But no matter what the cycle is, all studies and all experience have shown the same result as the one obtained for the expansion and compression cycle. We can therefore generalize. We consider any isolated system which contains any subsystem in which we are interested, any required thermal reservoirs, and any other systems which are capable of doing work or having work done on them. We find that whenever any process takes place in which the forces operating are not in equilibrium, it is not possible to operate in cycles and bring the entire isolated system back to its original state. Such processes are called irreversible processes. *The net result in such cycles is that some system in the isolated system will have done work and some thermal reservoir will have absorbed an equivalent quantity of heat.* Only in the limiting case that all processes which occur in the cyclic operation are reversible can the isolated system be brought back to its original state. Such processes are called reversible processes.

Reversible processes are therefore limiting processes in which the forces that are operating are always in equilibrium. If it is necessary to consider that the opposing forces differ by infinitesimal amounts in order that the process may take place, then we can define a reversible process as one whose direction may be reversed by an infinitesimal change of one of the forces involved in the process. All other processes are irreversible. Any real process or natural process can take place only when the forces which are operating in the process are not balanced and the direction of the process cannot be reversed by an infinitesimal change in one of the forces. *All natural processes are therefore irreversible.*

We thus come to a general conclusion based on experience. *No isolated system can be returned to its original state when a natural cyclic process takes place in the system.* This statement may be considered as one statement of the *second law of thermodynamics*. It is only in the idealized limit of a completely reversible cyclic process that an isolated system can be returned to its original state.

10.3   THE CARNOT CYCLE

We have seen in the preceding section that some net change always takes place in an isolated system for any real cyclic process, while for the completely reversible process no net change takes place. We have stated that the change is always one in which some subsystem in the isolated system has done work and some thermal reservoir has absorbed an equivalent quantity of heat. This statement is equivalent to the statement that no way has been found to remove the heat from the thermal reservoir and to use it to return to its original state the system which has done work, without causing changes in other systems. We seek to find a thermodynamic function related to the isolated system whose value will always change in the same direction whenever a natural cyclic process takes place in the isolated system and whose value will not change whenever the cyclic process is completely reversible.

The Carnot cycle, which is only one of many possible cycles, will be used to establish this function. But prior to doing so we use the Carnot cycle to establish the maximum efficiency of a cyclic process and to define the thermodynamic temperature scale. The Carnot cycle was named after the French military engineer Sadi Carnot, who was the first to describe this type of idealized reversible cycle (in a privately published brochure around 1820).

In the particular Carnot cycle described here we consider the system to be any fluid, single-phase substance. The system is contained in a frictionless piston and cylinder arrangement. We also use two thermal reservoirs, one at a higher temperature Θ_2 and one at a lower temperature Θ_1. The symbols Θ_2 and Θ_1 are used to indicate temperatures without reference, for the present, to any specific temperature scale. All processes in the cycle are *defined* to be reversible. The cycle is composed of four consecutive steps, as illustrated in Fig. 10.6. These steps are:

1. The isothermal, reversible expansion from the volume V_1 to the volume V_2 at the higher temperature Θ_2.

2. The adiabatic, reversible expansion from the volume V_2 to the volume V_3. In this step the temperature changes to Θ_1.

3. The isothermal, reversible compression from the volume V_3 to the volume V_4 at the temperature Θ_1.

4. The adiabatic, reversible compression from the volume V_4 to the original volume V_1, in which step the temperature changes back to Θ_2.

We may consider the initial state of the system to be at the point a at which the temperature of the system is Θ_2 and its volume V_1. The isothermal curve ab is thus fixed by choosing Θ_2. The point b is fixed by choosing a value for V_2. The adiabatic curve bc is determined by the point b and the properties of the system. The point c is fixed by choosing a value of either Θ_1 or the volume V_3; a choice of one fixes the value of the other. The determination of the point c determines the isothermal curve cd. The initial point

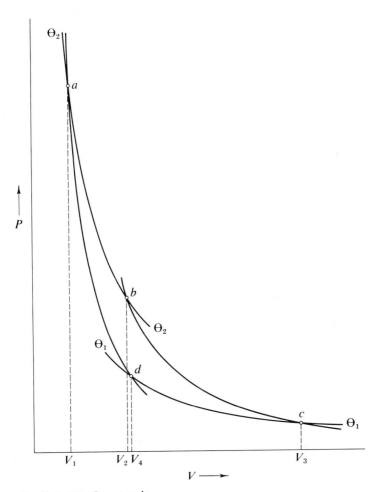

Fig. 10.6. The Carnot cycle.

a determines the adiabatic through *a*. Consequently the point *d* and the volume V_4 are fixed by the intersection of the adiabatic *ad* and the isotherm *cd*. We thus see that the independent variables for this cycle are V_1, V_2, Θ_2, and either V_3 or Θ_1. The equation used to determine the relationship between these independent variables and the dependent variables V_4 and either Θ_1 or V_3, as the case may be, is Eqs. (7.6) and (7.11),

$$dQ = C_V \, dT + T \left(\frac{\partial P}{\partial T} \right)_V dV = 0 \tag{10.11}$$

along an adiabatic path. The integration of this equation between limits involves two temperature variables and two volume variables, three of which are independent and the fourth dependent. Thus, if we choose V_2, Θ_1, and Θ_2 as independent, V_3 is determined (path *bc*). Similarly, if V_1, Θ_1, and Θ_2 are independent, then V_4 is dependent (path *ad*). The integration is difficult except for an ideal gas. Further discussion is postponed to Section 10.5.

In the first step of the cycle an amount of work W_1 will be done by the system on the surroundings; this amount of work is represented by the area under the curve *ab*. Moreover, a quantity of heat Q_2 will be absorbed by the system from the thermal reservoir. In the second step an amount of work W_2, represented by the area under the curve *bc*, will be done by the system on the surroundings; the heat absorbed by the system is zero. An amount of work W_3, represented by the area under the curve *cd*, will be done by the system on the surroundings in the third step; the numerical value of this work will be negative. Also a quantity of heat Q_1, which is also negative numerically, will be absorbed by the system from the thermal reservoir at the temperature Θ_1. Finally in the last step the amount of work done

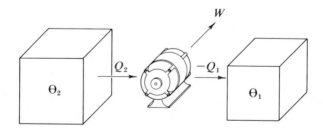

Fig. 10.7.   Illustration of the Carnot cycle.

by the system on the surroundings is W_4, represented by the area under the curve da; this work is also negative numerically. There is no heat absorbed by the system in this step. The net result of the cycle is that an amount of work W, which is the sum of W_1, W_2, W_3, and W_4, is done by the system on the surroundings. This quantity of work is represented by the area $abcd$. Also a quantity of heat has been transferred to the system at the temperature Θ_2 and some heat has been transferred from the system at the temperature Θ_1. These results are illustrated in Fig. 10.7. (Note that $-Q_1$ units of heat are transferred from the system to the thermal reservoir.) The change of energy of the system is zero and consequently

$$W = Q_2 + Q_1 \tag{10.12}$$

The efficiency of the cycle is defined as the ratio of the work done by the system to the amount of heat transferred to the system at the higher temperature; thus the efficiency e is given by†

$$e = \frac{W}{Q_2} \tag{10.13}$$

which, with the inclusion of Eq. (10.12), becomes

$$e = \frac{W}{Q_2} = \frac{Q_2 + Q_1}{Q_2} \tag{10.14}$$

10.4   THE THERMODYNAMIC OR
KELVIN TEMPERATURE SCALE

Kelvin showed that Eq. (10.13) can be used to define a thermodynamic temperature which is independent of the material used for the thermometric substance. First consider several adiabatics and two isothermals at

---

† The second law of thermodynamics is independent of the first law and the efficiency defined by Eq. (10.13) is independent of the first law. We introduce the first law here by use of Eq. (10.12) to obtain Eq. (10.14) in order to make the development of the thermodynamic temperature scale easier. The same results can be obtained by a more complicated argument without the use of the first law. Reference may be made to H. B. Callen, *Thermodynamics*. New York: Wiley, 1960.

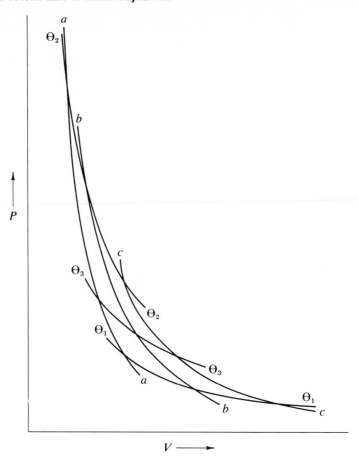

Fig. 10.8. Carnot cycles involving three temperatures.

the temperatures Θ_1 and Θ_2 as shown in Fig. 10.8. Equation (10.14) can be written in the form

$$\frac{Q_1}{Q_2} = e - 1 \tag{10.15}$$

Let us designate this ratio as $(Q_1/Q_2)'$ when the adiabatics a and b are used; as $(Q_1/Q_2)''$ when the adiabatics a and c are used; and as $(Q_1/Q_2)'''$ when the adiabatics b and c are used. The efficiency of a cycle using the same two temperatures is the same, independent of which two adiabatics are used. Therefore $(Q_1/Q_2)' = (Q_1/Q_2)'' = (Q_1/Q_2)'''$ and the ratio Q_1/Q_2 in general is a function only of the two temperatures Θ_1 and Θ_2.

Although we have discussed only one type of Carnot cycle involving a single-phase system and only pressure-volume work, the result expressed by Eqs. (10.13) and (10.14) is applicable to any Carnot cycle. The requirement is to determine or define the function $f(\Theta_1, \Theta_2)$ when we write $Q_1/Q_2 = f(\Theta_1, \Theta_2)$.

One comment needs to be made concerning the sign of Q_1. In the discussion of the Carnot cycle, Q_1 was the heat absorbed by the system for the isothermal reversible compression of the system and consequently was numerically negative. But in defining the temperature we desire to make all temperatures positive. Therefore we consider only the absolute values of Q_1 and Q_2 here. This point is discussed again at the end of this chapter.

Now consider three cycles involving three temperatures and two adiabatics as illustrated in Fig. 10.8. If we carry out Carnot cycles between the temperatures Θ_2 and Θ_1, Θ_2 and Θ_3, and Θ_1 and Θ_3, we find that

$$\frac{Q_1}{Q_2} = f(\Theta_1, \Theta_2) \tag{10.16}$$

$$\frac{Q_2}{Q_3} = f(\Theta_2, \Theta_3) \tag{10.17}$$

and

$$\frac{Q_1}{Q_3} = f(\Theta_1, \Theta_3) \tag{10.18}$$

but

$$\frac{Q_1}{Q_2} = \frac{Q_1}{Q_3} \cdot \frac{Q_3}{Q_2} = \frac{f(\Theta_1, \Theta_3)}{f(\Theta_2, \Theta_3)} = f(\Theta_1, \Theta_2) \tag{10.19}$$

That is, on dividing Eq. (10.18) by Eq. (10.17), the ratio of the two functions $f(\Theta_1, \Theta_3)$ and $f(\Theta_2, \Theta_3)$ becomes a function of Θ_1 and Θ_2 alone. We conclude that the function $f(\Theta_i, \Theta_j)$ may be written as the ratio of two functions, each of which is dependent on only one temperature. Thus $f(\Theta_1, \Theta_2)$ may be written as $\phi(\Theta_1)/\phi(\Theta_2)$, $f(\Theta_1, \Theta_3)$ as $\phi(\Theta_1)/\phi(\Theta_3)$, and $f(\Theta_2, \Theta_3)$ as $\phi(\Theta_2)/\phi(\Theta_3)$. Then $f(\Theta_1, \Theta_3)/f(\Theta_2, \Theta_3)$ equals $\phi(\Theta_1)/\phi(\Theta_2)$ which in turn equals $f(\Theta_1, \Theta_2)$. Therefore

$$\frac{Q_1}{Q_2} = \frac{\phi(\Theta_1)}{\phi(\Theta_2)} \tag{10.20}$$

We thus conclude that the heat absorbed by a given system along all isotherms bounded by the same two adiabatics depends only on the temperature of the isotherm.

The definition of a temperature scale follows from Eq. (10.20). It is presumed that Q_1 and Q_2 can be measured experimentally. The definition of the function $\phi(\Theta)$ and of the required number of fixed points suffices to determine the scale. The simplest definition, and the one actually used, is to make $\phi(\Theta)$ proportional to Θ so that Eq. (10.20) becomes

$$\frac{Q_1}{Q_2} = \frac{\Theta_1}{\Theta_2} \tag{10.21}$$

Equation (10.21) gives one equation relating the two unknown quantities Θ_1 and Θ_2. One additional relation is then sufficient to determine the numerical values of Θ_1 and Θ_2 for a given value of the ratio Q_1/Q_2. Prior to 1954 the difference between the temperature of the ice point and that of the normal boiling point of water was defined to be 100 deg. Thus, if Q_1 was determined at the ice point and Q_2 at the normal boiling point of water, then $\Theta_2 - \Theta_1$ would be 100 deg. Since 1954, as discussed in Chapter 4, the triple point of water has been used as the single defined temperature to establish a temperature scale. Thus we could determine Q_1 at the triple point of water and define Θ_1 to be 273.16° K. Then Θ_2 would be determined by the relation

$$\Theta_2 = 273.16\left(\frac{Q_2}{Q_{273.16}}\right) \tag{10.22}$$

and the thermodynamic temperature scale is defined.

One might question the suitability of defining a temperature scale based on the Carnot cycle because of the requirement of a reversible process. However, only the values of Q_1 and Q_2 determined along isothermal reversible paths between the same two adiabatics are required, and not the amount of work done in the cycle. The states of the system along the chosen adiabatics can be determined experimentally and Q_1 and Q_2 can be determined along the isotherms by processes which approach reversibility. The direction of the processes can always be the same so that the ratio of Q_1 to Q_2 is always positive. Consequently the thermodynamic scale defined in this way does have experimental meaning. The measurement of a temperature by the methods discussed here would be difficult and inconvenient. However, in the next section we demonstrate that the thermodynamic temperature scale and the ideal gas temperature scale are the same.

10.5 IDENTITY OF THE THERMODYNAMIC AND IDEAL GAS TEMPERATURE SCALES

The identity of the thermodynamic temperature scale and the ideal gas temperature scale is easily shown by considering an ideal gas in the Carnot cycle discussed in Section 10.3.

The first step in the cycle is the isothermal, reversible expansion of the gas from a volume V_1 to a volume V_2 at the temperature T_2 (Fig. 10.6). The work done by the gas on the surroundings and the heat absorbed by the gas from the thermal reservoir are equal because ΔE for this step is zero for the ideal gas. These quantities, Eq. (7.20), are

$$W_1 = Q_2 = nRT_2 \ln \frac{V_2}{V_1} \qquad (10.23)$$

Similarly, the work done on the surroundings by the gas and the heat absorbed by the gas from the thermostat at the temperature T_1 for the isothermal, reversible compression from V_3 to V_4 (the third step) is

$$W_3 = Q_1 = nRT_1 \ln \frac{V_4}{V_3} \qquad (10.24)$$

Since V_4 is less than V_3 both W_3 and Q_1 are numerically negative.

The pertinent equations for the adiabatic steps have been developed in Section 7.6(a). For the adiabatic reversible expansion (step 2) the work done

203

by the system is given by the relation, Eq. (7.25),

$$W_2 = -\Delta E = -\int_{T_2}^{T_1} C_V \, dT \tag{10.25}$$

and for the adiabatic, reversible compression (step 4) the work done by the system is given by

$$W_4 = -\Delta E = -\int_{T_1}^{T_2} C_V \, dT \tag{10.26}$$

These quantities, W_2 and W_4, are equal but opposite in sign for the ideal gas because the heat capacity at constant volume is independent of the volume and the limits of integration are the same but in opposite order. The sum of W_2 and W_4 is therefore zero.

The total work done by the system on the surroundings in the cycle is the sum of W_1 and W_3 which is

$$W = W_1 + W_3 = Q_2 + Q_1$$

$$= RT_2 \ln \frac{V_2}{V_1} + RT_1 \ln \frac{V_4}{V_3} \tag{10.27}$$

The ratios V_2/V_1 and V_4/V_3 are not independent. The relationship between them can be found by the use of Eq. (7.29). This equation for the second step is

$$\int_{T_2}^{T_1} \frac{C_V}{T} \, dT = -nR \ln \frac{V_3}{V_2} \tag{10.28}$$

and for the fourth step is

$$\int_{T_1}^{T_2} \frac{C_V}{T} \, dT = -nR \ln \frac{V_1}{V_4} \tag{10.29}$$

The integrals on the left-hand side of Eqs. (10.28) and (10.29) are equal in magnitude but opposite in sign. Therefore

$$\frac{V_3}{V_2} = \frac{V_4}{V_1}$$

or

$$\ln \frac{V_2}{V_1} = -\ln \frac{V_4}{V_3} \tag{10.30}$$

Equation (10.27) can now be written as

$$W = \left(R \ln \frac{V_2}{V_1}\right)(T_2 - T_1) \tag{10.31}$$

and the efficiency, Eq. (10.14), as

$$e = \frac{W}{Q_2} = \frac{T_2 - T_1}{T_2} \tag{10.32}$$

The ratio of Q_1 and Q_2 becomes

$$\frac{Q_1}{Q_2} = \frac{T_1}{T_2} \tag{10.33}$$

When we compare Eq. (10.33) to Eq. (10.21) we see that

$$\frac{\Theta_1}{\Theta_2} = \frac{T_1}{T_2} \tag{10.34}$$

for a cycle operating between the same two temperatures. Thus the ratio of the values of these two temperatures is the same on either scale. If we define both Θ_1 and T_1 to be 273.16° at the triple point of water, the two temperature scales become identical. We can then write Eq. (10.22) as

$$T = 273.16 \frac{Q_T}{Q_{273.16}} \tag{10.35}$$

where T represents any temperature on the Kelvin scale, Q_T is the heat absorbed by the system for an isothermal, reversible process at the temperature T between two adiabatics, and $Q_{273.16}$ is the heat absorbed by the system for a similar isothermal, reversible process between the same two adiabatics at the triple point of water.

The thermodynamic temperature scale defined in terms of the Carnot cycle has the advantage that it does not depend upon the properties of any particular substance. The result of using the Carnot cycle is independent of the substance. The requirement of determining experimentally the heats absorbed by the system at the triple point of water and at the temperature T does not lead, however, to the design of a convenient thermometer. Fortunately the identity of the thermodynamic temperature scale and the ideal gas temperature scale permits the development of a thermometer in terms of an ideal gas in a constant-volume or constant-pressure apparatus. The relationship of the ideal gas temperature scale to a practical scale has already been discussed in Chapter 4. The International Practical Temperature Scale is a close approximation to the thermodynamic scale.

10.6   EFFICIENCY OF A HEAT ENGINE

With the definition of the thermodynamic temperature scale we may return to a discussion of the efficiency of a heat engine operating in a Carnot cycle. The defining equation is

$$e = \frac{W}{Q_2} = \frac{Q_2 + Q_1}{Q_2} \tag{10.36}$$

and with the introduction of the temperature scale we can write

$$e = \frac{W}{Q_2} = \frac{T_2 - T_1}{T_2} \tag{10.37}$$

The efficiency of a heat engine operating in a Carnot cycle depends only on the two temperatures and primarily on the difference of the two temperatures between which the engine operates. The greater this difference, the greater the efficiency.

The fact that the efficiency obtained in a Carnot cycle is the maximum efficiency for any heat engine is proved in Section 10.9. Any real engine operating between the same two temperatures must have an efficiency less than that of a Carnot cycle. The steam turbine used for the generation of electric power has one of the higher efficiencies, but this efficiency is only about 40 to 50 percent of the maximum efficiency. A great deal of development has gone on and is still going on to increase the efficiency of various heat engines which absorb heat at a higher temperature, do work on the surroundings in cycles, and reject the difference between the heat absorbed and the work done as heat at the lower temperature.

Two special cases are of interest. (1) If T_1 equals T_2 then no work is done in the cycle. This is actually the case we discussed in Section 10.2, which concerned the isothermal expansion and compression of a fluid at the same temperature. In the limit of reversible processes the work done by the system on the expansion is equal to the work done on the system during the compression and no net work is done. (2) It is evident from Eq. (10.37) that T_1 must be zero in order to obtain 100 percent efficiency. Indeed, absolute zero may be defined as the temperature which the thermal reservoir at the lower temperature must have in order to obtain 100 percent efficiency in the cyclic operation of a heat engine.

10.7   THE REFRIGERATION CYCLE

If the Carnot cycle were operated in the direction opposite to that discussed in Section 10.3, the cycle would be a refrigeration cycle. In this case a quantity of heat, Q_1, would actually be absorbed by the system from the thermal reservoir at the temperature T_1, a quantity of work, W', equal to the area *adcb* would be *done* by the surroundings on the system (the work W done by the system on the surroundings is negative), and a quantity of heat, Q_2', would be transferred from the system to the thermal reservoir at the temperature T_2. For the cycle the quantity of heat transferred to the thermal reservoir at the temperature T_2 is the sum of the heat absorbed by the system at T_1 and the work done by the surroundings on the system, or

$$Q_2' = W' + Q_1 \tag{10.38}$$

because ΔE for the system is zero in the cycle.

The *coefficient of performance* is defined for the refrigeration cycle as Q_1/W'. With the use of Eq. (10.38) and the definition of the thermodynamic temperature scale, we obtain the relation

$$\frac{Q_1}{W'} = \frac{T_1}{T_2 - T_1} \qquad (10.39)$$

which gives the coefficient of performance for the cycle in terms of the two temperatures between which the cycle operates. According to this equation the work required to remove a given quantity of heat from the reservoir at the lower temperature increases with an increase in the difference between the two temperatures and with the decrease of the lower temperature. Household refrigerators operate at a coefficient of performance of about 2 to 7.

10.8   TWO STATEMENTS OF THE SECOND LAW OF THERMODYNAMICS

Having investigated the cyclic operation of heat engines we can now state two forms of the second law based on Eqs. (10.37) and (10.39). We have seen from Eq. (10.37) that the work done by a heat engine, operating in cycles, is zero when the two temperatures are the same. We then can state:

> *It is impossible to construct a heat engine which, operating in cycles, can perform work at the expense of heat obtained from a single thermal reservoir.*

This is the Kelvin-Planck statement of the second law. It is the denial of what is known as a perpetual motion machine of the second kind. As an example, it is impossible to operate a heat engine solely by the removal of heat from a thermal reservoir such as an ocean or a river. The first law may be thought of as the denial of a perpetual motion machine of the first kind, which is a heat engine operating in cycles that performs work without the absorption of an equivalent quantity of heat. The second law states that a heat engine, operating in cycles, can perform work only by absorbing a quantity of heat, greater than the work done, from some reservoir at a higher temperature and by rejecting the difference between the heat absorbed and the work done to some thermal reservoir at a lower temperature. Two thermal reservoirs are required.

The second statement is the Clausius statement of the second law, based on Eq. (10.39). Here we observe that work is required to transfer heat from a reservoir at a lower temperature to one at a higher temperature. The generalization of this observation leads to:

Heat of itself will not flow from a thermal reservoir at a lower temperature to one at a higher temperature. It is in no way possible for this to occur without the agency of some system operating as a heat engine in which work is done by the surroundings on this system.

Both statements are based on the experimental results of cyclic operation of heat engines. They are equivalent in the sense that either can be proved if the other is postulated.

There is no "proof" of the second law; like the first law, the second law is based on experience. In this chapter we have arrived at the second law by considering one type of cycle. Other cycles could be discussed and the treatment expanded to general cases. The results of these discussions would be the same as those obtained here. On this basis we accept the concepts which have been developed in this chapter as general concepts applicable to all systems and cyclic operations.

10.9 CARNOT'S THEOREM

In Section 10.8 we accepted the result that the maximum efficiency obtainable in the cyclic operation of any heat engine is that obtained in the Carnot cycle. It is possible to prove this with the second law.

We consider a Carnot engine C and any other heat engine I operating between the same two temperatures. We assume that the efficiency of the engine I is greater than that of the Carnot engine, so that

$$e_I > e_C \tag{10.40}$$

and

$$\frac{W_I}{Q_{2I}} > \frac{W_C}{Q_{2C}} \tag{10.41}$$

When Q_{2I} and Q_{2C} are equal, then

209

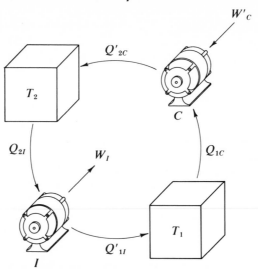

Fig. 10.9. Carnot's theorem.

$$W_I > W_C \tag{10.42}$$

or

$$(W_I - W_C) > 0 \tag{10.43}$$

We now allow engine I to drive the Carnot engine in a refrigeration cycle with the condition that $Q_{2I} = -Q_{2C} = Q'_{2C}$. The operation is illustrated in Fig. 10.9, where primes have been used again to designate positive quantities of heat and work, contrary to the usual definition of the symbols Q and W. Equation (10.43) may be written as

$$(W_I + W_C') > 0 \tag{10.44}$$

for the combined operation. But

$$W_I = Q_{2I} - Q'_{1I} \tag{10.45}$$

and

210

$$W_C' = -Q_{2C}' + Q_{1C} \tag{10.46}$$

Therefore

$$(Q_{1C} - Q_{1I}') > 0 \tag{10.47}$$

That is, heat is removed from the reservoir at the lower temperature. The result of the cyclic operation of the combined engines is that work is done by the engines at the expense of heat obtained from a single thermal reservoir at one temperature. This is contrary to experience and to the Kelvin-Planck statement of the second law, and so our original assumption must be incorrect. Thus e_I can only be equal to or less than e_C. *Carnot's theorem* states that no engine operating in cycles between two given temperatures can be more efficient than a Carnot engine operating between the same two temperatures.

The statement that two Carnot engines operating between the same two temperatures have the same efficiency is easily proved. We may consider two Carnot engines C_1 and C_2. In one case we operate C_1 as a heat engine to drive C_2 in a refrigeration cycle. From Carnot's theorem we know that $e_{C_1} \leqslant e_{C_2}$. When we use C_2 as the heat engine and C_1 as the refrigerator, we have $e_{C_1} \geqslant e_{C_2}$. Thus the two efficiencies must be equal in order to satisfy both equations. This conclusion is independent of the particular Carnot cycle used or the substance used in the cycle.

10.10   CONCLUDING COMMENTS

A number of important conclusions have been reached in this chapter. All of these have been based on experience and there is no proof of them other than experience. Although we have used specific examples to arrive at the conclusions, the conclusions themselves are general. They may be expressed in terms of three equivalent statements:

1. No isolated system can be returned to its original state whenever a natural cyclic process takes place in the system.
2. It is impossible to construct a heat engine which, operating in cycles, can perform work at the expense of heat obtained from a single thermal reservoir.

3. Heat of itself will not flow from a thermal reservoir at a lower temperature to one at a higher temperature.

In the development of these conclusions, reversible and irreversible processes have been defined. All natural processes are irreversible. Reversible
processes are necessarily quasi-static, but quasi-static processes can be
reversible or irreversible.

The maximum efficiency obtainable for any heat engine operating in cycles
depends only upon the temperatures of the two thermal reservoirs used in
the cycle and not at all upon the fluid used in the engine or the particular
type of cycle. The maximum efficiency can be obtained (in thought) only
when all processes in the cycle are reversible.

A thermodynamic temperature scale has been defined in terms of a reversible cycle involving two isotherms. Such a temperature scale is independent
of the thermometric fluid.

While we have made use of the first law in some of the discussion, the
second law is independent of the first law. In fact, historically, the second law
was understood prior to a complete acceptance of the first law.

Exercises

10.1   What is the maximum efficiency of a heat engine operating between
the two temperatures 300° K and 400° K ?

10.2   A heat engine operating between the two temperatures of 300° K and
500° K transfers 700 cal of heat to the reservoir at 300° K for every 1000
cal of heat absorbed from the reservoir at 500° K. Is the cycle
reversible ?

10.3   The temperature of a refrigerator is kept at 10° C and the temperature
of the thermal reservoir at the higher temperature is 40° C. What is the
minimum amount of work which must be done on the system per hour
when the heat leak into the refrigerator is 500 cal hr^{-1}.

10.4   We define a temperature scale in terms of a Carnot cycle operating
between two adiabatics and choose to make Q proportional to e^θ (e is
the natural base of logarithms).

(a) If we define the lowest possible temperature as the temperature
which the thermal reservoir must have in order to have 100 percent
efficiency, what is the lowest possible temperature on this scale?

(b) Would it ever be possible to obtain this lowest possible temperature?

(c) How could this scale be completely defined?

(d) If we desired to change from the present Kelvin scale to this scale and still make the two scales comparable, how would the new scale be defined?

10.5 Sketch diagrams of Carnot cycles for an ideal gas for each of the following sets of coordinates: (a) *P-V*; (b) *P-T*; (c) *T-V*; (d) *E-V*; (e) *E-T*; (f) *H-T*. For each pair of coordinates, take the first as the ordinate and the second as the abscissa.

10.6 An ideal strip of rubber had for its equation of state

$$f = (\text{const})(T)(\text{function of the length})$$

$$= KT\left[\frac{L}{L_0} - \left(\frac{L_0}{L}\right)^2\right]$$

in which f is the stretching force, K is a proportionality constant, L is the length of the rubber strip, and L_0 is the length under zero applied force. Assume that $E = C_L T + \text{const}$. Show how a rubber strip can be carried through a Carnot cycle. Show that the efficiency is the same as that for an ideal gas. Make a plot of f versus L for the cycle. C_L is the appropriate heat capacity.

10.7 Three moles of an ideal gas of C_V of 5 cal mole^{-1} deg^{-1} are carried through a Carnot cycle between the temperatures of 300° K and 500° K. For the isothermal step at 500° K the initial volume is 2 liters and the final volume is 10 liters. Calculate and tabulate ΔE, ΔH, Q, and W for each step in the Carnot cycle for this gas.

10.8 Which is the most effective way of increasing the efficiency of a Carnot engine: (a) changing T_2 at constant T_1, or (b) changing T_1 at constant T_2? ($T_2 > T_1$.)

10.9 Show that Eq. (10.37) is obtained when an ideal gas is used in a heat engine and the cycle is composed of two isotherms and two isobars. (C_P for an ideal gas is independent of the pressure.)

10.10 Show that Eq. (10.37) is obtained when an ideal gas is used in a heat engine and the cycle is composed of two isotherms and two isochores. (C_V for an ideal gas is independent of the volume.)

10.11 Discuss the efficiency of heating a home to be kept at 25° C when the out-of-doors temperature is 0° C by using a refrigeration cycle, that is, by refrigerating the out-of-doors.

11 The Entropy Function

In Chapter 10 we introduced the problem of finding a thermodynamic function whose properties are consistent with the behavior of isolated systems when irreversible and reversible processes take place within them. This function is the *entropy function*. Its value for an isolated system always increases whenever an irreversible process takes place within it; otherwise it remains constant. This property of the entropy function leads to the establishment of the conditions for equilibrium; these conditions are developed in Chapter 14.

In this chapter the result of the study of the Carnot cycle is used to define the entropy function. The study of the properties of the function as related to reversible and irreversible processes leads to Planck's statement of the second law of thermodynamics. The entropy is a function of the state variables which are used to define the state of the system; and the dependence of the function on the temperature, pressure, and volume is developed. Changes of the entropy for simple changes of state are also discussed. Finally, cyclic processes are reexamined in terms of entropy-temperature diagrams.

11.1 DEFINITION OF THE ENTROPY FUNCTION

The efficiency of the Carnot cycle was defined as

$$e = \frac{W}{Q_2} = \frac{Q_2 + Q_1}{Q_2} \tag{11.1}$$

which, with the definition of the Kelvin temperature scale, becomes

$$e = \frac{T_2 - T_1}{T_2} \tag{11.2}$$

From these two equations we obtain the relation

$$\frac{Q_2}{T_2} + \frac{Q_1}{T_1} = 0 \tag{11.3}$$

This result can be related to the four steps of the cycle (see Fig. 11.1). The quantity Q_2 is the heat absorbed by the system along the isothermal, reversible path ab at the temperature T_2, so that

$$\frac{Q_2}{T_2} = \int_a^b \frac{dQ}{T} \tag{11.4}$$

Along the adiabatic reversible path bc, Q is zero and

$$\int_b^c \frac{dQ}{T} = 0 \tag{11.5}$$

Along the isothermal, reversible path cd at the temperature T_1 we have

$$\frac{Q_1}{T_1} = \int_c^d \frac{dQ}{T} \tag{11.6}$$

Finally along the adiabatic reversible path da,

$$\int_d^a \frac{dQ}{T} = 0 \tag{11.7}$$

The sum of the four steps and Eq. (11.3) show that

$$\frac{Q_2}{T_2} + \frac{Q_1}{T_1} = \oint \frac{dQ_{rev}}{T} = 0 \tag{11.8}$$

or the cyclical integral of dQ_{rev}/T is equal to zero. The subscript "rev" is used to emphasize that dQ must be measured along a reversible path.

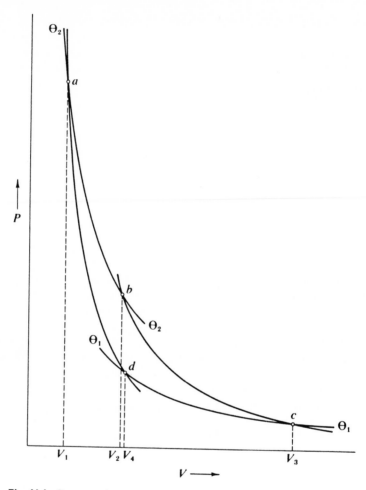

Fig. 11.1. Carnot cycle.

The result expressed by Eq. (11.8) has been obtained on the basis of a single Carnot cycle. This result can be generalized for any reversible cycle so that we may state (without further proof) that

$$\oint \frac{dQ_{rev}}{T} = 0 \tag{11.9}$$

for any reversible cycle taking place in a system. In words, this equation states that the integral around any reversible cycle of the differential quantity of heat absorbed by the system divided by the temperature at which the heat is absorbed is equal to zero. This relation is known as Clausius' theorem.

We know from the mathematical discussion in Chapter 2 that if $\oint dz = 0$ for any cycle then dz is an exact differential and z is a function. We therefore conclude that dQ_{rev}/T is an exact differential of a function of the independent variables which define the state of the system. This function is called the *entropy function* and given the symbol S. Thus the entropy function is defined by the relation

$$dS = \frac{dQ_{rev}}{T} \tag{11.10}$$

The entropy function is a function of the independent variables which are used to define the state of a system. It is an extensive function, not intensive. The change in the value of the entropy function (change of entropy) in going from one state to another is independent of the path, and the cyclic integral of dS for a cyclic change of state is always zero. This function is defined, like the energy function, in terms of a differential, and consequently the absolute value of the entropy function for a system in any state is not known. It is well to emphasize again that, while the change of the entropy function is independent of the path between two states of the system, the determination of the entropy change by the use of Eq. (11.10) must be along a reversible path.

The units of the entropy function are, in general, energy units divided by degrees, such as cal deg^{-1} or Btu deg^{-1}. The entropy per unit quantity of material is an intensive quantity with units such as cal deg^{-1} mole^{-1} or cal deg^{-1} g^{-1}.

11.2 ENTROPY CHANGE OF AN ISOLATED SYSTEM ALONG A REVERSIBLE PATH

The definition of the entropy function given by Eq. (11.10) permits the calculation of the change of the value of the entropy of a system for a change of state along a reversible path whether the system is isolated or not. We are interested here in changes in the value of the entropy function in isolated systems along reversible paths.

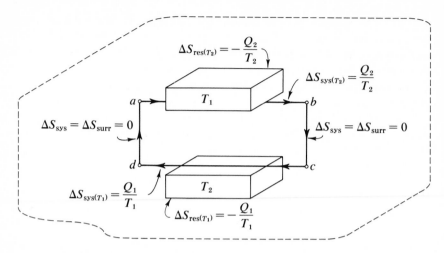

Fig. II.2.   Changes of state for a cyclic reversible process.

We return to the Carnot cycle once again (see Fig. 11.2). For the iso-thermal reversible expansion a quantity of heat, Q_2, is transferred to the fluid in the engine from a thermal reservoir at the temperature T_2. The entropy change of the fluid is then Q_2/T_2 while that of the reservoir is

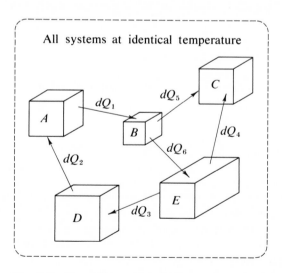

Fig. II.3.   Reversible transfer of differential quantities of heat.

$-Q_2/T_2$. Thus, when the reservoir and the engine are considered as a single isolated system, there is no change of entropy of the isolated system for the isothermal, reversible expansion. The same result is obtained for the isothermal, reversible compression where the change of entropy of the fluid is Q_1/T_1 while that for the thermal reservoir at the temperature T_1 is $-Q_1/T_1$. Along the reversible adiabatic paths, Q is zero and consequently the change of the entropy of the isolated system is zero. We then conclude that *the entropy change of an isolated system is zero for any reversible process taking place in that system.*

This statement can be elucidated by considering an isolated system to consist of any number of subsystems whose temperatures are all the same. We allow differential quantities of heat to be transferred between the subsystems. In Fig. 11.3, the subsystems are represented by the lettered blocks and the differential quantities of heat are indicated by the various dQ symbols. The differential entropy change of any system i is given by dQ_i/T. The differential change of the entropy function of the isolated system is then equal to

$$dS = \sum_i \frac{dQ_i}{T} \tag{11.11}$$

where the $\sum$ sign represents the sum taken over all subsystems. Because the temperatures are all equal we can factor $1/T$ from the sum and write

$$dS = \frac{1}{T} \sum_i dQ_i \tag{11.12}$$

But the sum of all the differential quantities of heat absorbed by the subsystems must be zero because the system is isolated, and therefore

$$dS = 0 \tag{11.13}$$

If Eq. (11.13) is true for differential changes of state then ΔS must be zero for finite changes of state along reversible paths.

In Section 10.2 we concluded that an isolated system can be brought back to its original state only when all processes taking place within the system are reversible. We now see that the entropy change of an isolated system is zero for all reversible processes which may take place in the isolated system. Thus there is a correlation between the conclusion arrived at in Section 10.2 and this one property of the entropy function.

11.3   ENTROPY CHANGE OF AN ISOLATED SYSTEM ALONG AN IRREVERSIBLE PATH

In order to determine the change of the value of the entropy function of an isolated system for an irreversible process taking place in the system, we allow the irreversible process to take place and then attempt to bring the system back to its original state by reversible processes. We do so because we can determine entropy changes *only* for reversible processes.

As an example consider the Joule expansion of an ideal gas (see Fig. 11.4). The gas is considered as the system and the system is isolated because the

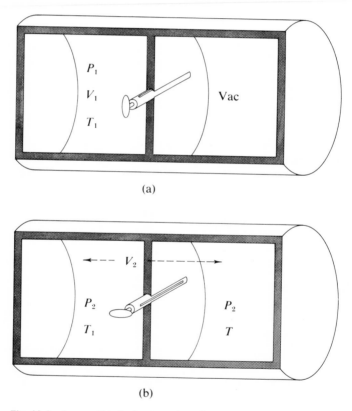

(a)

(b)

Fig. 11.4.   Irreversible Joule expansion of an ideal gas.

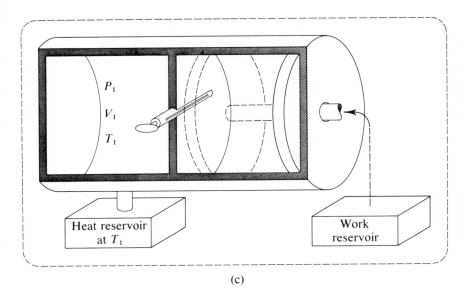

(c)

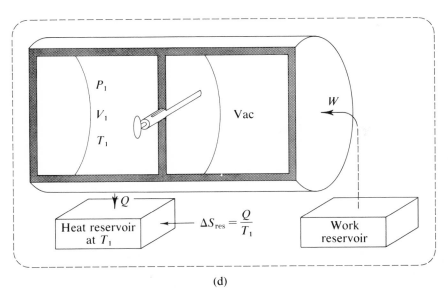

(d)

Fig. 11.4. (*cont.*)

expansion is adiabatic and the system is separated from the surroundings by a rigid wall. We have learned already that for an ideal gas, the temperature remains constant. The change of state that occurs then may be written as

$$nA(g, T, V_1) \rightarrow nA(g, T, V_2) \tag{11.14}$$

where V_1 is the initial volume and V_2 is the final volume of the gas. After the expansion has taken place, Fig. 11.4(b), we may return the gas to its original state by placing it in a piston and cylinder arrangement and carrying out an isothermal (at T_1), reversible compression of the gas from V_2 to V_1 as in Fig. 11.4(c). This removes the restriction of isolation. From our previous work we known that a quantity of heat Q equal to

$$Q = nRT \ln \frac{V_1}{V_2} \tag{11.15}$$

will be absorbed by the gas during the compression and that this quantity of heat is negative; that is, heat is transferred to the heat reservoir. The entropy change of the gas is then

$$\Delta S = \frac{Q}{T} = R \ln \frac{V_1}{V_2} \tag{11.16}$$

which is also negative. Thus the entropy of the gas has been decreased in the isothermal, reversible compression of the gas. But the gas is in the same state at the end of the compression as it was prior to the original expansion and consequently the value of the entropy function is the same. We must conclude, then, that the value of the entropy function was greater in the expanded state at V_2 than in the original state V_1. Therefore the entropy of the gas increased in the irreversible expansion. Since the gas was isolated, the condition in Fig. 11.4(b), we may state that in this case the value of the entropy of an isolated system increases in an irreversible process.

The generalization of this conclusion is relatively easy. In Section 10.2 we showed that when irreversible processes took place in an isolated system, we could not bring the entire system back to its original state; always some system had done work and some thermal reservoir had had heat transferred to it. In order to bring the system back to its original state, the isolation must be removed. For example, by the use of a heat engine external to the original system, work may be done reversibly on the system which had done work, thus restoring it to its original state. The process can be carried out in such a way that no heat is added to or removed from the system so that there is no change in the entropy of the system. In order to return to its original state the thermal reservoir which has had heat added to it, we may place another thermal reservoir in thermal contact with the original reservoir and reversibly remove the added heat from it. In removing the heat the entropy of the first thermal reservoir has been decreased. But the originally isolated system has been returned to its original state and the value of its entropy function is the same as that in the original state. Therefore the entropy of the isolated system increased during the irreversible process or processes which took place in the isolated system.

11.4   PLANCK'S STATEMENT OF THE SECOND LAW

Planck[†] has given a statement of the second law of thermodynamics which summarizes the conclusions developed in Sections 11.2 and 11.3.

Every physical and chemical process in nature takes place in such a way as to increase the sum of the entropies of all bodies taking any part in the process. In the limit, that is for reversible processes, the sum of the entropies remains unchanged.

It is important to remember that these statements refer to isolated systems. It is possible to increase or decrease the entropy of a system by either a reversible or irreversible process. But the system is not isolated and other systems must be involved in the process. When *all* systems involved in the process are considered, the value of the entropy function of the total system increases for irreversible processes and remains unchanged for reversible processes.

Moreover, the entropy function is a function of the independent variables used to define the state of the system. Therefore the change of the value of the entropy function of a given system is zero for any cyclic process which the system may undergo. But other systems will in general be involved in the

† M. Planck, *Treatise on Thermodynamics.* (New York: Dover, 1945, p.103.)

223

cyclic process. The statement given in this section applies to the combination of all systems involved, considered together as an isolated system.

11.5 DEPENDENCE OF ENTROPY ON TEMPERATURE

The state of a closed system can be defined by assigning values to two independent variables such as T and V or T and P. The entropy would then be a function of either T and V or T and P. For the first case we may set $S = S(T, V)$, and at constant volume

$$dS = \left(\frac{\partial S}{\partial T}\right)_V dT \quad \text{(const vol)} \tag{11.17}$$

The definition of the entropy function is

$$dS = \frac{dQ_{rev}}{T}$$

but

$$dQ = C \, dT$$

in general, where C is the heat capacity. For constant-volume, reversible processes,

$$dQ_{rev} = C_V \, dT$$

and

$$dS = \left(\frac{\partial S}{\partial T}\right)_V dT = \frac{C_V}{T} dT \tag{11.18}$$

Therefore we find that

$$\left(\frac{\partial S}{\partial T}\right)_V = \frac{C_V}{T} \tag{11.19}$$

When we express the entropy as a function of the temperature and pressure,

$S = S(T, P)$, we similarly obtain the relation

$$\left(\frac{\partial S}{\partial T}\right)_P = \frac{C_P}{T} \tag{11.20}$$

Equations (11.19) and (11.20) permit us to calculate the change of the value of the entropy function of a closed system for a change of temperature either at constant volume or at constant pressure. If either heat capacity is given in the form

$$C = a + bT + cT^2$$

where a, b, c are functions of the volume or pressure and hence constant at a constant volume or a constant pressure, as the case may be, the change of entropy for the change of the temperature of the system from T_1 to T_2 is

$$\Delta S = \int_{T_1}^{T_2} \left(\frac{a}{T} + b + cT\right) dT = a \ln \frac{T_2}{T_1} + b(T_2 - T_1)$$
$$+ \tfrac{1}{2}c(T_2{}^2 - T_1{}^2) \tag{11.21}$$

In this calculation no phase change is permitted between T_1 and T_2.

11.6   CHANGE OF THE VALUE OF THE ENTROPY FUNCTION FOR A PHASE CHANGE OF A PURE SUBSTANCE

The evaporation of a pure liquid, the melting of a pure solid, and the sublimation of a pure solid all take place at constant temperature when the pressure is held constant. The change of entropy of a pure substance for such changes of phase is then given by

$$\Delta S = \int \frac{dQ_{rev}}{T}$$

But the temperature is constant and the integral of dQ_{rev} simply equals Q_{rev} so that

$$\Delta S = \frac{Q_{rev}}{T} \tag{11.22}$$

The quantity Q_{rev} can be determined calorimetrically when the change of phase takes place in the calorimeter at constant pressure. Moreover, we know that ΔH equals Q for a change of state at constant pressure, so that we also have the relation

$$\Delta S = \frac{\Delta H}{T} \qquad \text{(const } T \text{ and } P) \qquad (11.23)$$

for phase changes.

As an example, the heat of evaporation for the change of state

$$H_2O(l, 373°, 1 \text{ atm}) = H_2O(g, 373°, 1 \text{ atm})$$

is 9700 cal. The molar change of enthalpy for this change of state is then 9700 cal mole^{-1} and the molar change of entropy is 26.0 cal deg^{-1} mole^{-1}.

11.7 DEPENDENCE OF THE ENTROPY FUNCTION ON VOLUME AND PRESSURE

The two partial derivatives required for the dependence of the entropy of a closed system on volume and on pressure are

$$\left(\frac{\partial S}{\partial V}\right)_T = \left(\frac{\partial P}{\partial T}\right)_V \qquad (11.24)$$

and

$$\left(\frac{\partial S}{\partial P}\right)_T = -\left(\frac{\partial V}{\partial T}\right)_P \qquad (11.25)$$

These relations are given without proof. Their derivation will be given in Chapter 12. These relations may be verified by experiment without resort to the first law.

As an example, consider the change of state

$$nA(g, T, V_1) = nA(g, T, V_2)$$

for an ideal gas. The differential of the entropy is

$$dS = \left(\frac{\partial P}{\partial T}\right)_V dV$$

and

$$\left(\frac{\partial P}{\partial T}\right)_V = \frac{nR}{V}$$

for an ideal gas. Therefore, for n moles of gas,

$$\Delta S = nR \int_{V_1}^{V_2} \frac{dV}{V} = nR \ln \frac{V_2}{V_1} \tag{11.26}$$

Equation (11.26) must be consistent with the original definition of the entropy. The indicated change of state can be accomplished by the isothermal, reversible expansion of the gas. For this process

$$Q = nRT \ln \frac{V_2}{V_1}$$

as $\Delta S = Q_{rev}/T$ for an isothermal process. The combination of these two relations yields Eq. (11.26). For a real gas an appropriate equation of state can be used to evaluate $(\partial P/\partial T)_V$ or $(\partial V/\partial T)_P$.

11.8 TEMPERATURE-ENTROPY DIAGRAMS

The Carnot cycle has been used to establish the second law and to define the entropy function. It is also instructive to consider the Carnot cycle in terms of temperature-entropy variables rather than pressure-volume variables. Figure 11.5 represents such a condition. The isothermal, reversible expansion at the temperature T_2 is represented by the horizontal line *ab*. As the expansion takes place the entropy of the fluid used in the cycle increases from S_1 to S_2. The adiabatic reversible expansion follows the isentropic line *bc* along which the entropy is constant. The isothermal reversible compression at the temperature T_1 takes place along the horizontal line *cd*. Along this line the entropy decreases from S_2 back to S_1. Finally the adiabatic, reversible compression follows the line ad at constant entropy. The area $abef$ represents the heat absorbed by the fluid at the higher temperature, since $Q_2 = T_2(S_2 - S_1) = T_2 \Delta S$.

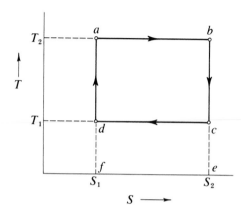

Fig. 11.5. Temperature-entropy diagram.

Similarly the heat transferred from the fluid to the thermal reservoir at the lower temperature is represented by the area $cdfe$. The net heat absorbed by the system is represented by the area $abcd$. This area also represents the net work done by the system on the surroundings. The efficiency of the cycle is the ratio of the area $abcd$ to $abef$. Here we see that the efficiency is given by

$$e = \frac{W}{Q_2} = \frac{Q_2 + Q_1}{Q_2} = \frac{T_2(\Delta S)_{T_2} - T_1(\Delta S)_{T_1}}{T_2(\Delta S)_{T_2}} \qquad (11.27)$$

It is evident from Fig. 11.5 that $(\Delta S)_{T_2}$ equals $(\Delta S)_{T_1}$ and consequently

$$e = \frac{T_2 - T_1}{T_2} \qquad (11.28)$$

Several other types of reversible cycles are easily discussed in terms of temperature-entropy diagrams. Two isothermal, reversible processes are involved in each cycle. These processes are indicated by the straight lines ab and cd in Fig. 11.6. We accept the previous results that the maximum

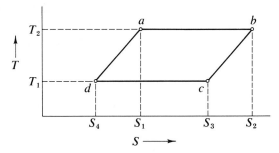

Fig. 11.6. Temperature-entropy diagram.

efficiency is given by the two relations

$$e = \frac{W}{Q_2} = \frac{Q_2 + Q_1}{Q_2} \qquad (11.29)$$

$$e = \frac{T_2 - T_1}{T_2} \qquad (11.30)$$

But

$$Q_2 = T_2(S_2 - S_1) \qquad (11.31)$$

and

$$Q_1 = T_1(S_4 - S_3) \qquad (11.32)$$

Then, in order that both Eq. (11.29) and Eq. (11.30) be satisfied, $(S_2 - S_1)$ must equal $(S_3 - S_4)$. Therefore the entropy changes in going along the two paths bc and da are equal but opposite in sign. (The lines bc and ad have been drawn as straight lines in Fig. 11.6 only for illustrative purposes; they may be curved.) This relationship must hold if the efficiency of the cycle in Fig. 11.6 is to be identical with the maximum efficiency of a Carnot cycle as given in Eq. (11.29). Sometimes the efficiency is described as the work done divided by the total heat absorbed. The efficiency defined in this way (in terms of the total heat absorbed) for the cycle shown in Fig. 11.6 would then be less than the maximum efficiency of the Carnot cycle. In the Carnot cycle

229

the processes along the lines bc and da are adiabatic and reversible so that the differences $(S_2 - S_3)$ and $(S_1 - S_4)$ are both zero.

The independent variables in the general cycle illustrated in Fig. 11.6 are T_2, S_1, S_2, T_1, and S_3. We may choose T_2 (the upper temperature) and S_1 which determines the initial state of the system. The extent of the line ab is determined by the choice of S_2. The point c is determined by the choice of T_1 (the lower temperature) and S_3. The entropy S_4 at d is dependent because of the requirement that $(S_3 - S_4)$ must equal $(S_2 - S_1)$. Here we have considered the entropy as an independent variable. But we have already shown that the entropy may be taken as a function of either the temperature and volume or the temperature and pressure. Therefore we could consider a volume or a pressure as an independent variable, in place of the entropy in each case.

The general case can be discussed by setting the entropy as a function (1) of the temperature and volume and (2) of the temperature and pressure. When we set the entropy as a function of the temperature and volume so that $S = S(T, V)$, we can write the differential dS as

$$dS = \frac{C_V}{T} dT + \left(\frac{\partial P}{\partial T}\right)_V dV \tag{11.33}$$

Equation (11.33) must be applicable along both paths bc and da. Moreover, the difference between T_2 and T_1 could be infinitesimal or finite, and therefore the differential entropy change along a differential portion of the path bc between the temperatures T and $T - dT$ must equal that along a differential portion of the path ad between the same two temperatures. Mathematically we have

$$(dS)_{bc} = (dS)_{ad} \tag{11.34}$$

and with the use of Eq. (11.33) we obtain the derivative

$$\frac{dV}{dT} = -\frac{(C_V/T)_{bc} - (C_V/T)_{ad}}{(\partial P/\partial T)_{V,bc} - (\partial P/\partial T)_{V,ad}} \tag{11.35}$$

This equation then shows how the volume of the system must be changed with a change of temperature along paths bc and ad so that the entropy changes along these two paths are equal.

If the processes along paths *bc* and *ad* are at constant volume, then we see that

$$\left(\frac{C_V}{T}\right)_{bc} = \left(\frac{C_V}{T}\right)_{ad} \tag{11.36}$$

The heat capacities in general are dependent on the volumes, and hence the condition expressed in Eq. (11.36) is not satisfied. The condition is satisfied by ideal gases because the heat capacities are independent of the volume. The efficiency of a reversible cycle composed of two isotherms and two isochores is the maximum efficiency when an ideal gas is used as the fluid, and is generally less than the maximum when other fluids are used.

Similar conclusions may be drawn when the entropy is expressed as a function of the temperature and pressure. Then the differential of the entropy is expressed as

$$dS = \frac{C_P}{T}\,dT - \left(\frac{\partial V}{\partial T}\right)_P dP \tag{11.37}$$

By the arguments used in the preceding paragraphs we find that the pressure must be changed with a change of temperature according to the equation

$$\frac{dP}{dT} = \frac{(C_P/T)_{bc} - (C_P/T)_{ad}}{(\partial V/\partial T)_{bc} - (\partial V/\partial T)_{ad}} \tag{11.38}$$

If now a reversible cycle is composed of two isotherms and two isobars, the use of an ideal gas as the fluid will give the maximum efficiency because the heat capacities are independent of pressure for an ideal gas. The efficiency is generally less than the maximum when other fluids are used.

11.9 CONCLUDING COMMENTS

The entropy function is defined in terms of its differential as

$$dS = \frac{dQ_{\text{rev}}}{T}$$

where dQ_{rev} is the differential heat absorbed by a system in a reversible process and T is the temperature at which the heat is absorbed. The entropy function of a system is a function of the independent variables used to define the state of the system. Therefore the change in the value of the entropy function in going from one state to another state is independent of the path used to connect the two states. However, the change in the value of the entropy function must be determined along a reversible path.

The change of entropy of an *isolated* system is zero for any *reversible* process taking place within the system. The value of the entropy function of an *isolated* system always increases for any *irreversible* process which takes place in the system.

The dependence on the temperature of the entropy function for a closed system is given by the two relations

$$\left(\frac{\partial S}{\partial T}\right)_V = \frac{C_V}{T}$$

and

$$\left(\frac{\partial S}{\partial V}\right)_T = \frac{C_P}{T}$$

The dependence on volume or pressure of the entropy function for a closed system at constant temperature is given by the two equations

$$\left(\frac{\partial S}{\partial V}\right)_T = \left(\frac{\partial P}{\partial T}\right)_V$$

$$\left(\frac{\partial S}{\partial P}\right)_T = -\left(\frac{\partial V}{\partial T}\right)_P$$

Exercises

11.1 A system undergoes a process in which the entropy change is 2.41 cal deg^{-1}. During the process, 1000 calories of heat are added to the system from a thermostat at a constant temperature of 500° K. Is the process reversible or irreversible?

11.2 Five grams of ice at $273°$ K are mixed adiabatically at a constant pressure of 1 atm with 25 g of water at $298°$ K. Find the final state of the system and its change of entropy. The specific heat at constant pressure of ice of 0.53 cal $\deg^{-1}$ g^{-1}; that of water is 1.0 cal $\deg^{-1}$ g^{-1}; and the specific heat of fusion of ice at 1 atm pressure is 80 cal g^{-1}.

11.3 The molar heat capacity of water vapor (in cal $\deg^{-1}$ $mole^{-1}$) is given by the equation $\tilde{C}_P = 7.187 + 0.00237T - 0.208 \times 10^{-6}T^2$ and that of liquid water is 18 cal $\deg^{-1}$ $mole^{-1}$. The molar change of enthalpy on evaporation at $373°$ K and 1 atm pressure is 9700 cal $\deg^{-1}$ $mole^{-1}$. Calculate ΔS for the change of state

$$3H_2O(l, 298° \text{ K, 1 atm}) = 3H_2O(g, 500° \text{ K, 1 atm})$$

11.4 One mole of an ideal gas at 10 atm pressure and $244°$ K is contained in a rigid cylinder. The cylinder is connected through a valve to a piston and cylinder arrangement. The rigid cylinder and the piston and cylinder are contained in a thermostat at $244°$ K. The volume between the valve and the face of the piston is negligible. The valve is now slightly opened and the gas leaks through slowly and pushes the piston against a constant pressure of 1 atm until the pressure of the gas becomes 1 atm. The temperature is kept constant at $244°$ K.
(a) What is ΔE of the gas?
(b) How much work is done by the gas?
(c) How much heat is added to the gas?
(d) What is ΔS of the gas for the change of state which takes place?

11.5 One mole of gas undergoes a Joule-Thomson expansion from 100 atm to 1 atm, starting at $373°$ K. With the use of the data below, calculate
(a) The final temperature.
(b) The change of the entropy of the gas for the change of state which takes place.
Data:

$$\left(\frac{\partial T}{\partial P}\right)_H = 0.21° \text{ K atm}^{-1}$$

$$\tilde{C}_P = \tfrac{5}{2}R$$

$$PV = RT(1 + B'P)$$

$$B' = -\frac{0.525}{T} \text{ atm}^{-1}$$

11.6 One mole of an ideal gas at 298° K and 1 atm pressure is expanded adiabatically into a vacuum, as in the Joule experiment. The final pressure of the gas is 0.1 atm. What is the change in entropy of the gas for the change of state that occurs?

11.7 When one mole of water is evaporated at 373° K and 1 atm pressure, 9700 cal of heat are absorbed by the water substance. Two vessels, one having a volume of 100 ml and the other having a volume of 1000 ml, are sealed together by means of a stopcock. The smaller vessel is filled with water and the larger vessel is evacuated. The entire assembly is placed in a thermostat at 373° K. The quantity of water in the smaller vessel is such that it just fills the vessel to the stopcock at this temperature and 1 atm pressure. After temperature equilibrium has been obtained the stopcock is opened and some of the water evaporates. Calculate ΔE, ΔH, and ΔS for the change of state that takes place and also Q and W for the process.

11.8 A block of copper weighing 50 g is placed in 100 g of H_2O for a short time. The copper is then removed from the water, with no adhering drops of water, and separated from it adiabatically. Temperature equilibrium is then established in both the copper and water. The entire process is carried out adiabatically at constant pressure. The initial temperature of the copper was 373° K and that of the water was 298° K. The final temperature of the copper block was 323° K. Consider the water and the block of copper as an isolated system and assume that the only transfer of heat was between the copper and water. The specific heat of copper at constant pressure is 0.093 cal deg^{-1} g^{-1} and that of water is 1.000 cal deg^{-1} g^{-1}. Calculate the entropy change of the isolated system.

11.9 The equation of state for one mole of a certain gas is given by

$$PV = RT\left(1 + \frac{B}{V}\right)$$

where $B = -11{,}000 + 20T$ cm^3 mole^{-1}, and
  (i)   A(g, 20,000 cm^3, 300° K) = A(g, 60,000 cm^3, 300° K)
  (ii) A(g, 60,000 cm^3, 300° K) = A(g, 60,000 cm^3, 500° K)
  (iii) A(g, 20,000 cm^3, 300° K) = A(g, 20,000 cm^3, 500° K)
  (iv) A(g, 20,000 cm^3, 500° K) = A(g, 60,000 cm^3, 500° K)
  (a) Calculate Q and ΔS for the isothermal, reversible expansion of the gas for the change of state represented by (i) and (iv).

(b) Calculate Q and ΔS for the isochoric, reversible process represented by (ii) and (iii).

(c) What is the total heat absorbed and the change of entropy for the sum of the two steps (i) and (ii); (iii) and (iv)?

(d) If the direction of the two steps (i) and (ii) are reversed so that the combination of the four steps results in a cycle, calculate Q and ΔS for the processes in (a) and (b). What is ΔS for the cycle? *Data:*

$$\tilde{C}_V = 3.0 + 2.5 \times 10^{-3}T \text{ cal deg}^{-1} \text{ mole}^{-1} \text{ at 20,000 cm}^3 \text{ mole}^{-1}$$

$$\tilde{C}_V = 3.0 + 5.2 \times 10^{-3}T \text{ cal deg}^{-1} \text{ mole}^{-1} \text{ at 60,000 cm}^3 \text{ mole}^{-1}$$

11.10 Two very large thermal reservoirs are connected by a good thermal conductor and the entire system is isolated. Reservoir A is at 400° K and reservoir B is at 300° K. If heat flows at a constant rate of 10 cal sec^{-1} from A to B, what is the entropy change per second for A? for B? for the entire isolated system? (Assume that the transfer of heat at each end of the thermal conductor takes place reversibly and that the state of the thermal conductor remains unchanged.)

12 The Helmholtz and Gibbs Free Energies

The first law of thermodynamics defines the energy function E and gives us the information that the value of the energy of an isolated system is constant. The second law of thermodynamics defines the entropy function S and gives us the knowledge that the value of the entropy always increases when an irreversible process takes place in an isolated system and that in the limit of a reversible process the value of the entropy of an isolated system does not change. Questions naturally arise as to how these two laws may be combined and what further useful functions may be defined and developed. The combination of the first and second laws leads to the definition of two new functions: the Helmholtz and Gibbs free energies. In this chapter we establish most of the relations which were introduced without proof in earlier chapters.

12.1 GENERAL CONSIDERATIONS

From the first law we have the expression

$$dE = dQ - P \, dV - dW \tag{12.1}$$

for the differential of the energy function. The work terms, other than the work of expansion or compression, are designated by the symbol dW. From the second law the entropy function is defined through the relations

$$dS = \frac{dQ_{rev}}{T} \quad \text{or} \quad dQ_{rev} = T\,dS \tag{12.2}$$

If the use of Eq. (12.1) is *limited* to reversible processes we can write

$$dE = dQ_{rev} - P\,dV - dW_{rev} \tag{12.3}$$

and on substituting $T\,dS$ for dQ_{rev} we obtain

$$dE = T\,dS - P\,dV - dW_{rev} \tag{12.4}$$

It should be emphasized that dE for an infinitesimal change of state and ΔE for a finite change of state are independent of the path and may be calculated by either Eq. (12.1) or Eq. (12.4). However, the calculations using Eq. (12.4) must be along a reversible path, while those using Eq. (12.1) may be along any path.

For the enthalpy we have

$$dH = dQ + V\,dP - dW \tag{12.5}$$

Again we may limit the use of Eq. (12.5) to reversible processes and substitute $T\,dS$ for dQ_{rev} to obtain

$$dH = T\,dS + V\,dP - dW_{rev} \tag{12.6}$$

The same conditions which applied to Eq. (12.4) also apply to Eq. (12.6).

The most convenient set of independent variables for use in Eq. (12.4) from a mathematical viewpoint, are the entropy and the volume and those associated with the other work terms. For Eq. (12.6) the most convenient set comprises the entropy, the pressure, and those associated with other work terms. However, from the practical viewpoint the entropy is a most inconvenient variable to use. There is no direct way by which we can change the entropy from one value to another; we can change the entropy only by a change of temperature, volume, pressure, or other quantities which are used to define the state of a system. It proves convenient to define some new functions by carrying out a change of variables. The same procedure was used earlier in the definition of the enthalpy.

12.2   THE HELMHOLTZ FREE ENERGY FUNCTION A

The definition of the Helmholtz free energy function is based on Eq. (12.4). By taking the differential of the product TS we obtain

$$d(TS) = T \, dS + S \, dT \tag{12.7}$$

Subtraction of Eq. (12.7) from Eq. (12.4) gives

$$d(E - TS) = -S \, dT - P \, dV - dW_{rev} \tag{12.8}$$

where the temperature rather than the entropy is now the independent variable. The quantity $d(E - TS)$ is the differential of a new function which is called the Helmholtz free energy function and is given the symbol A. Then

$$dA = d(E - TS)$$

and on integration this gives

$$A = E - TS + \text{const}$$

Since we do not know the absolute value of the entropy or energy functions, and we are here defining a new function, it is possible to make the constant zero so that

$$A = E - TS \tag{12.9}$$

This equation defines the Helmholtz free energy function A. The differential of A is exact, A is a state function and a thermodynamic property, and the value of ΔA is independent of the path between two states. The cyclical integral, $\oint dA$, equals zero.

From Eq. (12.8) we have that

$$dA = -S \, dT - P \, dV - dW_{rev} \tag{12.10}$$

which shows how the value of the Helmholtz free energy changes with temperature, with volume, and with the independent variables associated with the other work terms. The seeking of an understanding of A in terms of words leads back directly to interpreting Eq. (12.10) or variations of it in terms of words. For example, at constant temperature, Eq. (12.10) becomes

$$dA = -P\,dV - dW_{rev}$$

The quantity $P\,dV$ is the differential reversible work of expansion done by the system on the surroundings, and dW_{rev} is the differential of all other reversible work done by the system on the surroundings. Therefore dA, the differential change of the Helmholtz free energy, equals the negative of the differential of the total *reversible* work done by the system on the surroundings at *constant temperature*. In a similar fashion we could say, using Eq. (12.4), that dE is the differential of the total reversible work done by the system on the surroundings at *constant entropy*. Obviously, A is a much more practical property to use than E when considering the total reversible work done by the system. For a process that takes place at constant volume and temperature, A is a measure of the total reversible work done by the system, excluding pressure-volume work.

12.3   THE GIBBS FREE ENERGY FUNCTION G

The Gibbs free energy function† can be defined in a fashion similar to that for A by an appropriate change of variables. Subtraction of Eq. (12.7) from Eq. (12.6) gives

$$d(H - TS) = -S\,dT + V\,dP - dW_{rev} \qquad (12.11)$$

where the independent variables are now the convenient ones of temperature, pressure, and those associated with the other work terms. We define Gibbs free energy function to be

$$G = H - TS \qquad (12.12)$$

† Alternatively called the Gibbs free energy or sometimes (loosely) called simply the free energy.

and then we find

$$dG = -S\,dT + V\,dP - dW_{\text{rev}} \tag{12.13}$$

This equation tells us how the Gibbs free energy varies with changes in the temperature, the pressure, and any of the independent variables associated with the other work terms

For an interpretation in terms of words we consider changes of state at *constant temperature and pressure.* Under these conditions dG is equal to the negative of the differential of the reversible work done by the system on the surroundings *other* than the work of expansion or compression. According to Eq. (12.6), dH describes the same property under the conditions of *constant entropy and pressure.*

The Gibbs free energy is a state function, its differential is exact, and the value of the change in the Gibbs free energy for a change of state is dependent solely on the initial and final states. Although the values of ΔA and ΔG for a change of state are independent of the path, the development of Eqs. (12.10) and (12.13) implies that the integration of these equations to obtain values of ΔA and ΔG is along a reversible path.

12.4   A RÉSUMÉ CONCERNING E, H, S, A, and G

We have now established five functions: the energy, the enthalpy, the entropy, the Helmholtz free energy, and the Gibbs free energy. Of these five, H, A, and G were developed by suitable changes of variables to create functions with special useful characteristics. All five are functions of the independent variables which are used to define the state of a system. As such, the differential of each function is exact.

From the first law we have the two relations

$$dE = dQ - P\,dV - dW \tag{12.14}$$

and

$$dH = dQ + V\,dP - dW \tag{12.15}$$

The use of these equations for the determination of ΔE or ΔH is not limited to any particular path, be it reversible or irreversible. However, the inclusion of the terms $P\,dV$ and $V\,dP$, where P and V are properties of the system, indicates the use of quasi-static processes.

From the combination of the first and second laws we have four relations:

$$dE = T\,dS - P\,dV - dW_{rev} \qquad (12.16)$$

$$dH = T\,dS + V\,dP - dW_{rev} \qquad (12.17)$$

$$dA = -S\,dT - P\,dV - dW_{rev} \qquad (12.18)$$

$$dG = -S\,dT + V\,dP - dW_{rev} \qquad (12.19)$$

The calculation of ΔE, ΔH, ΔA, or ΔG for a given change of state by the integration of the appropriate equation in this list implies a reversible path. We note that Eqs. (12.16) through (12.19) give us the convenient independent variables which may be used for each of the four functions. Thus

$$
\begin{aligned}
E &= E(S, V, x) \\
H &= H(S, P, x) \\
A &= A(T, V, x) \\
G &= G(T, P, x)
\end{aligned}
\qquad (12.20)
$$

where the x refers to all independent variables associated with the other work terms. In many problems when the other work terms are zero, each x is constant, and the x's are omitted from Eq. (12.20). The most convenient independent variables for the energy are the entropy and volume; for the enthalpy, entropy and pressure; for the Helmholtz free energy, temperature and volume; and for the Gibbs free energy, temperature and pressure.

Although the most convenient independent variables to associate with the energy are the entropy and the volume, we are frequently concerned with the dependence of the energy on temperature and volume. Then it becomes more practical to write $E = E(T, V, x)$ rather than $E = E(S, V, x)$. We could also set the energy as a function of temperature and pressure, but the resulting differential expressions are much more complicated. The choice of the independent variables to use with a particular function for a particular problem is basically made in terms of convenience, simplicity of the relationships, and, of course, experience.

12.5   MAXWELL RELATIONS AND OTHER PARTIAL DERIVATIVES

We can derive many relations by the application of mathematics (refer to Chapter 2) to Eqs. (12.16) through (12.19). If we take $z = z(x, y)$, then

$$dz = \left(\frac{\partial z}{\partial x}\right)_y dx + \left(\frac{\partial z}{\partial y}\right)_x dy$$

If now we are given $dz = M\,dx + N\,dy$ and know that dz is the differential of a function, then we also know that M equals $(\partial z/\partial x)_y$ and N equals $(\partial z/\partial y)_x$. Applying these concepts to Eqs. (12.16) through (12.19) we have, from Eq. (12.16),

$$\left(\frac{\partial E}{\partial S}\right)_{V,x} = T \qquad \text{and} \qquad \left(\frac{\partial E}{\partial V}\right)_{S,x} = -P \tag{12.21}$$

and from Eq. (12.17),

$$\left(\frac{\partial H}{\partial S}\right)_{P,x} = T \qquad \text{and} \qquad \left(\frac{\partial H}{\partial P}\right)_{S,x} = V \tag{12.22}$$

and from Eq. (12.18),

$$\left(\frac{\partial A}{\partial T}\right)_{V,x} = -S \qquad \text{and} \qquad \left(\frac{\partial A}{\partial V}\right)_{T,x} = -P \tag{12.23}$$

and from Eq. (12.19),

$$\left(\frac{\partial G}{\partial T}\right)_{P,x} = -S \qquad \text{and} \qquad \left(\frac{\partial G}{\partial P}\right)_{T,x} = V \tag{12.24}$$

Each of these relations tells us how one dependent variable changes with a change of one independent variable, keeping the appropriate other variables constant.

We also know from Chapter 2 that when we are given $dz = M\,dx + N\,dy$

and know that dz is exact, then $(\partial M/\partial y)_x$ equals $(\partial N/\partial x)_y$. In Eqs. (12.16) through (12.19) we know that E, H, A, and G are functions of the state variables and therefore dE, dH, dA, and dG are exact. We then have the *Maxwell relations*:

$$\left(\frac{\partial T}{\partial V}\right)_{S,x} = -\left(\frac{\partial P}{\partial S}\right)_{V,x} \qquad (12.25)$$

$$\left(\frac{\partial T}{\partial P}\right)_{S,x} = \left(\frac{\partial V}{\partial S}\right)_{P,x} \qquad (12.26)$$

$$\left(\frac{\partial S}{\partial V}\right)_{T,x} = \left(\frac{\partial P}{\partial T}\right)_{V,x} \qquad (12.27)$$

$$\left(\frac{\partial S}{\partial P}\right)_{T,x} = -\left(\frac{\partial V}{\partial T}\right)_{P,x} \qquad (12.28)$$

If we invert the first two equations we have

$$\left(\frac{\partial S}{\partial P}\right)_{V,x} = -\left(\frac{\partial V}{\partial T}\right)_{S,x} \qquad (12.29)$$

$$\left(\frac{\partial S}{\partial V}\right)_{P,x} = \left(\frac{\partial P}{\partial T}\right)_{S,x} \qquad (12.30)$$

These last two equations give the change of entropy with pressure or volume at constant volume or pressure, respectively, in terms of the change of volume or pressure with temperature for an isentropic (adiabatic, reversible) process. The last two Maxwell relations, Eqs. (12.27) and (12.28), are of special importance because they relate changes of entropy to the experimentally observable quantities of pressure, volume, and temperature.

12.6   DERIVATION OF SOME ADDITIONAL USEFUL RELATIONS

We continue to consider closed systems and we also limit the changes of state so that all work terms other than the work of expansion or compression are zero. In this case we may set the entropy as a function of the temperature and volume. Thus

$$S = S(T, V)$$

and

$$dS = \left(\frac{\partial S}{\partial T}\right)_V dT + \left(\frac{\partial S}{\partial V}\right)_P dV \qquad (12.31)$$

From Eq. (11.19) we know that $(\partial S/\partial T)_V = C_V/T$ and from Eq. (12.27) that $(\partial S/\partial V)_T = (\partial P/\partial T)_V$, so that

$$dS = \frac{C_V}{T} dT + \left(\frac{\partial P}{\partial T}\right)_V dV \qquad (12.32)$$

The coefficients of dT and dV are thus expressed in terms of quantities that can be measured experimentally. Equation (12.32) can be integrated for any change of state involving a change of temperature and volume, by the methods which have been discussed previously.

We can also apply Eq. (12.32) to an isentropic change of state. For such changes of state dS is zero and therefore

$$\left(\frac{\partial T}{\partial V}\right)_S = -\frac{T(\partial P/\partial T)_V}{C_V} \qquad (12.33)$$

This equation can be derived from Eq. (12.25) by slightly different methods. It is equivalent to Eq. (7.27) for an ideal gas.

Similarly, we may set $S = S(T, P)$ and thus

$$dS = \left(\frac{\partial S}{\partial T}\right)_P dT + \left(\frac{\partial S}{\partial P}\right)_T dP \qquad (12.34)$$

We use Eqs. (12.28) and (11.20) to obtain

$$dS = \frac{C_P}{T} dT - \left(\frac{\partial V}{\partial T}\right)_P dP \qquad (12.35)$$

The coefficients of dT and dP in this equation are now expressed in terms of experimentally observable quantities, and the integration of the equation for a change of state involving a change of temperature and pressure can be readily carried out. When we consider an isentropic change of state we find that

$$\left(\frac{\partial T}{\partial P}\right)_S = \frac{T(\partial V/\partial T)_P}{C_P} \tag{12.36}$$

We may determine by means of this equation the change of temperature of a system with pressure for an adiabatic, reversible process. Equation (8.45) can be obtained from this equation.

We have frequently used the two relations

$$\left(\frac{\partial E}{\partial V}\right)_T = T\left(\frac{\partial P}{\partial T}\right)_V - P$$

and

$$\left(\frac{\partial H}{\partial P}\right)_T = V - T\left(\frac{\partial V}{\partial T}\right)_P$$

but have not derived them. For the first equation we start with Eq. (12.4), excluding the other work terms, namely

$$dE = T\,dS - P\,dV \tag{12.37}$$

At constant temperature, $dE = (\partial E/\partial V)_T\,dV$ and $dS = (\partial S/\partial T)_V\,dV$. We substitute these relations into Eq. (12.37) and cancel the differentials dV. Thus we obtain

$$\left(\frac{\partial E}{\partial V}\right)_T = T\left(\frac{\partial S}{\partial V}\right)_P - P \tag{12.38}$$

This equation becomes

$$\left(\frac{\partial E}{\partial V}\right)_T = T\left(\frac{\partial P}{\partial T}\right)_V - P \tag{12.39}$$

245

by the use of Eq. (12.27). We prove that

$$\left(\frac{\partial H}{\partial P}\right)_T = V - T\left(\frac{\partial V}{\partial T}\right)_P \tag{12.40}$$

with the use of similar arguments and Eqs. (12.6) and (12.28).

One final pair of relation concerns the dependence of the Helmholtz and Gibbs free energies on temperature. Equations (12.23) and (12.24) give these relations in terms of the entropy. It is only recently that data concerning the entropy have been accumulated, although there does exist a large amount of data concerning the energy and enthalpy. It is therefore important to obtain a relation between a temperature derivative of the free energies and the energy or enthalpy. The definitions of the two free energies are

$$A = E - TS \quad \text{and} \quad G = H - TS$$

and we know that $(\partial A/\partial T)_V = -S$ and $(\partial G/\partial T)_P = -S$. We can then write

$$A - T\left(\frac{\partial A}{\partial T}\right)_V = E \tag{12.41}$$

and

$$G - T\left(\frac{\partial G}{\partial T}\right)_P = H \tag{12.42}$$

Other forms of these last two equations can be obtained by mathematical manipulation. These are

$$\left(\frac{\partial(A/T)}{\partial T}\right)_V = -\frac{E}{T^2} \tag{12.43}$$

$$\left(\frac{\partial(A/T)}{\partial(1/T)}\right)_V = E \tag{12.44}$$

$$\left(\frac{\partial(G/T)}{\partial T}\right)_P = -\frac{H}{T^2} \tag{12.45}$$

$$\left(\frac{\partial(G/T)}{\partial(1/T)}\right)_P = H \tag{12.46}$$

In these four equations the function which is differentiated is A/T or G/T and the variable of differentiation is T or $1/T$. Equation (12.45) is called the Gibbs–Helmholtz equation.

12.7 FREE ENERGY FUNCTIONS AND IDEAL GASES

First we develop some general methods of evaluating ΔA and ΔG for a change of state and then apply some of these relations to the special case of the ideal gas. We assume in this development that the only work which is done on or by the system is pressure-volume work. We write Eqs. (12.18) and (12.19) as

$$dA = -S(T, V)\, dT - P(T, V)\, dV \tag{12.47}$$

$$dG = -S(T, P)\, dT + V(T, P)\, dP \tag{12.48}$$

where the independent variables are included explicitly to show that the entropy, volume, and pressure are themselves dependent on the independent variables.

It is evident that in the case of *non*isothermal changes of state it is necessary to know the *absolute* value of the entropy as a function of T and P or T and V. Although it will develop that under certain conditions it is possible to evaluate absolute entropies, it is much simpler to evaluate changes in the Helmholtz and Gibbs free energies for isothermal processes. In this latter case Eqs. (12.47) and (12.48) reduce to

$$dA = -P(T, V)\, dV \qquad \text{or} \qquad \Delta A = -\int P(T, V)\, dV \tag{12.49}$$

$$dG = V(T, P)\, dP \qquad \text{or} \qquad \Delta G = \int V(T, P)\, dP \tag{12.50}$$

By substituting an appropriate equation of state for $P(T, V)$ or $V(T, P)$, ΔA and ΔG may be evaluated for isothermal changes of state.

For n moles of an ideal gas Eqs. (12.49) and (12.50) become

$$\Delta A = -nRT \int_{V_i}^{V_f} \frac{dV}{V} = -nRT \ln \frac{V_f}{V_i} \tag{12.51}$$

$$\Delta G = nRT \int_{P_i}^{P_f} \frac{dP}{P} = nRT \ln \frac{P_f}{P_i} \tag{12.52}$$

from which it is evident that for an isothermal change of state of an ideal gas ΔA equals ΔG.

12.8   FREE ENERGY CHANGES FOR PHASE CHANGES IN A PURE SUBSTANCE

Phase transitions in one-component systems can be carried out reversibly at constant temperature and constant pressure. For such changes of state, $\Delta G = 0$ and $\Delta A = -P \, \Delta V$. Thus, for the change of state

$$nH_2O(l, 373° \text{ K, 1 atm}) = nH_2O(g, 373° \text{ K, 1 atm})$$

ΔG is zero. The pressure is constant and thus

$$\Delta A = -P(V_g - V_l) \tag{12.53}$$

where V_g represents the volume of n moles of water vapor at 373° K and 1 atm, and V_l the volume of n moles of liquid water under the same conditions. In many cases the molar volume of the liquid is very small with respect to the molar volume of the gas and $(V_g - V_l)$ can be approximated by V_g, the volume of the gas alone. Then ΔA becomes

$$\Delta A \cong -PV_g$$

which in the approximation of the ideal gas law is

$$\Delta A \cong -nRT \tag{12.54}$$

For the simpler closed systems with which we have been concerned, no change of state can take place under conditions of constant temperature and constant volume.

12.9   CONCLUDING COMMENTS

In this chapter two new functions were introduced. They are the Helmholtz free energy function defined by $A = E - TS$ or $dA = -S\,dT - P\,dV - dW_{\text{rev}}$, and the Gibbs free energy function, defined as $G = H - TS$ or $dG = -S\,dT + V\,dP - dW_{\text{rev}}$. Many general relationships between the functions E, H, S, A, and G were developed, and in particular the Maxwell relations were derived. The full significance of the Helmholtz and Gibbs free energies will be realized as they are applied to various processes in subsequent chapters.

Exercises

12.1   Derive the Maxwell relations, starting with Eqs. (12.16) through (12.19). Then derive Eqs. (12.16) through (12.19).

12.2   Three moles of oxygen for which $\tilde{C}_V$ is 4.97 cal mole^{-1} deg^{-1}, expand reversibly and isothermally from 10 liters and 300° K to 75 liters. Assume ideal gas behavior. Calculate ΔE, ΔH, ΔA, ΔS, and ΔG for this change of state and Q and W for this process.

12.3   Five moles of helium initially at 300° K and 10 liters, for which $\tilde{C}_V$ is 3.01 cal mole^{-1} deg^{-1}, expand reversibly and adiabatically to 75 liters. Assume ideal gas behavior. (a) Calculate ΔE, ΔH, and ΔS for the change of state and Q and W for the process. (b) Calculate the same quantities if this process is an adiabatic free expansion. (c) Can ΔA and ΔG be calculated for the change of state in part (a)?

12.4   Obtain expressions for ΔA and ΔG for each of the two changes of state:

$$n\text{M}(g,\ T,\ V_1) = n\text{M}(g,\ T,\ V_2)$$

$$n\text{M}(g,\ T,\ P_1) = n\text{M}(g,\ T,\ P_2)$$

with the assumption that the substance M obeys the ideal gas equation of state.

249

12.5 Calculate ΔA and ΔG for the change of state

$$H_2O(l, 298° K, 1 atm) = H_2O(l, 298° K, 10 atm)$$

with the assumption that the molar volume of water is constant over this pressure range.

12.6 For a given process, ΔG is -20.5 kcal mole^{-1} at 298° K and -20.0 kcal mole^{-1} at 308° K. Calculate for this process approximate values of ΔS and ΔH at 303° K.

12.7 Consider the transition at a constant pressure of 1 atm of 10 g of water (liquid) at 263° K to 10 g of water (solid) at 263° K. At 263° K the density of water is 0.998 g cc^{-1} and of ice, 0.92 g cc^{-1}. Assume that the C_P's are constant at 0.48 cal g^{-1} deg^{-1} for ice and 1.01 cal g^{-1} deg^{-1} for water. $\Delta H_f(H_2O) = 80$ cal g^{-1}. Calculate $\Delta H, \Delta S, \Delta G, \Delta A, \Delta E, W,$ and Q for this transition.

12.8 (a) Given $S = S(T, V)$, show that $C_V \ln (T_2/T_1) = -nR \ln (V_2/V_1)$ for an adiabatic, reversible expansion of an ideal gas. Assume C_V is a constant.

(b) Given $S = S(T, P)$, show that $C_P \ln (T_2/T_1) = nR \ln (P_2/P_1)$ for an adiabatic, reversible expansion of an ideal gas. Assume C_P is a constant.

(c) Combine these two expressions to prove that $PV^\gamma = k$ where $\gamma = C_P/C_V$ for the adiabatic equation of state of an ideal gas.

12.9 One mole of a monatomic ideal gas for which $\tilde{C}_V = \frac{3}{2} R$ is expanded adiabatically and reversibly from a volume of 20,000 cm^3 to 40,000 cm^3 starting at 300° K. Calculate the final temperature.

12.10 Starting with $H = E + PV$, obtain a relation for $C_P - C_V$ in terms of experimentally observable quantities.

12.11 The change of enthalpy for the change of state

$$H_2O(l, 373° K, 1 atm) = H_2O(g, 373° K, 1 atm)$$

is 9700 cal. Calculate $\Delta A, \Delta G,$ and ΔS for this change of state.

12.12 One mole of an ideal gas at 298° K and 1 atm pressure is expanded adiabatically into a vacuum, as in the Joule experiment. The final pressure of the gas is 0.1 atm. What are $\Delta E, \Delta H, \Delta A, \Delta G,$ and ΔS for the gas for the change of state that occurs?

12.13 Calculate ΔA and ΔG for the change of state described in Exercise 11.7.

12.14 The equation of state for one mole of a certain gas is given by

$$PV = RT\left(1 + \frac{B}{V}\right)$$

where $B = -11{,}000 + 20T$ cm^3 mole^{-1}, and
  (i) A(g, 20,000 cm^3, 300° K) = A(g, 60,000 cm^3, 300° K).
 (ii) A(g, 60,000 cm^3, 300° K) = A(g, 60,000 cm^3, 500° K).
(iii) A(g, 20,000 cm^3, 300° K) = A(g, 20,000 cm^3, 500° K).
(iv) A(g, 20,000 cm^3, 500° K) = A(g, 60,000 cm^3, 500° K).
 (a) Calculate ΔA and ΔG for the isothermal, reversible expansion of
    the gas for the changes of state represented by (i) and (iv).
 (b) Consider the cycle composed of the four changes of state shown.
    What can be said about ΔA and ΔG for the changes of state repre-
    sented by (ii) and (iii)?

13 Open Systems— The Chemical Potential

The entire development of thermodynamics studied up to this point has been restricted to closed systems. But for many problems in thermodynamics, particularly those involving chemical equilibria, we must consider open systems, those in which the mass may be altered. The units we use here for mass are moles of a substance rather than actual mass units because of the simpler relations between moles of substances in chemical reactions. In this discussion we consider only the work terms for expansion and compression and we assume other work terms to be zero.

13.1 CHEMICAL POTENTIAL AND OPEN SYSTEMS

We recognize that the energy of a system does depend upon the mass of the substances which are used to form the system. If, then, we have a system made up of n_1 moles of the first component, n_2 moles of a second component, n_3 moles of a third component, and so forth, we may set the energy to be a function of the entropy, volume, and the number of moles of each component, so that

$$E = E(S, V, n_1, n_2, n_3, \ldots) \tag{13.1}$$

The differential of the energy is then

$$dE = \left(\frac{\partial E}{\partial S}\right)_{V,n_1,n_2,n_3...} dS + \left(\frac{\partial E}{\partial V}\right)_{S,n_1,n_2,n_3...} dV$$

$$+ \left(\frac{\partial E}{\partial n_1}\right)_{S,V,n_2,n_3...} dn_1 + \left(\frac{\partial E}{\partial n_2}\right)_{S,V,n_1,n_3...} dn_2$$

$$+ \left(\frac{\partial E}{\partial n_3}\right)_{S,V,n_1,n_2,...} dn_3 \cdots \tag{13.2}$$

This expression may be shortened by the use of a summation symbol so that

$$dE = \left(\frac{\partial E}{\partial S}\right)_{V,n} dS + \left(\frac{\partial E}{\partial V}\right)_{S,n} dV + \sum_i \left(\frac{\partial E}{\partial n_i}\right)_{S,V,n} dn_i \tag{13.3}$$

Here we let the subscript i designate any single substance and the summation sign represent a sum of the terms which follow. The sum is taken over all the components of the system. The subscript n on a derivative indicates that the number of moles of every component is kept constant except for those derivatives which are taken with respect to a specific component; in this case only the number of moles of the specific component is varied and the number of moles of every other component is kept constant. We know that $(\partial E/\partial S)_{V,n} = T$ and $(\partial E/\partial V)_{S,n} = -P$. We give a new symbol, μ_i, to the partial derivative $(\partial E/\partial n_i)_{S,V,n}$ so that

$$\left(\frac{\partial E}{\partial n_i}\right)_{S,V,n} = \mu_i \tag{13.4}$$

This quantity is so important to considerations of chemical equilibrium that it is given a special name and is called the *chemical potential*. With these relations we can rewrite Eq. (13.3) in compact form as

$$dE = T\,dS - P\,dV + \sum_i \mu_i\,dn_i \tag{13.5}$$

This equation is the fundamental equation which will be used to discuss the conditions for equilibrium. But it has the same difficulty which was discussed previously in that both the entropy and volume are the convenient independent

253

variables. The differentials of the enthalpy and of the two free energies are obtained by means of the same methods which were used in the earlier chapters. When this is done we obtain three other equations:

$$dH = T\,dS + V\,dP + \sum_i \mu_i\,dn_i \tag{13.6}$$

$$dA = -Sd\,T - P\,dV + \sum_i \mu_i\,dn_i \tag{13.7}$$

$$dG = -S\,dT + V\,dP + \sum_i \mu_i\,dn_i \tag{13.8}$$

Equation (13.8) is probably the most important of these equations because the independent variables are temperature, pressure, and the number of moles of each component. The definitions of H, A, and G are preserved in open systems.

13.2   HOMOGENEOUS FUNCTIONS AND EULER'S THEOREM

Consider a function $z = z(x, y)$ and the value of the function at two points x_1, y_1 and x_2, y_2 so that $z_1 = z(x_1, y_1)$ and $z_2 = z(x_2, y_2)$. Further, let $x_2 = kx_1$ and $y_2 = ky_1$ where k is the same factor; that is, both x_2 and y_2 are changed from x_1 and y_1, respectively, by the same factor. Then if

$$z_2 = k^n z_1$$

the function z is said to be homogeneous in degree n. A simple example of a homogeneous function of degree 2 is

$$z = ax^2 + bxy + cy^2$$

Euler's theorem states that if a function $z = z(x, y)$ is homogeneous in degree n then

$$nz = x\left(\frac{\partial z}{\partial x}\right)_y + y\left(\frac{\partial z}{\partial y}\right)_x \tag{13.9}$$

13.3 APPLICATION OF EULER'S THEOREM TO THERMODYNAMICS

The entropy and volume are extensive variables, that is, variables which are proportional to the mass of a system. Experience has shown that the energy of a system is a homogeneous function of degree 1 in the entropy, volume, and the number of moles of each component in the system. Euler's theorem then yields the equation

$$E = S\left(\frac{\partial E}{\partial S}\right)_{V,n} + V\left(\frac{\partial E}{\partial V}\right)_{S,n} + \sum_i n_i\left(\frac{\partial E}{\partial n_i}\right)_{S,V,n} \tag{13.10}$$

and, with the evaluation of the derivatives,

$$E = TS - PV + \sum_i \mu_i n_i \tag{13.11}$$

From the definitions of the other thermodynamic functions (for instance, $H = E + PV$)

$$H = TS + \sum_i \mu_i n_i \tag{13.12}$$

$$A = -PV + \sum_i \mu_i n_i \tag{13.13}$$

and

$$G = \sum_i \mu_i n_i \tag{13.14}$$

The important Eq. (13.14) states that the Gibbs free energy of a system is the sum of products of the chemical potential and the number of moles of each component.

13.4 CHEMICAL POTENTIALS

The chemical potentials are very important in chemical and phase equilibria. From their definition, Eq. (13.4) and Eqs. (13.5), (13.6), (13.7), and

(13.8), we see that the chemical potentials may be considered as functions of several combinations of variables:

$$\mu_i = \left(\frac{\partial E}{\partial n_i}\right)_{S,V,n} = \left(\frac{\partial H}{\partial n_i}\right)_{S,P,n} = \left(\frac{\partial A}{\partial n_i}\right)_{T,V,n} = \left(\frac{\partial G}{\partial n_i}\right)_{T,P,n} \tag{13.15}$$

The last derivative is the most important because the convenient independent variables in addition to the number of moles of each component are the temperature and pressure. We then express the chemical potential of a component as

$$\mu_i = \mu_i(T, P, n_1, n_2, n_3 \cdots) \tag{13.16}$$

because $G = G(T, P, n_1, n_2, n_3 \cdots)$. Equation (13.16) states that the chemical potential of a substance is a function of the temperature, pressure, and the number of moles of each component.

In many systems several different phases which contain the same components may exist together. The equations developed here apply to a single phase considered as a system as well as to the whole system. For a single phase the dependence of the chemical potentials on the moles of each component can be changed to composition variables such as mole fractions or molalities. The argument is that the derivative of a homogeneous function of degree n is itself a homogeneous function of degree $(n - 1)$. Thus, if G is a homogeneous function of degree n in the number of moles of each component at constant temperature and pressure, μ_i is a homogeneous function of degree zero in the number of moles of each component also at constant temperature and pressure. In more physical terms the chemical potential of a component is an intensive quantity which depends upon the values of intensive variables.

The mole fraction of a component, j, is defined as

$$x_j = \frac{n_j}{\sum_i n_i} \tag{13.17}$$

where n_j is the number of moles of a specific component. The molality is defined as

$$m_j = \frac{1000 n_j}{M_1 n_1} \tag{13.18}$$

where M_1 is the molecular weight of the component designated as component 1 (usually the solvent). Both the mole fraction and the molality are homogeneous functions of degree zero in the mole numbers. Consequently we may make the chemical potentials functions of the mole fractions or molalities of the components as well as the temperature and pressure. Thus we may write

$$\mu_i = \mu_i(T, P, x_1, x_2, x_3 \cdots) \tag{13.19}$$

or

$$\mu_i = \mu_i(T, P, m_1, m_2, m_3 \cdots) \tag{13.20}$$

In each case the number of independent composition variables is one less than the number of components. The sum of mole fractions for any system must equal 1.

13.5 CONCLUDING COMMENTS

In this brief chapter, open systems in which the mass may change have been introduced and discussed. The chemical potential was defined. The importance of the chemical potential will become evident in subsequent chapters where the concepts of chemical equilibria and phase equilibria are developed. (Euler's theorem and partial derivatives with respect to mole numbers are important in the thermodynamics of solutions, but this is a subject which will not be covered in this book.)†

Exercises

13.1 A mixture is made of 500 g of ethanol and 500 g of water. The density of ethanol at 298° K is 0.79 g cc^{-1} and its molecular weight is 46 g mole^{-1}. The density of water at 298° K is 1.00 g cc^{-1} and its molecular weight is 18 g mole^{-1}. Calculate the mole fraction, weight percent, and molality of both ethanol and water in this solution.

13.2 (a) Derive the identities in Eq. (13.15). (b) Derive Eq. (13.14).

† See I. M. Klotz, *Chemical Thermodynamics*, New York: Benjamin, 1964.

13.3 If the volume of a binary solution is a homogeneous function of degree 1 in terms of the mole numbers of the components, show that

(a) $$V = n_1 \left(\frac{\partial V}{\partial n_1} \right)_{T,P,n_2} + n_2 \left(\frac{\partial V}{\partial n_2} \right)_{T,P,n_1}.$$

(b) What is the graphical significance of $(\partial V/\partial n_1)_{T,P,n_2}$ on a plot of V versus n_1 (at constant n_2)?

13.4 If $dG = 0$ at constant temperature and pressure, what does Eq. (13.8) reduce to? For these conditions and a binary system, what is the relationship between μ_1 and μ_2?

13.5 The Gibbs free energy is not a homogeneous function of the temperature and pressure, but at constant temperature and pressure it is a homogeneous function of degree 1 of the mole numbers. Derive Eq. (13.14) on the basis of this statement.

13.6 The solubility of sulfur (atomic weight 32.06 g mole^{-1}) at 298° K in benzene is 18.5 g liter^{-1} and in toluene is 17.8 g liter^{-1}. The molecular weight of benzene is 78.11 g mole^{-1} and its density at 298° K is 0.879 g ml^{-1}. The same data for toluene is 92.13 g mole^{-1} and 0.867 g ml^{-1}. What is the solubility of sulfur as S_8 in benzene and toluene at 298° K expressed as molality, weight percent, and mole fraction? Assume that the densities of the solutions are those of the pure solvents.

14 Conditions of Equilibrium

The study of systems at equilibrium constitutes one of the main uses of thermodynamics. In the field of chemistry the studies yield information concerning the properties of a system when two or more phases are in equilibrium, such as the change in the vapor pressure of a pure liquid with temperature. Other examples are the dependence of the vapor pressure of a solution on temperature and composition and the dependence of the freezing point or boiling point of a solution on composition and pressure. Expressions for the equilibrium constant for a chemical reaction and the dependence of this constant on temperature and pressure are derived from thermodynamics. Many of the problems encountered in engineering require the application of the concepts of thermodynamic equilibrium.

The fundamental concepts of thermodynamic equilibrium are developed in this chapter on the basis of the first two laws of thermodynamics. The initial approach concerns solely the energy, volume, and entropy of a system. The conditions of equilibrium expressed in these quantities are extended to include the other thermodynamic functions. Finally the conditions of equilibrium for both phase and chemical equilibria are derived in terms of the chemical potentials.

14.1 FUNDAMENTAL CONDITIONS OF EQUILIBRIUM

We consider any closed isolated system. For such an isolated system the energy and volume will necessarily be constant. We know from experience

259

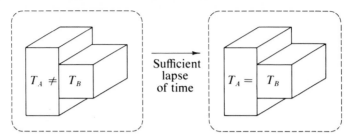

Fig. I4.I. Isolated bodies A and B originally at different temperatures.

that any such system when left to itself approaches a state of equilibrium if it is not already at equilibrium. As examples, we know (see Fig. 14.1) that the temperature of any two bodies will approach the same value when the two bodies are placed in thermal contact with each other and then isolated from the surroundings. We know that when a soluble substance is placed in a solvent, the substance will be distributed uniformly throughout the solvent, when sufficient time is allowed. We know that a mixture of substances which are capable of reacting will react over a period of time (which may be long or short) until equilibrium is obtained. And we know that any pressure difference between parts of the system will decrease in time so that the pressure becomes uniform throughout the system (unless prevented by some mechanical means).

Any isolated system left to itself will approach a state of equilibrium, a state in which all forces are balanced by equal and opposite forces and a state which does not change with time. But all processes which take place in an isolated system in the approach to equilibrium are of necessity irreversible. We also know that the entropy of an isolated system increases for any irreversible process which takes place in the system. Therefore, as an isolated system approaches a state of equilibrium, its entropy will approach the largest possible value consistent with the energy and volume of the system.

We start with an isolated system which is not at equilibrium. The entropy function for such a system will not have its maximum value consistent with the energy and volume of the isolated system. When this isolated system has attained equilibrium the entropy of the system has increased. If we now consider that the original nonequilibrium state was displaced only to an infinitesimal extent from the equilibrium state, then we can state that

$$(dS)_{E,V,n} \geqq 0 \tag{14.1}$$

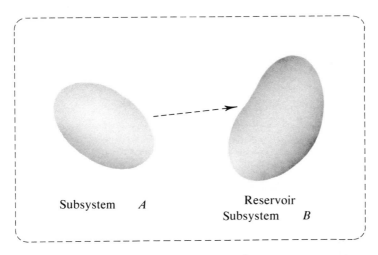

Fig. 14.2. An isolated system composed of two subsystems.

as the result of the process of attaining equilibrium. (The equality sign in Eq. (14.1) refers to possible infinitesimal reversible processes occuring under conditions of equilibrium and also indicates that the system is potentially at equilibrium.) Such a process of moving from a nonequilibrium to an equilibrium state (in an isolated system) is naturally an irreversible one. The following illustration will serve to clarify the condition in Eq. (14.1) and extend the criterion for the attainment of equilibrium to include the energy function.

Let us consider an isolated system at the temperature T, consisting of two subsystems: subsystem A is the one of interest, and subsystem B is a reservoir (see Fig. 14.2). The subsystem A then undergoes an infinitesimal irreversible process and at the same time the subsystem B undergoes an infinitesimal reversible change of state. Since in the entire isolated system an irreversible process takes place,

$$(dS)_{E,V,n} = dS_A + dS_B > 0 \tag{14.2}$$

During this process a differential quantity of heat is transferred from system

A to system B such that $dQ_A = -dQ_B$. The entropy change for system B is given by

$$dS_B = \frac{dQ_B}{T} \tag{14.3}$$

and we may write Eq. (14.2) as

$$dS_A - \frac{dQ_A}{T} > 0 \quad \text{or} \quad T\, dS_A - dQ_A > 0 \tag{14.4}$$

If system A undergoes a reversible process, dQ_A becomes dQ_A and Eq. (14.4) becomes

$$T\, dS_A - dQ_A = 0 \tag{14.5}$$

To include this possibility we rewrite Eq. (14.4) as

$$T\, dS_A - dQ_A \geq 0 \tag{14.6}$$

where the inequality sign indicates that an irreversible process has taken place and the equality sign indicates that a reversible process has occurred.

From the first law the differential quantity dQ_A must be equal to $dE_A + P_A dV_A$ or

$$T\, dS_A - dE_A - P_A\, dV_A \geq 0 \tag{14.7}$$

In terms of the energy function this can be rearranged to give

$$dE_A \leq T\, dS_A - P_A\, dV_A \tag{14.8}$$

For a process which takes place under conditions of constant entropy and volume, Eq. (14.8) reduces to

$$(dE_A)_{S,V} \leq 0 \tag{14.9}$$

In this equation the inequality sign refers to spontaneous, natural, or irreversible processes. The equality sign refers to possible infinitesimal reversible processes occurring under conditions of equilibrium, and also indicates that the system is at equilibrium.

Equations (14.1) and (14.9) express equivalent conditions for equilibrium. They state that it is the minimization of energy (in a system at constant entropy and volume) and the maximization of entropy (in an isolated system) that lead to the condition of equilibrium.

In the preceding discussion we examined the effect on the energy and entropy for the case where the initial state was a nonequilibrium state. Now let us start with an isolated system *at equilibrium* and consider possible states of the system which are variations of the original but which have the same energy and volume of the original system. At equilibrium the entropy function will have its largest possible value for the original system consistent with the values of the energy and volume. When only first orders of infinitesimal variations are considered, the value of the varied system must be either the same or *less* than that of the original system.† We can therefore write

$$(\delta S)_{E,V,n} \leq 0 \tag{14.10}$$

Here δS is the entropy change associated with an arbitrary virtual variation of the original system.

The condition of equilibrium expressed by the relation given in Eq.(14.10) is one of the two equivalent conditions used by Gibbs. This second condition is that for a system *at equilibrium* with a fixed value of the entropy and volume that for any virtual variation of such a system the energy can only increase or remain unchanged. We can thus write

$$(\delta E)_{S,V,n} \geq 0 \tag{14.11}$$

In order to elucidate the two conditions, (14.10) and (14.11), we consider a single-component two-phase system at equilibrium. The value of the entropy, energy, volume, and mole number of each phase is fixed. For Eq. (14.10) a virtual variation of this system is one in which the energy of one phase is slightly less than in the original system, but the volume and number of moles are the same. For the same total energy, volume, and mole number of the entire system the energy of the second phase must be larger by the same

†When higher orders of infinitesimal variations are considered the entropy of a varied system can be only less than that of the original system.

amount as the decrease of energy of the first phase, but the volume and number of moles of the second phase must be the same as in the original system. The entropy of the varied system can be only the same or less than that of the original system but it can never be greater. Similarly for Eq. (14.11), the entropy of one phase may be slightly less than in the original system but with the same volume and number of moles. The entropy of the second phase must then be larger by the same amount but with the same volume and number of moles. The energy of this varied system can be only the same or greater than that of the original system.

How such variations may be accomplished is not important to the argument, but an understanding of the result of the variations may be helpful. The increase of the entropy or energy of one phase may be caused by or result in an increase in temperature with an accompanying increase of pressure in order to keep the volume of the phase constant without transferring mass from one phase to the other. The corresponding decrease of the entropy or energy of the second phase may be caused by or result in a decrease in temperature with an accompanying decrease in pressure. If the varied system is still to be in equilibrium, an adiabatic and rigid wall would have to be placed between the two phases.

We return to the conditions of equilibrium and observe that it is the minimization of the energy and the maximization of the entropy which lead to a condition of equilibrium.

14.2   OTHER CONDITIONS OF EQUILIBRIUM

From Eq. (14.7) we see that for any system undergoing an irreversible process, the value of $dE - T dS + P dV$ must be less than zero, and for a reversible process it must be zero. When the definitions of the other thermodynamic functions are substituted for dE in this expression we obtain

$$dH - T \, dS - V \, dP \leqq 0$$

$$dA + S \, dT - P \, dV \leqq 0$$

and

$$dG + S \, dT - V \, dP \leqq 0$$

where the inequality sign refers to irreversible processes and the equality sign to a reversible process. If now, we consider systems at equilibrium and possible variations of the system we arrive at conditions of equilibrium expressed as

$$(\delta H)_{S,P,n} \geq 0 \tag{14.12}$$

$$(\delta A)_{T,V,n} \geq 0 \tag{14.13}$$

and

$$(\delta G)_{T,P,n} \geq 0 \tag{14.14}$$

These equations can also be derived by substituting the definitions of the appropriate thermodynamic function in Eq. (14.8) and choosing the inequality to mean changes away from the equilibrium condition. Note in Eqs. (14.12), (14.13), and (14.14), and in Eqs. (14.10) and(14.11) that we are concerned with possible changes of one function under the condition that the two variables which are most convenient for that function are held constant. For the energy, the enthalpy, the Helmholtz free energy, and the Gibbs free energy the only possible values for the change of the function for a system at equilibrium are either zero or positive. For example, at equilibrium the Gibbs free energy has the lowest possible value consistent with the value of the temperature and pressure of the system.

Equation (14.14) is probably the most useful condition of equilibrium other than Eq. (14.10) or Eq. (14.11) because of the convenience of the temperature and pressure variables.

14.3 CONDITION OF EQUILIBRIUM IN TERMS OF WORK

The change of energy of any closed system is given by the equation

$$dE = T\,dS - P\,dV - dW_{rev}$$

With the use of Eq. (14.7) we see that dW_{rev} at equilibrium can be only zero or less than zero or, mathematically,

$$dW_{rev} \leq 0 \tag{14.15}$$

Thus, while work may be done on the system by the surroundings at constant entropy and volume, a system at equilibrium can do no work on the surroundings. This condition is consistent, of course, with our normal expectation concerning systems at equilibrium.

14.4 PHASE EQUILIBRIA

We have discussed the conditions of equilibrium from a rather general point of view. We can now inquire how these general conditions may be further developed to furnish more useful conditions and how such conditions may be applied to specific types of systems. In this section we discuss conditions of equilibrium in the case that two or more phases are in equilibrium and discuss in the following section the conditions for equilibrium in chemical reactions.

For the simplest case we consider two-phase equilibria of a pure substance. The phases may be solid, liquid, or gas, so that we may have a system which consists of two solid phases, a solid and a liquid phase, a solid and a gas phase, or a liquid and a gas phase. We choose to use Eq. (14.14) to express the condition of equilibrium. The system contains $n°$ moles of component at a specified temperature and pressure and is closed. However, we consider each phase as an open system (a subsystem) because we may transfer material from one phase to another. We know from experience that when the phases are in contact with each other the temperature of each phase must be the same, and also the pressure of each phase must be the same. (This in itself can be proved by using the second law.) In applying Eq. (14.14) we consider only the equality sign for simplicity. Then we know that

$$(dG)_{T,P} = 0 \qquad (14.16)$$

for equilibrium of the entire system. We can apply the equation

$$dG = -S\,dT + V\,dP + \sum_i \mu_i\,dn_i$$

to each phase as an open system so that for each phase

$$dG = \mu\,dn \qquad (14.17)$$

at constant temperature and pressure in the one-component system. The change of the Gibbs free energy for the entire system is the sum of the changes for each phase so that

$$dG = dG' + dG''$$
(14.18)

where the primes are used to designate the phases. The combination of Eqs. (14.16), (14.17), and (14.18) then leads to the condition that

$$\mu' \, dn' + \mu'' \, dn'' = 0$$
(14.19)

The total system is closed so that the number of moles of the component in each phase must add to give the original number of moles in the system, and any decrease in the number of moles of one phase must cause an increase of the number of moles in the other phase. Mathematically we have

$$n° = n' + n'' \quad \text{and} \quad dn' + dn'' = 0$$
(14.20)

When we eliminate dn'' in Eq. (14.19) by the use of Eq. (14.20) we obtain

$$(\mu' - \mu'') \, dn' = 0$$
(14.21)

The differential dn' is independent and can have any value we choose, positive or negative. Therefore we conclude that

$$\mu' = \mu''$$
(14.22)

in order to satisfy Eq. (14.21). Thus we see that the chemical potential of the component must be identical in each of the two phases.

The result expressed by Eq. (14.22) is quite general. We consider a closed system at a given temperature and pressure containing $n_1°, n_2°, n_3°, \ldots$ moles of the components $1, 2, 3, \ldots$. The system may exist in many phases, indicated by primed quantities in the following equations. The differential of the Gibbs free energy of the several phases at constant temperature and pressure may then be written as

$$dG' = \mu_1' \, dn_1' + \mu_2' \, dn_2' + \mu_3' \, dn_3' + \cdots$$
$$dG'' = \mu_1'' \, dn_1'' + \mu_2'' \, dn_2'' + \mu_3'' \, dn_3'' + \cdots$$
$$dG''' = \mu_1''' \, dn_1''' + \mu_2''' \, dn_2''' + \cdots$$
$$\vdots$$
$$\vdots$$
(14.23)

These equations can be combined by use of an equation similar to Eq. (14.18),

$$dG = dG' + dG'' + dG''' + \cdots \tag{14.24}$$

and Eq. (14.16). The result is

$$
\begin{aligned}
\mu_1' \, dn_1' + \mu_1'' \, dn_1'' + \mu_1''' \, dn_1''' + \cdots \\
+ \mu_2' \, dn_2' + \mu_2'' \, dn_2'' + \mu_2''' \, dn_2''' + \cdots \\
+ \mu_3' \, dn_3' + \mu_3'' \, dn_3'' + \mu_3''' \, dn_3''' + \cdots = 0
\end{aligned}
\tag{14.25}
$$

Equation (14.25) is subject to the conditions that

$$
\begin{aligned}
dn_1{}^\circ &= 0 = dn_1' + dn_1'' + dn_1''' + \cdots \\
dn_2{}^\circ &= 0 = dn_2' + dn_2'' + dn_3''' + \cdots \\
dn_3{}^\circ &= 0 = dn_3' + dn_3'' + dn_3''' + \cdots \\
&\ \vdots
\end{aligned}
\tag{14.26}
$$

By the use of these mass balance equations for each component, one dn_1, one dn_2, one dn_3, and so forth may be eliminated in Eq. (14.25). If we eliminate the dn' terms, the result is

$$
\begin{aligned}
(\mu_1'' - \mu_1') \, dn_1'' + (\mu_1''' - \mu_1') \, dn_1''' + \cdots \\
+ (\mu_2'' - \mu_2') \, dn_2'' + (\mu_2''' - \mu_2') \, dn_2''' + \cdots \\
+ (\mu_3'' - \mu_3') \, dn_3'' + (\mu_3''' - \mu_3') \, dn_3''' + \cdots = 0
\end{aligned}
\tag{14.27}
$$

Each remaining dn quantity is independent. Therefore each coefficient of the dn quantities in Eq. (14.27) must be zero. We thus obtain the more general conditions

$$
\begin{aligned}
\mu_1' &= \mu_1'' = \mu_1''' = \cdots \\
\mu_2' &= \mu_2'' = \mu_2''' = \cdots \\
\mu_3' &= \mu_3'' = \mu_3''' = \cdots
\end{aligned}
\tag{14.28}
$$

In words, *at equilibrium the chemical potential of a component must have the same value in each phase in which the component exists.* These conditions are of prime importance for any thermodynamic study of phase equilibria. The use of these conditions is illustrated in Chapter 16.

14.5 CONDITIONS FOR CHEMICAL EQUILIBRIUM

As a first simple case consider the equilibrium represented by the balanced chemical equation

$$N_2(g) + 3H_2(g) = 2NH_3(g)$$

We then define the system as a closed system containing originally $n_{N_2}^\circ$ moles of nitrogen and $n_{H_2}^\circ$ moles of hydrogen at a given temperature and pressure. Here we consider the components of the system to be nitrogen and hydrogen Only one phase will exist in the system. We then write the change of the Gibbs free energy in terms of the species (nitrogen, hydrogen, and ammonia) to give

$$dG = \mu_{N_2}\, dn_{N_2} + \mu_{H_2}\, dn_{H_2} + \mu_{NH_3}\, dn_{NH_3} \tag{14.29}$$

subject to the conditions that $n_{N_2}^\circ$ and $n_{H_2}^\circ$ are constant. The mass balance equations are

$$n_{N_2}^\circ = n_{N_2} + \tfrac{1}{2}n_{NH_3} \tag{14.30}$$

and

$$n_{H_2}^\circ = n_{H_2} + \tfrac{3}{2}n_{NH_3} \tag{14.31}$$

where the ns represent the number of moles of the designated species at equilibrium. Equations (14.30) and (14.31) demand that

$$dn_{N_2} = -\tfrac{1}{2}\, dn_{NH_3} \tag{14.32}$$

and

$$dn_{H_2} = -\tfrac{3}{2}\, dn_{NH_3} \tag{14.33}$$

269

With the elimination of dn_{N_2} and dn_{H_2} in Eq. (14.29) by the use of Eqs. (14.32) and (14.33), Eq. (14.29) becomes

$$dG = (\mu_{NH_3} - \tfrac{1}{2}\mu_{N_2} - \tfrac{3}{2}\mu_{NH_3})\, dn_{NH_3} \tag{14.34}$$

But according to Eq. (14.14), dG must be zero for a system at equilibrium at constant temperature and pressure. In Eq. (14.34), dn_{NH_3} is independent and may have any value we choose to give it. Thus the coefficient must be zero; that is,

$$2\mu_{NH_3} - \mu_{N_2} - 3\mu_{H_2} = 0 \tag{14.35}$$

This equation is the required condition of equilibrium for the ammonia equilibrium.

For a more general case we may write the chemical reaction as

$$\nu_A A + \nu_B B = \nu_M M + \nu_N N \tag{14.36}$$

and for simplicity we assume that this reaction has come to equilibrium in a single-phase system. The νs are the stoichiometric coefficients for the *balanced* equation and A, B, M, and N are substances. Again we define the system to be a closed system at a given temperature and pressure containing $n_A{}^\circ$ moles of A, $n_B{}^\circ$ moles of B, and $n_M{}^\circ$ moles of M. (Three components are required for this system and we arbitrarily have chosen the substances A, B, and M as the components.) At equilibrium we then have the relation, from Eq. (14.14),

$$\mu_A\, dn_A + \mu_B\, dn_B + \mu_M\, dn_M + \mu_N\, dn_N = 0 \tag{14.37}$$

at constant temperature and pressure. The variables n_A, n_B, n_M, and n_N are subject to the condition of constant mass. The mass balance equations are

$$n_A{}^\circ = n_A + \frac{\nu_A}{\nu_N} n_N \tag{14.38}$$

$$n_B{}^\circ = n_B + \frac{\nu_B}{\nu_N} n_N \tag{14.39}$$

$$n_M{}^\circ = n_M + \frac{\nu_M}{\nu_N} n_N \tag{14.40}$$

from which we obtain on differentiation, knowing that $n_A{}^\circ$, $n_B{}^\circ$ and $n_M{}^\circ$ are constant,

$$dn_A = -\frac{v_A}{v_N} dn_N \tag{14.41}$$

$$dn_B = -\frac{v_B}{v_N} dn_N \tag{14.42}$$

$$dn_M = +\frac{v_M}{v_N} dn_N \tag{14.43}$$

Substitution of Eqs, (14.41), (14.42), and (14.43) into (14.37) yields the equation

$$(v_M\mu_M + v_N\mu_N - v_A\mu_A - v_B\mu_B)\, dn_N = 0 \tag{14.44}$$

As before, the coefficient in this equation must be zero because now dn_N is independent. Therefore

$$v_M\mu_M + v_N\mu_N - v_A\mu_A - v_B\mu_B = 0 \tag{14.45}$$

at equilibrium. This is the condition of equilibrium required for the chemical equilibrium given in Eq. (14.36). Note that if Eq. (14.36) is written as

$$v_M M + v_N N - v_A A - v_B B = 0 \tag{14.46}$$

then Eq. (14.45) is of the same form with the chemical potentials of the substances being written in place of the chemical formulas of the substances involved in the reaction.

One comment needs to be made concerning signs. The form of Eq. (14.45), in which the terms for the products of the chemical reaction as given in Eq. (14.36) are given positive signs and those for the reagents are given negative signs, has been adopted by convention. If Eq. (14.36) were written as

$$v_M M + v_N N = v_A A + v_B B$$

then Eq. (14.45) would be written as

$$v_A\mu_A + v_B\mu_B - v_M\mu_M + v_N\mu_N = 0.$$

The development presented here for the condition for chemical equilibrium has been limited to single-phase systems. The general condition of equilibrium represented by Eq. (14.45) is not limited, however, to homogeneous systems. Such a condition of equilibrium is valid for any chemical reaction taking place in any number of phases.

14.6 CONCLUDING COMMENTS

Criteria for thermodynamic equilibrium can be stated for a closed system in terms of the energy, enthalpy, entropy, Gibbs free energy, or Helmholtz free energy. For example, for equilibrium in a closed system at constant energy and volume the entropy has its largest possible value; at constant temperature and pressure the Gibbs free energy has its lowest possible value. When phase equilibria are considered, the criterion for a closed system at constant temperature and pressure is that the chemical potential of a component must be the same in each phase in which the component exists. For chemical equilibria in a closed system at constant temperature and pressure the stoichiometric coefficients of each species in the balanced equation must be taken into account, and for the generalized balanced equation,

$$v_A A + v_B B = v_M M + v_N N$$

the condition for equilibrium is that

$$v_M \mu_M + v_n \mu_M - v_A \mu_A - v_B \mu_B = 0.$$

Chemical equilibria and phase equilibria are discussed in more detail in Chapters 15 and 16.

Exercises

14.1 What is meant by a system's being in (a) thermal equilibrium? (b) chemical equilibrium? (c) mechanical equilibrium? (d) thermodynamic equilibrium?

14.2 Is time a factor in the determination of whether or not a system is in equilibrium? Explain.

14.3 If a system originally at equilibrium is changed to a nonequilibrium state, show that $(dS)_{E,V} \leq 0$. Explain the statement that a closed isolated system in equilibrium at constant energy and volume has the largest possible value of the entropy.

14.4 Consider the case illustrated in Fig. 14.3, in which the two mutually

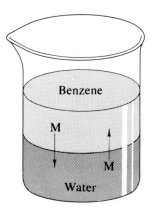

Fig. 14.3.

immiscible solvents, benzene and water, are present. A solute M, is soluble in both benzene and water. Let us add some M, shake the solution, and let it come to equilibrium at constant temperature and pressure. (a) If the concentration of M in the benzene layer is C_B and in water is C_W, what is the relationship between the chemical potential of M in each layer? (b) If $\mu_M = a \ln C_B + b$ and $\mu_M = \alpha \ln C_W + \beta$, where a, b, α and β are constants, what can you state about the ratio C_B/C_W? (c) If additional M is added, what can you state about the ratio C_B/C_W at equilibrium? (d) Will changing the temperature or pressure affect the ratio C_B/C_W?

14.5 What is meant by a "mass balance?" How is this concept applied to chemical equilibria? Make up an example.

14.6 (a) In Eq. (14.29) if dn_{NH_3} is positive, what must be the sign of dn_{N_2}? (b) If dn_{NH_3} is $+2.5 \times 10^{-3}$ moles, what is dn_{N_2} and dn_{H_2}? (c) Justify the statement made in parenthesis between Eq. (14.36) and (14.37) that only three components are required for this system.

14.7 For the gas-phase reaction

$$C_2H_6(g) + 3\tfrac{1}{2}O_2(g) = CO_2(g) + 3H_2O(g)$$

find general relations for $dn_{C_2H_6}$, dn_{O_2}, and dn_{CO_2} in terms of dn_{H_2O}. (b) At equilibrium what is the relation between the chemical potentials of the species in the equation above?

15 Chemical Equilibrium —Electromotive Force of Cells

Many real processes take place under controlled conditions of temperature and pressure. The Gibbs free energy is the most useful thermodynamic function to use in the study of such processes and the changes of state associated with them. In this chapter we study the application of the Gibbs free energy to chemical equilibrium, to the electromotive force of cells, and to the prediction of the direction of chemical reactions.

An important and remarkable success of thermodynamics is the ability to calculate equilibrium constants for an enormous number of chemical reactions using tables of changes of the standard Gibbs free energy of formation. The criterion for chemical equilibrium centered on the Gibbs free energy is related by means of the chemical potential to equilibrium constants for chemical reactions. The application of this condition of equilibrium to chemical reactions is discussed.

The equilibrium constant for a chemical reaction is obtained from the equilibrium condition and gives the relation $\Delta G° = -RT \ln K$ which connects the equilibrium constant K with changes in the standard Gibbs free energy. The problem of establishing tables of data for standard changes in the Gibbs free energy of formation is discussed and such a table is presented. For this development we find it convenient to introduce expressions for the chemical potential of a substance in terms of experimentally observable quantities and from these expressions to introduce again the concept of standard states.

275

The temperature dependence of the equilibrium constant is derived. From knowledge of the change of enthalpy for a reaction, the equilibrium constant at one temperature, and heat capacity data for the reactants and products as a function of temperature, the values of the equilibrium constant at other temperatures may be calculated.

Many chemical reactions involve oxidation and reduction processes wherein there is (usually) a transfer of electrons. In many cases it is possible to carry out such processes in electrochemical cells. The electromotive force of such cells is directly related to the changes of the Gibbs free energy for the change of state which takes place in the cell. A study of these cells is made in the last part of this chapter.

15.1 EXPRESSIONS FOR THE CHEMICAL POTENTIALS

For the purposes of this text we can give only the required expressions for mixtures of ideal gases, for ideal solutions, and for very dilute solutions. These expressions are given without derivation. We know that the chemical potential of a substance in a single phase containing more than one substance is a function of the temperature, pressure, and the composition variables. If we indicate a particular substance by the subscript i, we have

$$\mu_i = \mu_i(T, P, x_1, x_2, \ldots, x_i, \ldots)$$

We consider, then, the chemical potential of a substance in a mixture at a given temperature and pressure and show how its value depends upon the composition variable. However, we do not know the absolute value of the chemical potential and consequently we introduce a standard state for the substance. We can always determine the *difference* between the chemical potential of a substance in some given state and its standard state.

For a substance in an ideal gas mixture, the required expressions are

$$\mu_i(T, P, y) = RT \ln Py_i + \mu_i^\circ(T, 1 \text{ atm, pure}) \tag{15.1}$$

$$\mu_i(T, P, y) = RT \ln P_i + \mu_i^\circ(T, 1 \text{ atm, pure}) \tag{15.2}$$

In these equations we use y to indicate mole fractions in the gas phase rather

276

than x, which is used for liquid phases. The left-hand side of the equation indicates the chemical potential of the ith substance at a given temperature, pressure, and set of mole fractions, which determine the composition of the mixture. The quantity $\mu_i°(T, 1 \text{ atm}, \text{pure})$ represents the chemical potential of the substance in its standard state, which is the pure substance at the same temperature as the mixture and at 1 atm pressure. In the term $RT \ln Py_i$, P is the total pressure and y_i is the mole fraction of the substance. The partial pressure of the ith substance, P_i, is defined as Py_i.

For a substance in an ideal liquid solution, the required expression is

$$\mu_i(T, P, x) = RT \ln x_i + \mu_i°(T, P, \text{pure}) \tag{15.3}$$

In this case the standard state is the pure substance in the liquid phase at the same temperature and pressure as those of the solution. The state of the solution is indicated by the left-hand side of the equation; this state is at a given temperature and pressure of the solution with a set of mole fractions to give the composition of the solution.

For a substance considered as a solute in a very dilute solution in a given solvent, the required expression is

$$\mu_i(T, P, m) = RT \ln m_i + \mu_i° (T, P) \tag{15.4}$$

Here the state of the solution is at a given temperature and pressure and at concentrations of solutes expressed in terms of molalities. The chemical potential of the substance in its standard state is given by the symbol, $\mu_i°(T, P)$, indicating that the standard state is at the same temperature and pressure as those of the solution. For the simple relation given here the composition of the solution for the solute is unit molality. However, in a real case the composition of the standard state is not unit molality. Fortunately a knowledge of the actual composition of the standard state is seldom required. The solutions to which Eq. (15.4) is usually applied are those in which the range of concentration of the solutes is very limited; such solutions are aqueous solutions of gases, salts, and similar constituents.

For pure solids and liquids the standard state is simply the pure state at the given conditions of temperature and pressure, so that

$$\mu_i(T, P, \text{pure}) = \mu_i° (T, P, \text{pure}) \tag{15.5}$$

15.2 CHEMICAL EQUILIBRIA

Let us consider a chemical equilibrium given by the chemical equation

$$v_A A(g) + v_B B(g) = v_M M(g) + v_N N(g) \tag{15.6}$$

where for the present we have assumed that all substances are in the gas phase. For equilibrium, Eq. (14.45),

$$v_M \mu_M + v_N \mu_N - v_A \mu_A - v_B \mu_B = 0 \tag{15.7}$$

When we use Eq. (15.2) for the chemical potentials we obtain the equation

$$v_M RT \ln P_M + v_N RT \ln P_N - v_A RT \ln P_A - v_B RT \ln P_B$$
$$+ v_M \mu_M{}^\circ + v_N \mu_N{}^\circ - v_A \mu_A{}^\circ - v_B \mu_B{}^\circ = 0 \tag{15.8}$$

which may be rewritten as

$$v_M \mu_M{}^\circ + v_N \mu_N{}^\circ - v_A \mu_A{}^\circ - v_B \mu_B{}^\circ = - RT \ln \left[\frac{P_M{}^{v_M} P_N{}^{v_N}}{P_A{}^{v_A} P_B{}^{v_B}} \right] \tag{15.9}$$

Each $\mu_i{}^\circ$ is a function of the temperature alone. Consequently the right-hand side of the equation is a function of the temperature alone, and at a given temperature is a constant. Thus, at constant temperature, we may write

$$\frac{P_M{}^{v_M} P_N{}^{v_N}}{P_A{}^{v_A} P_B{}^{v_B}} = K(T) \tag{15.10}$$

The quantity K is the *equilibrium constant* for the chemical reaction given in Eq. (15.6) and is a function only of the temperature. For a given temperature the quotient of equilibrium pressures given by Eq. (15.10) will be the same no matter what amounts of the different gases are put into the reaction vessel at the start. Here we have followed the usual convention of expressing the partial pressures of the products in the numerator and those of the reagents in the denominator.

Consider now the specific example

$$Fe_2O_3(s) + 3H_2(g) = 2Fe(l) + 3H_2O(g) \qquad (15.11)$$

where we consider $Fe_2O_3(s)$ and $Fe(l)$ to be pure phases and the temperature to be sufficiently high so that the iron is liquid and water is in the vapor state. From the condition of equilibrium we can immediately write

$$2\mu_{Fe}^\circ(l, T, P) + 3\mu_{H_2O}^\circ(g, T, 1 \text{ atm}) - \mu_{Fe_2O_3}^\circ(s, T, P)$$

$$- 3\mu_{H_2}^\circ(g, T, 1 \text{ atm}) = - RT \ln \frac{P_{H_2O}^3}{P_{H_2}^3} = - RT \ln K \quad (15.12)$$

where K is the equilibrium constant and is given by

$$K(T, P) = \frac{P_{H_2O}^3}{P_{H_2}^3} \qquad (15.13)$$

Note that because both $\mu_{Fe_2O_3}^\circ$ and μ_{Fe}° are dependent upon the temperature and pressure the equilibrium constant depends upon the temperature and pressure. As a final example consider the ionization of a weak acid presented by the symbol HA. The chemical reaction may be written as

$$HA(m_{HA}) = H^+(m_{H^+}) + A^-(m_{A^-}) \qquad (15.14)$$

The equilibrium condition, with Eq. (15.4), yields the equation

$$\mu_{H^+}^\circ(T, P) + \mu_{A^-}^\circ(T, P) - \mu_{HA}^\circ(T, P) = - RT \ln \frac{m_{H^+} m_{A^-}}{m_{HA}}$$

$$= - RT \ln K \quad (15.15)$$

We see that the equilibrium constant is a function of the temperature and pressure and not of the composition of the solution.

We can now generalize. For any chemical reaction written as

$$\nu_A A + \nu_B B = \nu_M M + \nu_N N \qquad (15.16)$$

279

we have the equation

$$\nu_M\mu_M^\circ + \nu_N\mu_N^\circ - \nu_A\mu_A^\circ - \nu_B\mu_B^\circ = -RT \ln K \tag{15.17}$$

This expression can be shortened by defining ΔG° as

$$\Delta G^\circ = \nu_M\mu_M^\circ + \nu_N\mu_N^\circ - \nu_A\mu_A^\circ - \nu_B\mu_B^\circ \tag{15.18}$$

so that

$$\Delta G^\circ = -RT \ln K \tag{15.19}$$

In general, ΔG°, and consequently K, is a function of the temperature and the pressure but independent of the composition. For ideal gases ΔG° and K as defined here are functions of the temperature alone.

We can interpret ΔG° on the basis of Eqs. (15.16) and (15.18). We see that this quantity is the difference of the Gibbs free energy of the products and that of the reactants when the products and reactants are in their standard states. Another statement is that ΔG° is the change of free energy for the change of state given by Eq. (15.16) when the products and the reactants are in their standard states. It is this quantity that is related to the equilibrium constant for the reaction by Eq. (15.19).

A clear understanding of the relationship between ΔG° and K for a chemical reaction is exceedingly important. For this discussion, consider the change of state

$$N_2(g, T, P_{N_2}) + 3H_2(g, T, P_{H_2}) = 2NH_3(g, T, P_{NH_3})$$

where P_{N_2}, P_{H_2}, and P_{NH_3} are equilibrium partial pressures. Then ΔG for this change of state is zero. Now ΔG° refers to the change of state

$$N_2(g, T, 1\ atm) + 3H_2(g, T, 1\ atm) = 2NH_3(g, T, 1\ atm)$$

which is not an equilibrium state and ΔG° has a finite value which may be positive or negative. Equation (15.19) relates the two quantities ΔG° and K.

Thus two changes of state are involved in Eq. (15.19), the standard change of state for $\Delta G°$ and the equilibrium change of state for K.

15.3 STANDARD GIBBS FREE ENERGIES OF FORMATION

It is evident from Eq. (15.18) that we could determine $\Delta G°$ and hence K for any chemical reaction if we had knowledge of the values of the chemical potentials of the substances taking part in the reaction in their standard states. Unfortunately this knowledge is not ordinarily available. However, we know that every chemical reaction can be obtained as an algebraic sum of reactions depicting the formation of a compound from the elements (Section 8.8). Then, if we have knowledge of the change of the Gibbs free energy for the formation of a compound from the elements, the compound and the elements being in their standard states, we can obtain $\Delta G°$ as the algebraic sum of the standard Gibbs free energies of formation of the compounds, $\Delta G°_{f,i}$. Thus, for the reaction expressed in Eq. (15.16),

$$\Delta G° = \nu_M \, \Delta G°_{f,M} + \nu_N \, \Delta G°_{f,N} - \nu_A \, \Delta G°_{f,A} - \nu_B \, \Delta G°_{f,B} \qquad (15.20)$$

Equation (15.19) coupled with Eq. (15.20) affords a means of determining the standard free energies of formation. Thus, if the chemical reaction itself is one of formation, such as

$$2H_2 + O_2 = 2H_2O \qquad \text{or} \qquad N_2 + O_2 = 2NO$$

determination of the equilibrium constant for the reactions at a given temperature and pressure gives $\Delta G°$ for the change of state at the same temperature and pressure. This $\Delta G°$ is $\Delta G_f°$ for the substance involved. Then the determination of the equilibrium constants for other reactions yields $\Delta G°$ for the reaction; if all but one of the standard free energies of formation are known, that one may be calculated from Eq. (15.20) if the equilibrium constant is measured.

As has been discussed, the standard free energies of formation are functions of the temperature and pressure, so that a different value is obtained for each temperature and pressure. For purposes of compilation of data a standard temperature of $298.15° \, K$ and a standard pressure of 1 atm has been chosen.

Some representative values of ΔG_f° are given in Table 15.1. The change of ΔG° and $\Delta G_{f,i}^\circ$ with temperature is discussed in the next section. The dependence upon pressure is usually small and will be omitted in this discussion.

The state of aggregation of an element in its standard state is taken as the naturally occurring state at the chosen temperature and pressure. When two states of aggregation are stable at the chosen temperature and pressure,

Table 15.1   Standard Gibbs Free Energy of Formation (kcal mole^{-1}) at 298.15° K[a]

Substance	ΔG°	Substance	ΔG°
$H(g)$	48.575	$H_2S(g)$	−7.892
$H_2(g)$	0.0	$N(g)$	108.870
$O(g)$	54.994	$NO(g)$	20.719
$O_2(g)$	0.0	$NO_2(g)$	12.390
$O_3(g)$	39.06	$NH_3(g)$	−3.976
$OH(g)$	8.93	$NOCl(g)$	15.86
$H_2O(g)$	−54.635	$C(g)$	160.845
$H_2O(l)$	−56.690	$C(s, diamond)$	0.6850
$HF(g)$	−64.7	$C(s, graphite)$	0.0
$Cl(g)$	25.192	$CO(g)$	−32.808
$Cl_2(g)$	0.0	$CO_2(g)$	−94.260
$HCl(g)$	−22.769	$CH_4(g)$	−12.140
$Br(g)$	19.69	$C_2H_2(g)$	50.0
$Br_2(l)$	0.0	$C_2H_4(g)$	16.282
$Br_2(g)$	0.751	$C_2H_6(g)$	−7.860
$S(g)$	43.57	$C_6H_6(g)$	30.989
$S(s, rhombic)$	0.0	$C_6H_6(l)$	41.30
$S(s, monoclinic)$	0.023	$CH_3OH(g)$	−38.70
$SO_2(g)$	−71.79	$CH_3OH(l)$	−39.75
$SO_3(g)$	−88.52	$C_2H_5OH(g)$	−40.30
$Si(g)$	77.41	$C_2H_5OH(l)$	−41.77
$Si(s)$	0.0	$CCl_4(g)$	−15.35
$SiO_2(s, quartz)$	−192.4	$CCl_4(l)$	−16.43
$KCl(s)$	−97.592	$Fe(g)$	85.76
$KClO_3(s)$	−69.290		

[a] From "Selected Values of Chemical Thermodynamic Properties," *Natl. Bur. Standards (U.S.) Cir. 500* (1952), and *Selected Values of Physical and Thermodynamic Properties of Hydrocarbons*, Am. Petrol. Inst. Project 44, 1953.

then one state is chosen as standard by convention. Thus graphite rather than diamond is chosen as the standard state of aggregation for carbon. Of course the standard free energy of formation of an element from itself in the same state of aggregation is zero.

15.4 DEPENDENCE OF $\Delta G°$, $\Delta G°_{f,i}$, AND K UPON THE TEMPERATURE

We have previously shown, Eq. (12.45), that

$$\left(\frac{\partial(G/T)}{\partial T}\right)_P = -\frac{H}{T^2} \tag{15.21}$$

It is important to realize that it is the function G/T that is differentiated. If now we divide Eq. (15.18) by the temperature and then differentiate with respect to T, keeping the pressure of each substance in its standard state constant, we obtain the equation

$$\left(\frac{\partial(\Delta G°/T)}{\partial T}\right)_P = -\nu_M \frac{\tilde{H}_M°}{T^2} - \nu_N \frac{\tilde{H}_N°}{T^2} + \nu_A \frac{\tilde{H}_A°}{T^2} + \nu_B \frac{\tilde{H}_B°}{T^2} \tag{15.22}$$

where each $\tilde{H}_i°$ is the molar enthalpy of the substance in its standard state. We define $\Delta H°$ as

$$\Delta H° = \nu_M \tilde{H}_M° + \nu_N \tilde{H}_N° - \nu_A \tilde{H}_A° - \nu_B \tilde{H}_B° \tag{15.23}$$

where the change of enthalpy for the indicated change of state when the products and the reactants are in their standard states is $\Delta H°$. Equation (15.22) can then be written as

$$\left(\frac{\partial(\Delta G°/T)}{\partial T}\right)_P = -\frac{\Delta H°}{T^2} \tag{15.24}$$

By the same arguments we get

$$\left(\frac{\partial(\Delta G°_{f,i}/T)}{\partial T}\right)_P = -\frac{\Delta H°_{f,i}}{T^2} \tag{15.25}$$

Finally, if we use

$$\ln K = -\frac{\Delta G^{\circ}}{RT} \tag{15.26}$$

we obtain

$$\frac{d \ln K}{dT} = \frac{\Delta H^{\circ}}{RT^2} \tag{15.27}$$

Thus we see that if we determine the value of the equilibrium constant as a function of the temperature, we can calculate ΔH° by Eq. (15.27). Conversely, if we know ΔH° we can determine ΔG° or K at any temperature, provided we know ΔG° or K at one temperature.

The integration of Eq. (15.24) or Eq. (15.27) depends upon whether ΔH° is a constant (independent of the temperature) or a function of the temperature. When ΔH° is a constant the integration is straightforward. However, when ΔH° is a function of the temperature the function must be known before integrating. We note from Eq. (8.71) that

$$\left(\frac{\partial \Delta H^{\circ}}{\partial T}\right)_P = v_{\mathrm{M}}\tilde{C}^{\circ}_{P_{\mathrm{M}}} + v_{\mathrm{N}}\tilde{C}^{\circ}_{P_{\mathrm{N}}} - v_{\mathrm{A}}\tilde{C}^{\circ}_{P_{\mathrm{A}}} - v_{\mathrm{B}}\tilde{C}^{\circ}_{P_{\mathrm{B}}} \tag{15.28}$$

or

$$\left(\frac{\partial \Delta H^{\circ}}{\partial T}\right) = \Delta C_P{}^{\circ} \tag{15.29}$$

where the subscript P means that the pressure of each substance is kept constant. Therefore we need to know the standard state heat capacities at constant pressure of all the substances taking part in the chemical reaction. Integration of $\Delta C_P{}^{\circ}$ by use of an indefinite integral yields the desired function when ΔH° at one temperature is known. The introduction of this function into Eq. (15.24) or Eq. (15.27) allows the integration of these equations to determine ΔG° or K either as a function of the temperature or at a fixed temperature when the value of ΔG° or K is known at some one temperature. It will be noted that $\Delta C_P{}^{\circ}$ and ΔH° can be integrated rather than $\tilde{C}^{\circ}_{P,i}$ or $\Delta \tilde{H}^{\circ}_{f,i}$ separately because the temperature of all substances involved in a chemical reaction must be the same at equilibrium.

One complication enters into these calculations when a change of the state of aggregation occurs with the change of temperature. As an example, let us consider the change of state

$$C_2H_4(g, 700° \text{ K, 1 atm}) + H_2O(g, 700° \text{ K, 1 atm})$$
$$= C_2H_5OH(g, 700° \text{ K, 1 atm}) \quad (15.30)$$

We desire to know $\Delta G°$ for this change of state and K for the equilibrium at 700° K. We may assume that we know $\Delta G°_{f,i}$ for the substances in their standard states at 298° K. In these states both water and ethanol are liquids. Consequently the change of state at 298° K is

$$C_2H_4(g, 298° \text{ K, 1 atm}) + H_2O(l, 298°\text{K, 1 atm})$$
$$= C_2H_5OH(l, 298°\text{K}, 1 \text{ atm}) \quad (15.31)$$

for which

$$\Delta G° = \Delta G°_{f,C_2H_5OH} - \Delta G°_{f,C_2H_4} - \Delta G°_{f,H_2O}$$

where $\Delta G_f°$ of each substance are for the states indicated. Now we know that the chemical potentials of a pure substance in the gas and liquid phases are equal at equilibrium and that the standard state of the gas and liquid phases are both at 1 atm. Therefore, at the normal boiling points of ethanol and of water, we have $\tilde{G}°(l) = \tilde{G}°(g)$. The boiling point of ethanol at 1 atm pressure is 351.4° K. We can now perform the following series of calculations. We start with the change of state given by Eq. (15.30) and by integration of Eq. (15.24) between the limits of 298° and 351° we can obtain $\Delta G°$ at 351° for the change of state

$$C_2H_4(g, 351°\text{K, 1 atm}) + H_2O(l, 351° \text{ K, 1 atm})$$
$$= C_2H_5OH(l, 351°\text{K}, 1 \text{ atm}) \quad (15.32)$$

The values of $\Delta H°$ and $\Delta C_P°$ used in this integration would be determined for both liquid water and liquid ethanol. At 351.4° K we have the change of state

$$C_2H_5OH(l, 351° \text{ K, 1 atm}) = C_2H_5OH(g, 351° \text{ K, 1 atm})$$

285

for which $\Delta G°$ is zero, and $\Delta G°$ for the change of state

$$C_2H_5(g, 351° K, 1 \text{ atm}) + H_2O(l, 351° K, 1 \text{ atm})$$
$$= C_2H_5OH(g, 351° K, 1 \text{ atm}) \quad (15.33)$$

is the same as that for Eq. (15.32). But $\Delta H°$ for Eq. (15.33) differs from that of Eq. (15.32) by the molar change of enthalpy on evaporating ethanol at its boiling point. We now integrate Eq. (15.24) between 351.4° K and 373.15° K with $\Delta H°$ and $\Delta C_p°$ based on values of ethanol vapor. The calculations for $\Delta H°$ are the same as those discussed for enthalpy changes with temperature. With this calculation we have the value of $\Delta G°$ at 373.15° K for the change of state

$$C_2H_4(g, 373° K, 1 \text{ atm}) + H_2O(l, 373° K, 1 \text{ atm})$$
$$= C_2H_5OH(g, 373° K, 1 \text{ atm}) \quad (15.34)$$

By the arguments used for ethanol we determine that $\Delta G°$ for the change of state

$$C_2H_4(g, 373° K, 1 \text{ atm}) + H_2O(g, 373° K, 1 \text{ atm})$$
$$= C_2H_5OH(g, 373° K, 1 \text{ atm}) \quad (15.35)$$

is the same as that for Eq. (15.34). But, just as for ethanol, $\Delta H°$ for Eq. (15.35) differs from that of Eq. (15.34) by the molar change of enthalpy for the evaporation of water at 373° K. Finally we integrate Eq. (15.24) from 373° K to 700° K, taking care again to use the correct function for $\Delta H°$ and $\Delta C_p°$ based on water vapor as well as ethanol vapor.

15.5 CHANGE OF GIBBS FREE ENERGY FOR SYSTEMS NOT AT EQUILIBRIUM

From the discussion on equilibrium we know that the Gibbs free energy of a system at equilibrium must have the lowest possible value at a given temperature and pressure. Therefore, if we have a system at constant temperature and pressure which is not at equilibrium, the change of the Gibbs free energy must be negative as the system moves toward equilibrium at constant temperature and pressure. This condition is used to determine the spontaneity of a chemical reaction.

Let us consider the change of state

$$v_A A(g, T, P_A) + v_B B(g, T, P_B) = v_M M(g, T, P_M) + v_N N(g, T, P_N)$$

where, for simplicity, all the substances have been chosen to be gases. The quantities P_A, P_B, P_M, and P_N are the pressures, chosen arbitrarily, of the species in the system. Now, if the system is not at equilibrium under these conditions, then either A or B would react together to form M and N and the corresponding change of the Gibbs free energy would be negative, or M and N will react to form A and B, and the change of the Gibbs free energy (for the reaction as written) would be positive. The problem is to express ΔG for the change of state in terms of the arbitrary conditions which have been chosen.

The change of the Gibbs free energy for this change of state is given by the equation

$$\Delta G = v_M \mu_M + v_N \mu_N - v_A \mu_A - v_B \mu_B \tag{15.36}$$

Substitution of Eq. (15.2) for each μ_i yields the equation

$$\Delta G = v_M RT \ln P_M + v_N RT \ln P_N - v_A RT \ln P_A - v_B RT \ln P_B$$
$$+ v_M \mu_M{}^\circ + v_N \mu_N{}^\circ - v_A \mu_A{}^\circ - v_B \mu_B{}^\circ \tag{15.37}$$

We can rearrange this equation to give two alternative forms:

$$\Delta G = RT \ln \frac{P_M{}^{v_M} P_N{}^{v_N}}{P_A{}^{v_M} P_B{}^{v_B}} + \Delta G^\circ \tag{15.38}$$

or

$$\Delta G = RT \ln \frac{P_M{}^{v_M} P_N{}^{v_N}}{P_A{}^{v_A} P_B{}^{v_B}} - RT \ln K \tag{15.39}$$

In these last two equations ΔG is the change of free energy for the change of state taking place under the *arbitrary* conditions which have been chosen;

the partial pressures P_A, P_B, P_M, and P_N are these arbitrarily chosen conditions; $\Delta G°$ is the change of free energy for the similar change of state taking place under *standard* conditions; and K is the equilibrium constant for the chemical reaction. (Note in Eq. (15.9) that the partial pressures there are equilibrium partial pressures).

The use of Eqs. (15.3) or (15.4) would yield similar equations in which the mole fractions or molalities are used instead of the partial pressures. Therefore we may generalize Eqs. (15.38) and (15.39) to

$$\Delta G = RT \ln Q + \Delta G° \tag{15.40}$$

or

$$\Delta G = RT \ln Q - RT \ln K \tag{15.41}$$

Here Q is used to represent the quotient of pressures in which the arbitrary conditions are used. In form it is exactly the same as the equilibrium constant.

For the determination of whether a reaction will proceed it is then necessary to determine ΔG for the arbitrarily chosen conditions by using Eq. (15.40) or Eq. (15.41). The change of state will proceed if this value of ΔG is negative; the reverse change will proceed if it is positive. The entire system, of course, is closed. If the reaction can take place both at constant pressure and constant temperature, then

$$dG = -dW'_{rev} \tag{15.42}$$

or

$$\Delta G = -W'_{rev} \tag{15.43}$$

Therefore the value of ΔG will give the value of the reversible work, other than the work of expansion or compression, which the system may do on the surroundings (for example, in the form of electrical work).

15.6 ELECTROCHEMICAL CELLS

In a closed system the differential of the Gibbs free energy is

$$dG = V \, dP - S \, dT - dW_{rev} \tag{15.44}$$

Electrical work (see Chapter 6) is given by the following relation

$$\text{Electrical work} = \int \mathcal{E}\, dc \qquad (15.45)$$

where $\mathcal{E}$ is the emf of the electrochemical cell and dc is the differential of the charge. If $\mathcal{E}$ is expressed in volts and c in coulombs, the work is in joules.

For an electrochemical cell with a reversible passage of n moles of charge (where n is the number of electrons transferred per molecule of substance) through the cell at constant temperature and pressure,

$$\Delta G_{cell} = -W_{rev} = \int_{c=0}^{c=n\mathcal{F}} \mathcal{E}_{cell}\, dc \qquad (15.46)$$

where $\mathcal{F}$ is the Faraday, which is almost exactly 96,500 coulombs mole^{-1} of electrons. If the states of all the substances participating in the cell reaction are constant, the emf of the cell is also constant and

$$\Delta G_{cell} = -n\mathcal{F}\mathcal{E} \qquad (15.47)$$

If the cell reaction is one in which the products and reactants are in their respective standard states, then $\mathcal{E}$ becomes $\mathcal{E}^\circ$ and

$$\Delta G^\circ_{cell} = -n\mathcal{F}\mathcal{E}^\circ = -RT \ln K \qquad (15.48)$$

or

$$\mathcal{E}^\circ = \frac{RT}{n\mathcal{F}} \ln K \qquad (15.49)$$

Equation (15.48) thus permits the calculation of equilibrium constants, by measuring the emfs of cells, or the calculation of cell emfs from equilibrium constants. The first is the more usual application.

By appropriately combining Eqs. (15.40), (15.47), and (15.49) we obtain

$$\mathcal{E} = \mathcal{E}^\circ - \frac{RT}{n\mathcal{F}} \ln Q \qquad (15.50)$$

for the emf $\mathcal{E}$ of a cell where the arbitrary conditions applying to Q pertain. Equation (15.50) is known as the Nernst equation.

By measuring the emf as a function of temperature, it also becomes possible to determine changes in the enthalpy and entropy by recalling that, from Eqs. (12.24) and (15.24),

$$\left(\frac{\partial \Delta G^\circ}{\partial T}\right)_P = \Delta S^\circ \quad \text{and} \quad \left(\frac{\partial (\Delta G^\circ / T)}{\partial T}\right)_P = -\frac{\Delta H^\circ}{T^2} \tag{15.51}$$

Applying these relations gives

$$\Delta S^\circ = n\mathscr{F}\left(\frac{\partial \mathcal{E}^\circ}{\partial T}\right)_P \tag{15.52}$$

and

$$\Delta H^\circ = n\mathscr{F}\left[T\left(\frac{\partial \mathcal{E}^\circ}{\partial T}\right)_P - \mathcal{E}^\circ\right] \tag{15.53}$$

15.7 AN EXAMPLE OF AN ELECTROCHEMICAL CELL

To illustrate the use of the equations developed in the preceding section we discuss one simple cell. The cell as shown in Fig. 15.1, consists of a hydrogen electrode and a silver-silver chloride electrode. The electrolyte is an aqueous solution of hydrochloric acid at a given molality. The hydrogen electrode consists of a piece of platinum foil over which is passed hydrogen gas at a given pressure. The silver-silver chloride electrode consists of a piece of silver wire on which some silver chloride has been deposited. Such a cell may be depicted either as

$$\text{Pt(s), } H_2(g, P_{H_2}) \,|\, HCl(m_{HCl}) \,|\, AgCl(s), \text{ Ag(s)} \tag{15.54}$$

or

$$\text{Ag(s), AgCl(s)} \,|\, HCl(m_{HCl}) \,|\, H_2(g, P_{H_2}), \text{ Pt(s)} \tag{15.55}$$

In either case the electrode on the left is taken to be the anode, the electrode

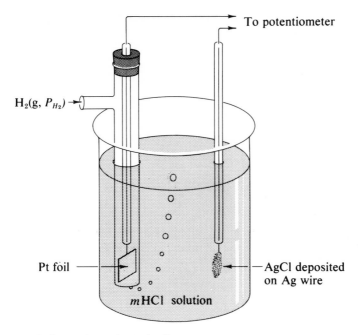

Fig. 15.1. An electrochemical cell.

at which oxidation takes place; and the electrode on the right is taken to be the cathode, the electrode at which reduction takes place.† The sign of the electromotive force of the cell in Eq. (15.55) is opposite to that of the cell in Eq. (15.54). In practice, the reaction for which the emf is positive will be the one which actually takes place in the cell.

In Eq. (15.54), the oxidation reaction taking place at the anode is

$$H_2(g, P_{H_2}) = 2H^+(m_{H^+}) + 2e^- \tag{15.56}$$

when two Faradays of electricity are passed through the cell. The correspond-

---

† Depending on the mode of presentation this convention is variously represented as: (1) electrons move from the left-hand electrode to the right-hand electrode through the external circuit; (2) positive electricity (conventional current flow) moves from the left-hand electrode to the right-hand electrode through the cell; and (3) electrons move from the right-hand electrode to the left-hand electrode through the cell.

ing reduction reaction taking place at the cathode is

$$2AgCl(s) + 2e^- = 2Ag(s) + 2Cl^-(m_{Cl^-}) \tag{15.57}$$

The net cell reaction is the sum of Eqs. (15.56) and (15.57) and is

$$H_2(g, P_{H_2}) + 2AgCl(s) = 2Ag(s) + 2H^+(m_{H^+}) + 2Cl^-(m_{Cl^-}) \tag{15.58}$$

The emf of the cell is then given by, Eq. (15.50),

$$\mathscr{E} = \mathscr{E}^\circ - \frac{RT}{2\mathscr{F}} \ln \frac{m_{H^+} m_{Cl^-}}{P_{H_2}} \tag{15.59}$$

Quantities referring to silver and silver chloride do not appear in Eq. (15.59) because these substances are in their standard states in the cell. For this cell, $\mathscr{E}^\circ$ equals 0.222 V at 298° K. The equation for the cell depicted in Eq. (15.55) is

$$\mathscr{E} = \mathscr{E}^\circ - \frac{RT}{2\mathscr{F}} \ln \frac{P_{H_2}}{m_{H^+} m_{Cl^-}} \tag{15.60}$$

and $\mathscr{E}^\circ$ for this cell is -0.222 V at 298° K.

For a reversible cell reaction (the only type we can discuss here) the emf of the cell can be measured by using a potentiometer which is a device for measuring the emf by balancing a precisely known emf against the cell emf. In this procedure no current is drawn from the cell and the direction of the cell reaction can (in principle) be reversed by changing the opposing voltage an infinitesimal amount.

If the emf of the cell as written is positive, then the cell reaction is spontaneous and proceeds as written. If the emf is negative, then the reaction proceeds spontaneously in the reverse direction. This, of course, follows from Eq. (15.47).

15.8   THE STANDARD ELECTROMOTIVE FORCE OF HALF-CELLS—OXIDATION POTENTIALS

Equations (15.56) and (15.57) indicated that the net cell reaction can be considered as the sum of two half-cell reactions. We can, then, consider the electromotive force of the cell as the *sum* of two electrode potentials, one associated with the anode and the other associated with the cathode. For the standard emf of the cell we write

$$\mathscr{E}^\circ_{cell} = \mathscr{E}^\circ_{anode} + \mathscr{E}^\circ_{cathode} \tag{15.61}$$

The individual electrode potentials cannot be determined experimentally; it is only $\mathscr{E}^\circ_{cell}$ that is obtained from experiment. However, for the purpose of the compilation of data we can obtain a consistent set of electrode potentials by assigning an arbitrary potential to *one* electrode reaction. By convention the standard electrode potential for the hydrogen half-cell, called the standard emf of the hydrogen half-cell, is given the value zero at all temperatures.

Thus, for the cell depicted in (15.54), $\mathscr{E}^\circ$ is $+0.222$ V and consequently $\mathscr{E}^\circ_{cathode}$ is $+0.222$ V at 298° K for the half-cell

$$Cl^- \,|\, AgCl(s), Ag(s)$$

For the cell depicted in (15.55), $\mathscr{E}^\circ$ is -0.222 V at 298° K and $\mathscr{E}^\circ_{anode}$ is -0.222 V at 298° K for the half-cell

$$Ag(s), AgCl(s) \,|\, Cl^-$$

Note that the values for the oxidation reaction and for the corresponding reduction reaction differ only in sign.

Two tables of values of the standard emf of half-cells can thus be developed, one for oxidation reactions and one for reduction reactions. The two tables would differ only in sign. We choose to give the table only for oxidation reactions. Table 15.2 lists the standard emf of various half-cells for oxidation reactions, called standard oxidation potentials, at 298° K.

With the use of oxidation potentials Eq. (15.61) would have to be changed to

$$\mathscr{E}^\circ_{cell} = \mathscr{E}^\circ_{anode} - \mathscr{E}^\circ_{cathode} \tag{15.62}$$

where *now the $\mathscr{E}^\circ$ refer only to oxidation reactions*. Thus, for the cell

$$Ag(s), AgCl(s) \,|\, NaCl(m_{NaCl}) \,|\, Cl_2(g)$$

293

Table 15.2 Standard Oxidation Potentials at 298° K[a]

Half-Cell Reaction	$\mathcal{E}°$(volts)
$K(s) = K^+ + e^-$	2.925
$Na(s) = Na^+ + e^-$	2.714
$Zn(s) = Zn^{++} + 2e^-$	0.763
$Fe(s) = Fe^{++} + 2e^-$	0.440
$Pb(s) + SO_4^= = PbSO_4(s) + 2e^-$	0.356
$Pb(s) = Pb^{++} + 2e^-$	0.126
$H_2(g) = 2H^+ + 2e^-$	0.000
$Ag(s) + Cl^- = AgCl(s) + e^-$	-0.222
$2Hg(l) + 2Cl^- = Hg_2Cl_2(s) + 2e^-$	-0.268
$Cu(s) = Cu^{++} + 2e^-$	-0.337
$2I^- = I_2(s) + 2e^-$	-0.536
$Fe^{++} = Fe^{3+} + e^-$	-0.771
$2Hg(l) = Hg_2^{++} + 2e^-$	-0.789
$Ag(s) = Ag^+ + e^-$	-0.799
$2Cl^- = Cl_2(g) + 2e^-$	-1.360
$PbSO_4(s) + 2H_2O(l) = PbO_2(s) + SO_4^= + 4H^+ + 2e^-$	-1.685

[a] W. M. Latimer, *Oxidation Potentials*, 2d ed.. Englewood Cliffs, N. J.: Prentice-Hall, 1952.

the two electrode reactions are

$$Ag(s) + Cl^- = AgCl(s) + e^-$$

and

$$\tfrac{1}{2}Cl_2(g) + e^- = Cl^-$$

so that the cell reaction is

$$Ag(s) + \tfrac{1}{2}Cl_2(g) = AgCl(s)$$

and

$$\mathcal{E}°_{cell} = \mathcal{E}°_{anode} - \mathcal{E}°_{cathode} = -0.799 - (-1.360) = +0.561 \text{ V}$$

For cells in which a common electrolyte is not possible the two half-cells are separated by a salt bridge which keeps the solutions from mixing while providing an electrical path.† An example is the cell

$$Zn(s) \,|\, ZnCl_2(m_{ZnCl_2}) \,\|\, AgNO_3(m_{AgNO_3}) \,|\, Ag(s) \qquad (15.63)$$

Here the double vertical line indicates that the two half-cells are separated by a salt bridge. The $\mathscr{E}^\circ$ of this cell is $+0.763 - (-0.799)$, or $+1.562$ V.

15.9 CONCLUDING COMMENTS

The relationship between changes in the standard Gibbs free energy and the equilibrium constant is $\Delta G^\circ = -RT \ln K$. This equation permits the calculation of a very large number of equilibrium constants from tables of thermochemical data and standard free energies of formation. Equations have been developed in this chapter to calculate the temperature dependence of equilibrium constants. In order to do this it is necessary to know the standard enthalpy change for the reaction and the heat capacities of reactants and products as a function of temperature.

Electrochemical cells have been discussed and the interrelationships among emf, the thermodynamic equilibrium constant, and the Gibbs free energy have been developed. It is noteworthy that it is possible to determine equilibrium constants and changes in the Gibbs free energy from emf measurements, and that the temperature dependence of emf measurements yields information from which enthalpy and entropy changes may be evaluated.

Exercises

15.1 Assume that for some given reaction you have the following information: $\Delta G^\circ_{298^\circ}$, $\Delta H^\circ_{298^\circ}$, and $\Delta C_p{}^\circ = a + bT + cT^2$ where a, b, and c are constants. Find expressions for (a) ΔH° as a function of the temperature; (b) ΔG° as a function of the temperature; (c) K as a function of the temperature; (d) $\ln K$ as a function of the temperature; and (e) ΔS° as a function of the temperature.

† Complications such as liquid junction potentials will be ignored in this book. Many of the references cited at the end of Chapter 1 cover the subject of electrochemical cells more fully. The reader is also referred to J. O'M. Bockris, *Modern Aspects of Electrochemistry*. New York: Academic, 1954.

15.2 Calculate the equilibrium pressure of oxygen at $298° K$ for the reaction

$$KClO_3(s) = KCl(s) + \tfrac{3}{2}O_2(g)$$

15.3 Determine whether any appreciable amount of ammonia would be present at equilibrium at $298° K$ in a mixture of N_2 and H_2.

15.4 (a) Calculate ΔG for the change of state at $298° K$

$$Cl_2(g, 1 \text{ atm}) = Cl_2(g, 7 \text{ atm})$$

assuming that the gas is ideal.

(b) The vapor pressure of $Cl_2(l)$ at $298° K$ is 7 atm. What is the standard free energy of formation of $Cl_2(l)$? Neglect the change of the free energy of liquid chlorine with pressure.

15.5 Calculate the standard free energy of formation of $SO_3(g)$ from the following data and the standard free energy of formation of $SO_2(g)$ at $298° K$. The equilibrium constants for the reaction

$$SO_2(g) + \tfrac{1}{2}O_2(g) = SO_3(g)$$

are $31.3 \text{ atm}^{-1/2}$ at $800° K$ and $6.56 \text{ atm}^{-1/2}$ at $900° K$.

15.6 Using the standard free energy of formation at $298° K$, calculate the thermodynamic equilibrium constant for the dissociation of the following substances into their elements at $298° K$: (a) $HCl(g)$, (b) $Br_2(g)$, (c) $H_2S(g)$, (d) $NO(g)$. (The dissociation reaction for HCl would be $HCl(g) = \tfrac{1}{2}H_2(g) + \tfrac{1}{2}Cl_2(g)$).

15.7 At a total pressure of 1 atm and at $457° K$, NO_2 is 5 percent decomposed according to the equation

$$2NO_2(g) = 2NO(g) + O_2(g)$$

Calculate $\Delta G°$ and K_P (the thermodynamic equilibrium constant in terms of the partial pressures of the reactants and products) for the equilibrium.

15.8 For each of the following reactions at $298° K$, calculate $\Delta G°$ and K_P.

(a) $CO(g) + H_2O(g) = CO_2(g) + H_2(g)$.

(b) $3C_2H_2(g) = C_6H_6(g)$.

(c) $3C_2H_2(g) = C_6H_6(l)$.

(d) $C_2H_2(g) + H_2(g) = C_2H_4(g)$.

(e) $C_2H_2(g) + 2H_2(g) = C_2H_6(g)$.

(f) $C_6H_6(l) = C_6H_6(g)$.

(g) $2NO(g) + Cl_2(g) = 2NOCl(g)$.

15.9 Calculate the change in the standard Gibbs free energy at $298°$ K for the following reactions:

(a) $H_2O(g) = 2H(g) + O(g)$.

(b) $H_2O(g) = H_2(g) + O(g)$.

(c) $NO_2(g) = N(g) + 2O(g)$.

(d) $NO_2(g) = N(g) + O_2(g)$.

(e) $CH_4(g) = C(s, \text{graphite}) + 4H(g)$.

(f) $SiO_2(s, \text{quartz}) = Si(s) + 2O(g)$.

15.10 For the reaction $2H_2(g) + S_2(g) = 2H_2S(g)$

$$\Delta G° = 38,810 + 1\,5.41T \log T - 2.07 \times 10^{-3} T^2 - 25.02T$$

Deduce expressions for $\ln K_P$, $\Delta H°$, $\Delta S°$ and ΔC_P for this reaction as a function of temperature.

15.11 (a) What can you state from the fact that $\Delta G°$ for a given reaction is negative? positive? zero? (b) What can you state from the fact that ΔG for a given reaction is negative? positive? zero? (c) What are the standard states used for defining standard Gibbs free energy changes?

15.12 (a) Derive Eq. (15.19).
(b) In this equation what are the units of $\Delta G°$, R, T, and K?
(c) Can a log term have dimensions? Explain.

15.13 The temperature dependence at $298°$ K of $\mathscr{E}°$ for a cell is 0.0018 V deg^{-1}. $\mathscr{E}°$ for the cell at $298°$ K is -1.44 V. Calculate $\Delta G°$, K, $\Delta S°$, and $\Delta H°$ for this cell at $298°$ K on the basis of 2 faradays.

15.14 Assuming that the reactions indicated in Exercise 15.9 could be realized in a chemical cell, calculate the $\mathscr{E}°$ at 298° K for each of these reactions.

15.15 Show that $(RT/\mathscr{F}) \ln Q = 0.059 \log Q$ at 298° K.

15.16 What is the emf of a cell at 298° K composed of a zinc electrode and a standard hydrogen electrode if the Zn^{++} concentration in solution is $1.0\,m$? $0.5\,m$? $0.1\,m$?

15.17 Consider the following cell

$$Zn\,|\,Zn^{++}(0.5\ m)\,\|\,Ag^{+}(0.5\ m)\,|\,Ag$$

(a) Write balanced equations for each half-cell reaction and for the cell reaction.

(b) Write an equation expressing the emf as a function of $\mathscr{E}°$ and concentration for each half-cell.

(c) Combine the equations in (b) to obtain an expression for the emf of the cell as a function of the Zn^{++} and Ag^{+} concentrations.

(d) What is the emf of the cell at 298° K?

(e) What is the equilibrium constant for this reaction?

(f) Does the reaction proceed spontaneously as written?

15.18 Carry out the same steps as in Exercise 15.17 for the following cells:

(a) $Ag\,|\,Ag^{+}\,(0.1\ m)\,\|\,Fe^{++}\,(0.5\ m)\,|\,Fe.$

(b) $Cu\,|\,Cu^{++}\,(0.7\ m)\,\|\,Zn^{++}(0.9\ m)\,|\,Zn.$

(c) $Pt,\ H_2\,(1\ atm)|H^{+}(1\ m)\,\|\,Cl^{-}(0.5\ m)\,|\,AgCl(s),\ Ag(s).$

15.19 Calculate $\Delta G_f°$ for $Hg_2Cl_2(s)$ at 298° K from values given in Table 15.2.

15.20 The lead storage battery may be depicted as

$$Pb(s),\ PbSO_4(s)\,|\,SO_4^{--}(m_{SO_4--})\,|\,PbSO_4(s),\ PbO_2(s),\ Pb$$

The overall cell reaction is

$$Pb(s) + PbO_2(s) + 4H^{+}(m_{H+}) + 2SO_4^{--}\ (m_{SO_4--})$$
$$= 2PbSO_4(s) + 2H_2O$$

(a) Write equations for the reactions taking place in each half-cell.

(b) What is the $\mathscr{E}°$ value for the cell at $298°\,K$?

(c) Using the information in Table 15.2, calculate the emf of this cell at $298°\,K$ when $m_{H^+} = 2m_{SO_4^{--}} = 2\,m$.

(d) When the lead storage battery is charged the current flow is reversed by impressing an outside emf on the cell. What happens to the hydrogen ion concentration during the charging process? during the discharging process?

15.21 For an exothermic reaction ΔH is negative. Does the equilibrium constant increase or decrease for an exothermic reaction? Explain.

16 The Gibbs Phase Rule—Phase Equilibria

There are many vantage points from which to investigate natural phenomena and many different ways to organize, systematize, and subdivide these phenomena. One way of subdividing matter is to talk about states of aggregation, and these fall basically into the two categories of fluid and solid. The fluid state is divided into the liquid and gaseous states, where the liquid state is taken to be the denser state, and the term *vapor* applies to the gaseous state below the critical temperature.

These states of aggregation are called phases, and a phase may be defined as any region of matter whose properties are either constant throughout the region or continuously varying. Phases are separated by physical boundaries across which some properties are discontinuous. Portions of matter which may be separated in space but which have identical properties are considered as one phase, such as a collection of salt crystals. A mixture of liquid water and ice consists of two phases whether the ice is present as one chunk or many pieces. Density and concentration gradients exist in a single phase where the phase is sufficiently extended in a gravitational or centrifugal field. For the purpose of this text only phases of uniform density and concentration will be considered. We also restrict our discussion to particles which are sufficiently large so that surface effects are negligible. In this chapter, then, we are concerned with describing the characteristics of phases in equilibrium for simple systems.

The third law of thermodynamics is discussed at the end of the chapter.

16.1 THE CLAPEYRON EQUATION

We consider as illustrative only one-component two-phase systems. In this case we are concerned with the equilibrium between two solid phases, solid and liquid, solid and gas, or liquid and gas. For a pure phase the chemical potential is a function of the temperature and pressure. Consequently we are interested in the relation between the temperature and pressure along the transition curve, the melting curve, the sublimation curve, and the vapor pressure curve.

From the condition of equilibrium, we know that the chemical potential of the component in one phase (double prime) must be equal to that in the other phase (prime phase). Now if we change the system by a change of temperature or a change in pressure but still maintain equilibrium, the chemical potential in the two phases must remain equal. Consequently the differential change of the chemical potential in the two phases must be equal and

$$d\mu'' = d\mu' \tag{16.1}$$

We take the chemical potential of a pure substance to be a function of the temperature and pressure which gives

$$d\mu = \left(\frac{\partial \mu}{\partial T}\right)_P dT + \left(\frac{\partial \mu}{\partial P}\right)_T dP \tag{16.2}$$

For a pure substance

$$G = n\mu$$

from which we obtain

$$\left(\frac{\partial \mu}{\partial T}\right)_P = -\tilde{S} \tag{16.3}$$

and

$$\left(\frac{\partial \mu}{\partial P}\right)_T = \tilde{V} \tag{16.4}$$

where $\tilde{S}$ and $\tilde{V}$ are the molar entropy and volume of the substance, respectively. Combination of Eqs. (16.1), (16.2), (16.3), and (16.4) yields the relation

$$- \tilde{S}'' \, dT + \tilde{V}'' \, dP = - \tilde{S}' \, dT + \tilde{V}' \, dP \tag{16.5}$$

which on rearrangement gives

$$\frac{dP}{dT} = \frac{\tilde{S}'' - \tilde{S}'}{\tilde{V}'' - \tilde{V}''} \tag{16.6}$$

This equation is known as the Clapeyron equation. We observe from this equation that for the one-component two-phase system, the pressure is a function of the temperature or, conversely, the temperature is a function of the pressure. Thus the vapor pressure of a liquid or the sublimation pressure of a solid depends only on the temperature. Similarly, the melting point of a solid depends only on the pressure. In Eq. (16.6), the quantity $\tilde{S}'' - \tilde{S}'$ is the difference in the molar entropy of the substance in the two phases when the two phases are in equilibrium with each other at the stated temperature or pressure. Similarly, $\tilde{V}'' - \tilde{V}'$ is the difference in the molar volume of the substance in the two phases at equilibrium.

Equation (16.6) may be written in a slightly different form. We have already determined that $T(\tilde{S}'' - \tilde{S}') = \tilde{H}'' - \tilde{H}'$ for a change of state of aggregation under equilibrium conditions. This change takes place reversibly at constant temperature and pressure. Consequently Eq. (16.6) may be written as

$$\frac{dP}{dT} = \frac{\tilde{H}'' - \tilde{H}'}{T(\tilde{V}'' - \tilde{V}')} = \frac{\Delta \tilde{H}}{T \, \Delta \tilde{V}} \tag{16.7}$$

The integration of Eq. (16.6) or Eq. (16.7) introduces certain problems. In general, each entropy, enthalpy, and volume is a function of the temperature and pressure. We could determine this dependence from heat capacities and equations of state for the entropy and enthalpy, and from equations of state alone for the volume, but no adequate algebraic equations of state are available for the solid and liquid phases. Moreover, the variables do not separate in general and the integration of the equations is usually not possible. Of course we can consider the equations to be a relation among three quantities ΔS or ΔH, ΔV, and dP/dT. A knowledge of any two at a point of equilibrium permits the calculation of the third.

16.2 THE CLAUSIUS-CLAPEYRON EQUATION

When the use of Eq. (16.6) or Eq. (16.7) is limited to an equilibrium between a liquid phase and a gas phase not too close to the critical point or to an equilibrium between a solid phase and a gas phase, the equation may be simplified by appropriate assumptions and the integration can be readily performed. The molar volume of a gas is very large with respect to the molar volume of a solid or that of a liquid (when the temperature is far removed from the critical temperature). Then the difference in the volumes may be approximated by the molar volume of the gas:

$$\tilde{V}(g) - \tilde{V}(s) \cong \tilde{V}(g)$$

or

$$\tilde{V}(g) - \tilde{V}(l) \cong \tilde{V}(g)$$

The second assumption requires the pressure to be sufficiently small so that the ideal gas equation may be used to express the molar volume of the gas as a function of the temperature and pressure. With the use of these two assumptions or approximations Eq. (16.6) may be written as

$$\frac{d \ln P}{dT} = \frac{\Delta \tilde{S}}{RT} \tag{16.8}$$

and Eq. (16.7) as

$$\frac{d \ln P}{dT} = \frac{\Delta \tilde{H}}{RT^2} \tag{16.9}$$

Equation (16.9) is the one used most often and is called the Clausius-Clapeyron equation.

The quantity $\Delta \tilde{H}$ is either $\tilde{H}(g) - \tilde{H}(s)$ or $\tilde{H}(g) - \tilde{H}(l)$. We know that the enthalpy of an ideal gas is not a function of the pressure. For a real gas, liquid, or solid the enthalpy is only a slowly varying function of the pressure. Therefore we assume that the dependence of $\Delta \tilde{H}$ on the pressure is negligible unless the range of integration is large. Then $\Delta \tilde{H}$ is a function of the temperature alone and Eq. (16.9) may be integrated.

Two cases may be singled out for the integration of Eq. (16.9): (1) $\Delta\tilde{H}$ is constant or (2) $\Delta\tilde{H}$ is a function of the temperature. When $\Delta\tilde{H}$ is a constant or approximately a constant over the temperature range of integration, the integrated form of Eq. (16.9) is

$$\ln\frac{P_2}{P_1} = \frac{\Delta\tilde{H}}{R}\left(\frac{T_2 - T_1}{T_1 T_2}\right) \tag{16.10}$$

where P_2, T_2, and P_1, T_1 are the limits of integration. For the second case, $\Delta\tilde{H}$ must be known as a function of the temperature. We know that

$$\Delta\tilde{H} = \tilde{H}'' - \tilde{H}'$$

and that

$$\left(\frac{\partial H}{\partial T}\right)_P = C_P$$

so that

$$\frac{d\,\Delta H}{dT} = \tilde{C}_P{}'' - \tilde{C}_P{}' = \Delta\tilde{C}_P \tag{16.11}$$

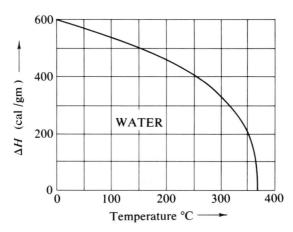

Fig. 16.1. Heat of vaporization of water.

We then need to know the molar heat capacity of each phase as a function of temperature, from which $\Delta \tilde{C}_P$ can be obtained. The integation of Eq. (16.11) with the use of an indefinite integral and a knowledge of $\Delta \tilde{H}$ at one temperature would give $\Delta \tilde{H}$ as a function of the temperature. When this function is substituted into Eq. (16.9), the integration of Eq. (16.9) proceeds with the use of either a definite or an indefinite integral. In either case the pressure must be known at one temperature. The variation of ΔH of vaporization of water as a function of temperature is shown in Fig. 16.1. The point at which the enthalpy of vaporization becomes zero is the critical temperature (374.15° C) of water.

16.3 SOME APPLICATIONS OF THE CLAPEYRON AND THE CLAUSIUS-CLAPEYRON EQUATIONS

In this section the Clapeyron and Clausius-Clapeyron equations will be applied to a number of simple phase transitions. Table 16.1 provides a

Table 16.1 Enthalpies of Vaporization, Fusion, and Sublimation for Some Common Substances

Substance	T_b °K	$\Delta \tilde{H}_{evap}$ cal mole^{-1}	T_m °K	$\Delta \tilde{H}_{fus}$ cal mole^{-1}	Substance	$\Delta \tilde{H}_{sub}$ kcal mole^{-1}
Ne	27.2	415	24.5	80.1	Ag^a	67.0
Ar	87.3	1,560	83.8	281	Au	92.2
O_2	90.2	1,630	54	106	Fe	95
N_2	77.3	1,330	63	171	Hg	15.4
H_2O	373	9,717	273	1415	K	21.9
CH_4	112	1,955	91.5	224	Mg	34.8
CF_4	145	3,010	84.6	168	Pt	125
CCl_4	350	7,140	250	647	Na	26.07
C_2H_6	185	3,517	101	668	W	210
C_4H_{10}	273	5,307	134	1050		
C_6H_6	353	7,350	279	2363		
CH_3OH	338	8,416	176	757		
C_2H_5OH	352	9,384	156	1105		
Li	1599	30,800	459	830		
Na	1156	21,800	370	630		
Hg	630	14,100	234	560		

^{a} Enthalpy of sublimation of the crystal at the absolute zero of temperature.

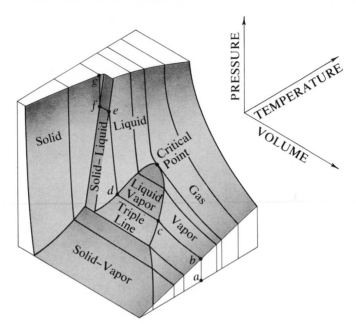

Fig. 16.2. *P-V-T surface for a substance that contracts on freezing (some isotherms sketched in).*

collection of enthalpies of vaporization, fusion, and sublimation for a number of common substances.

For the changes of state solid to liquid, liquid to vapor, and solid to vapor the change in the enthalpy is always positive. That is, the second phase in each case has a higher enthalpy than the first phase. For vaporizations and sublimations the vapor phase always has a larger volume than the condensed phase. For the melting process there is an increase in volume for most substances; water is the most common exception to this rule. Thus, based on the Clapeyron equation, the slope dP/dT will be positive (ΔH and ΔV both positive) for all common substances (except water) for sublimations, meltings, and vaporizations. For water the slope dP/dT is negative for melting (ΔH is positive, but ΔV is negative). The P-V-T surface for common substances is shown schematically in Fig. 16.2 and for substances (like water) where there is a volume expansion on freezing in Fig. 16.3.

This discussion may be better understood with reference to the *P-T*

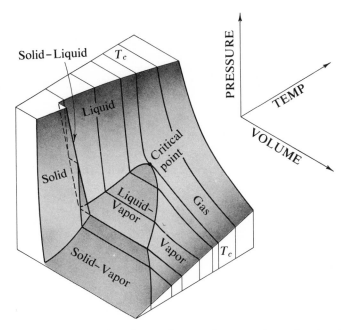

Fig. 16.3. *P-V-T* surface for a substance that expands on freezing (some iso-therms sketched in).

projections shown in Fig. 16.4(a) and (c). Starting at point *a*, Fig. 16.4(a), and proceeding along the isobar to point *b*, the temperature of the solid increases and its volume increases (although very slowly). Point *b* is on the solid-liquid coexistence curve, which is a locus of those points where the solid and liquid may be in equilibrium. In the transition from solid to liquid at *b* the volume increases. If the pressure were 1 atm, this would be the "normal melting point." The volume of the liquid increases from *b* to *c*, and *c* is on the liquid-vapor coexistence curve. There is a large increase in volume in going from liquid to vapor. The rule of thumb is (at atmospheric pressure) that the volume increases about 10 percent on melting and about a thousand-fold on vaporiz-ation. Again, if the pressure were 1 atm, point *c* would be the "normal boiling point."

It is of interest to note that although it is possible to pass from the liquid to the vapor state by crossing a liquid-vapor coexistence curve where there is a large discontinuous change in density, it is also possible to pass from liquid to

307

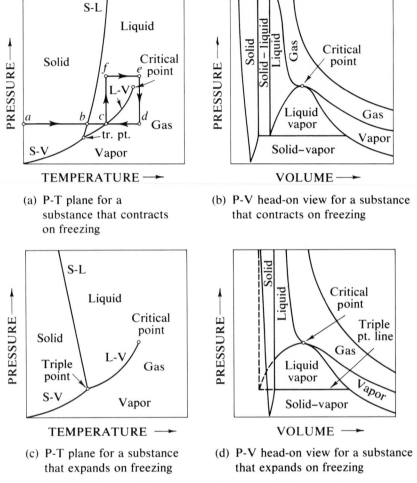

(a) P-T plane for a substance that contracts on freezing

(b) P-V head-on view for a substance that contracts on freezing

(c) P-T plane for a substance that expands on freezing

(d) P-V head-on view for a substance that expands on freezing

Fig. 16.4. *P-T and P-V projections.*

vapor without a discontinuous change in the density. This change of state can be carried out across c or from c to f to e to d and back to c.

The primary use of the Clausius-Clapeyron equation is for evaluating heats of vaporization from vapor-pressure data. Equation (16.10) is one of the equations which is often used, but we may arrive at a more convenient form via Eq. (16.9) and recognizing that dT/T^2 is $-d(1/T)$. This gives

$$\frac{d \ln P}{d(1/T)} = -\frac{\Delta \tilde{H}}{R} \tag{16.12}$$

The slope of a graph of $\ln P$ versus $1/T$ is then just $-\Delta \tilde{H}/R$. This is why vapor pressure data are most frequently represented in terms of the reciprocal of the absolute temperature.

16.4 THE GIBBS PHASE RULE

The Gibbs phase rule is named in honor of the great American physicist Josiah Willard Gibbs (1839–1903) who was for most of his life professor of mathematical physics at Yale University. Of Gibbs, the noted physicist Max Planck wrote " ... whose name, not only in America but in the whole world, will ever be reckoned among the most renowned theoretical physicists of all times ... ." This great man worked at Yale for many years without any regular salary although he did receive some money which bore a direct relation to the number of students he taught. It was only when Johns Hopkins University in 1879 offered him a position at $3000 per annum that Yale finally began to pay him the regular salary of $2000 per annum.

Although people frequently refer to Gibbs as being not known or honored in his time, this is certainly not true.[†] The great physicists and physical chemists of the time knew of his work and corresponded frequently with him. His three papers entitled " On the Equilibrium of Heterogeneous Substances " were published in the *Transactions of the Connecticut Academy of Sciences*. Even though the members of the academy professed that they could not understand the papers, they agreed that they were sufficiently important to publish. The papers were very long, and to defray the cost of publication the president of the Connecticut Academy had to solicit funds from the faculty and businessmen of New Haven. Their confidence in Gibbs' work was a truly outstanding act of prescience!

Gibbs great contributions were in the areas of thermodynamics and statistical mechanics. He formulated the idea of the chemical potential and

[†] L. P. Wheeler, *Josiah Willard Gibbs*. New Haven: Yale University Press, 1951. This definitive biography contains much of interest to the student of thermodynamics and is strongly recommended.

applied this to many phenomena, including equilibria, the phase rule, and electrochemical cells. We shall discuss the phase rule in this section.

The Gibbs phase rule concerns heterogeneous equilibria (that is, in more than one phase) and specifies the relationships between the *intensive* variables describing the system. The Gibbs phase rule is

$$F = C - P + 2 \tag{16.13}$$

and is applicable only to systems in equilibrium. P is the number of phases present. C is the number of components present. F is the number of degrees of freedom, that is, the number of intensive variables whose values may be arbitrarily changed (within limits) while still maintaining the specified number of phases. The intensive variables used ordinarily will be the temperature, pressure, and concentration variables such as mole fractions of the components in the phases.

The development of the phase rule is based on the elementary theorem of algebra that, given a set of simultaneous, independent equations, the number of variables to which values may be assigned arbitrarily is equal to the total number of variables minus the number of equations relating the variables. Consider a closed system containing P phases made up of C components. The composition of each phase is given by $(C - 1)$ composition variables. Also the temperature and pressure are intensive variables for the whole system. For P phases there are $P(C - 1) + 2$ intensive variables.

In Chapter 14 we showed that at equilibrium the chemical potential of a component must have the same value in each phase in which the component exists. This was represented in Eq. (14.28), namely,

$$\mu_1' = \mu_1'' = \mu_1''' = \cdots$$
$$\mu_2' = \mu_2'' = \mu_2''' = \cdots \tag{16.14}$$
$$\vdots$$
$$\mu_i' = \mu_i'' = \mu_i''' = \cdots$$

Each chemical potential of a component in a given phase is a function of the composition variables for the phase. Thus each independent equality sign in this set of equations signifies an additional condition between the composition variables, and each of these conditions decreases the number of degrees of freedom by one. There are $C(P - 1)$ such independent equalities for P phases and C components.

The number of degrees of freedom is then the total number of variables less the number of dependent variables, or

$$F = P(C - 1) + 2 - C(P - 1) \tag{16.15}$$

or

$$F = C - P + 2$$

Consider the following equilibrium:

$$CaCO_3(s) = CaO(s) + CO_2(g) \tag{16.16}$$

There are three phases ($CaCO_3(s)$, $CaO(s)$, and $CO_2(g)$) present, the number of components is 2, and the number of degrees of freedom is then $2 - 3 + 2$, or 1. This means that once the pressure is specified, the temperature is fixed, or that once the temperature is specified, the pressure is fixed. Thus the pressure is a function of the temperature, or vice versa. No composition variables are considered in this system because each phase is pure.

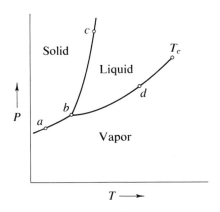

Fig. 16.5. *P-T diagram for a pure component.*

Consider the phase diagram for a single pure component as shown in the *P-T* diagram in Fig. 16.5. In any of the areas marked solid, liquid, or vapor the number of degrees of freedom is $1 - 1 + 2$, or 2. In these areas both

311

pressure and temperature may be varied while maintaining a single phase. Along the two-phase equilibrium lines ab, bc, and bd there is only one degree of freedom, which can be chosen as either the pressure *or* the temperature. At the triple point b there are no degrees of freedom, since $F = 1 - 3 + 2 = 0$; and the change of P or T will cause the disappearance of a phase. Thus the triple point is a fixed and invariant point for a pure substance as long as all three phases are in equilibrium. (The considerations discussed here were discussed earlier with respect to the necessity of fixed points for the establishment of temperature scales.)

One additional example will be discussed, the simple† vapor-liquid equilibrium for a two-component system. Figure 16.6 shows the *P-x* diagram

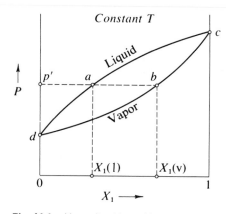

Fig. 16.6.   Vapor-liquid equilibrium.

(at constant temperature) for such a system. At the pressure P' and the first temperature the liquid and vapor are in equilibrium. At this pressure the composition of the liquid is $x_1(l)$ and of the vapor $x_1(v)$. The curve *dac* is the liquid coexistence curve, and the curve *dbc* is the vapor coexistence curve. The line connecting the points a and b is called a tie-line. Where there are two phases in equilibrium, $P = 2$, $C = 2$, and $F = 2 - 2 + 2 = 2$. But since the temperature has been fixed, $F = 2 - 1$, or 1. Thus, if either

---

† For a more complete discussion of phase equilibria for multicomponent systems, see any standard physical chemistry, metallurgy, or chemical engineering text. The paperback edition of A. Findlay's *The Phase Rule* (New York: Dover, 1951), is the classic work on applications of the Gibbs phase rule.

the total pressure or the composition of either phase is fixed, the system is determined. Once again the Gibbs phase rule is not concerned with the quantity of material in each phase—it is the intensive variables which are important.

16.5 OSMOTIC PRESSURE

The phenomenon of osmotic pressure and the transport of matter through membranes is of prime importance to biologists, but there are also some desalination projects which use membranes. The methods of thermodynamics permit an easy derivation of an important equation concerning osmotic pressure.

Consider a system in two parts, (1) pure solvent and (2) an ideal binary solution, separated by a rigid membrane permeable only to the solvent. (See Fig. 16.7.) The membrane is diathermic and therefore the temperatures of both parts are equal. The entire system may also be placed in a thermostat. Let P be the pressure on the pure solvent and P' be the pressure on the solution. Then at equilibrium we have

$$\mu_1{}^\circ(T, P) = \mu_1(T, P', x) \tag{16.17}$$

because the chemical potential of the solvent must be the same in both phases. For the solution we can write

$$\mu_1(T, P', x) = RT \ln x_1 + \mu_1{}^\circ(T, P') \tag{16.18}$$

where x_1 is the mole fraction of the solvent in the solution and $\mu_1{}^\circ(T, P')$ is

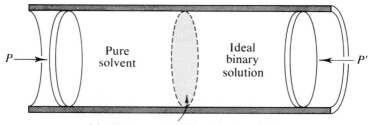

$P \longrightarrow$ Pure solvent | Ideal binary solution | $\longleftarrow P'$

Membrane permeable only to solvent

Fig. 16.7. Osmotic pressure.

313

the pure solvent standard state. Then

$$\mu_1{}^\circ(T, P) = RT \ln x_1 + \mu_1{}^\circ(T, P') \tag{16.19}$$

and

$$RT \ln x_1 = \mu_1{}^\circ(T, P) - \mu_1{}^\circ(T, P') \tag{16.20}$$

The pressure P' must be greater than P, since $x_1 < 1$ and $RT \ln x_1$ is therefore negative. Thus, $\mu_1{}^\circ(T, P') > \mu_1{}^\circ(T, P)$. The right-hand side of Eq. (16.20) at constant temperature is just the integral of $\tilde{V}_1{}^\circ \, dP$ between the two pressures, where $\tilde{V}_1{}^\circ$ is the molar volume of the pure solvent. Thus

$$RT \ln x_1 = \int_{P'}^{P} \tilde{V}_1{}^\circ \, dP \tag{16.21}$$

When we assume that $\tilde{V}_1{}^\circ$ is essentially constant over the small pressure range involved, then

$$(P - P') \tilde{V}_1{}^\circ = RT \ln x_1 \tag{16.22}$$

The osmotic pressure π is defined as $P' - P$ and our final relationship is

$$\pi \tilde{V}_1{}^\circ = - RT \ln x_1 \tag{16.23}$$

The units of π, $\tilde{V}_1{}^\circ$, and R should all be chosen to be compatible. Equations similar to (16.23) could have been derived using molality rather than the mole fraction. In the case of very dilute solutions, (16.23) can be simplified by making a number of assumptions, but in (16.23) itself we have already made two assumptions: (1) that the solution is ideal and (2) that $\tilde{V}_1{}^\circ$ is constant. The treatment of real solutions is more difficult and beyond the scope of this book.

16.6 THE THIRD LAW OF THERMODYNAMICS

In this section we take up the third law of thermodynamics which is concerned with the behavior of substances at the absolute zero of temperature. The third law provides a useful method for calculating entropy changes.

We can approach this subject by first quoting the Lewis and Randall statement of the third law (as modified by Glasstone). They state

Every substance has a finite positive entropy, but at the absolute zero of temperature the entropy may become zero, and does so become in the case of a perfect crystalline substance.

In a way this statement serves as a basis for establishing a standard state for all perfect crystalline substances at the absolute zero, and also defines the entropy of these substances to be zero at the absolute zero of temperature. There is quite good evidence from a number of sources that the third law is valid for perfect crystalline substances. However, the entropy of substances which are not in a perfectly crystalline state at the absolute zero will be some finite positive value.

The major usefulness of the third law is in the establishment of values of the absolute entropies of substances at 298° K (and in an appropriate standard state) by the determination of heat capacities over a range of temperatures starting at absolute zero with the addition of the necessary enthalpies of transition. When the heat capacity at constant pressure is known as a function of the temperature, the relation

$$\Delta S = S_{T_2} - S_{T_1} = \int_{T_1}^{T_2} C_p \, d \ln T \tag{16.24}$$

may be used. Heat capacity data are usually available down to 15° or 20° K. In the region below 20° K the heat capacity may be approximated by the Debye T^3 law, which in its simplest form is

$$C_P \cong C_V = kT^3 \tag{16.25}$$

where k is a constant characteristic of each substance. In the temperature interval 0° to 15° or 20° K we may use

$$\Delta S = S_T - S_0 = S_T = \int_0^T kT^3 \, \frac{dT}{T}$$

$$= \int_0^T T^2 \, dT = \frac{kT^3}{3} = \frac{C_P \, (\text{at } T)}{3} \tag{16.26}$$

The term C_P (at T) refers to the heat capacity measured at the lowest available temperature for that substance.

As an example we calculate the absolute entropy of gaseous cyclopropane at its boiling point.† For the first step, the transition is

(1) $C_3H_6(s, 0°\,K) = C_3H_6(s, 15°\,K)$ $\Delta\tilde{S}_1 = 0.243$ cal mole^{-1} deg^{-1}

$\Delta\tilde{S}_1$ was evaluated using the Debye T^3 law. The second step is

(2) $C_3H_6(s, 15°\,K) = C_3H_6(s, 145.54°\,K)$
$\Delta\tilde{S}_2 = 15.733$ cal mole^{-1} deg^{-1}

The remaining steps are

(3) $C_3H_6(s, 145.54°\,K) = C_3H_6(l, 145.54°\,K)$

$$\Delta\tilde{S}_3 = \frac{\Delta\tilde{H}_{fus}}{145.54} = 8.939 \text{ cal mole}^{-1} \text{ deg}^{-1}$$

(4) $C_3H_6(l, 145.54°\,K) = C_3H_6(l, 240.30°\,K)$
$\Delta\tilde{S}_4 = 9.176$ cal mole^{-1} deg^{-1}

(5) $C_3H_6(l, 240.30°\,K) = C_3H_6$ (real gas, $240.30°\,K$)

$$\Delta\tilde{S}_5 = \frac{\Delta\tilde{H}_{vap}}{240.30} = 19.946 \text{ cal mole}^{-1} \text{ deg}^{-1}$$

In summarizing steps (1) through (5) we get

(6) $C_3H_6(s, 0°\,K) = C_3H_6$ (real gas, $240.30°\,K$)

$$\Delta\tilde{S} = \sum_1^5 \Delta\tilde{S}_i = 54.04 \text{ cal mole}^{-1} \text{ deg}^{-1}$$

There is a small correction for the entropy change involved in going from the real gas to the standard condition of the ideal gas at $240.30°\,K$, and this is given by

† After Klotz, using the data of Ruhrwein and Powell.

(7) $C_3H(_6$ real gas, $240.30°$ K) = C_3H_6 (ideal gas, $240.30°$ K)

$\Delta \tilde{S}_7 = 0.13$ cal mole^{-1} deg^{-1}

Finally the absolute entropy of gaseous cyclopropane in its standard state at $240.30°$ K is given by the sum of (6) and (7) and is

$\tilde{S}_{240.30°}^\circ = 54.17$ cal mole^{-1} deg^{-1}

The entropy effects in steps (2) and (4) are found by a graphical integration of the heat capacity at constant temperature in the appropriate temperature interval. Some representative absolute entropies of various substances in their standard state at $298°$ K are tabulated in Table 16.2.

Table 16.2 Some Representative Standard Absolute Entropies at $298°$ K

Substance	$\tilde{S}_{298°}^\circ$ cal mole^{-1}deg^{-1}	Substance	$\tilde{S}_{298°}^\circ$ cal mole^{-1} deg^{-1}
Al(s)	6.77	NO(g)	50.34
C (graphite)	1.36	SO_2(g)	59.29
Cl_2(g)	53.29	SO_3(g)	61.24
Fe(s)	6.49	CH_4(g)	44.50
I_2(g)	27.76	C_2H_6(g)	54.85
N_2(g)	45.77	C_3H_8(g)	64.54
O_2(g)	49.01	C_2H_2(g)	48.00
H_2(g)	31.21	C_2H_4(g)	52.45
CO(g)	47.31	C_6H_6(g)	64.34
CO_2(g)	51.08	C_6H_6(l)	29.76
H_2O(l)	16.73	C_6H_{12}(g)	71.28
H_2O(g)	45.11	C_2H_5OH(g)	67.4
HCl(g)	44.64	C_2H_5OH(l)	38.4

The tabulated values of the absolute entropies may be used to calculate entropy changes for reactions as long as attention is paid to all the changes of state involved. The absolute entropies listed in Table 16.2 are for the substances in their respective standard states at $298°$ K. This table may be used to calculate standard state changes in the Gibbs free energy according to the equation

$$\Delta G^\circ = \sum_i v_i \Delta \tilde{G}^\circ_{f,i} = \sum_i v_i \Delta \tilde{H}^\circ_{f,i} - T \Delta S^\circ \tag{16.27}$$

where

$$\Delta S^\circ = \sum_i v_i \tilde{S}_i^{\ \circ}$$

16.7   CONCLUDING COMMENTS

The criteria for equilibrium have been applied in this chapter to a few one-component and multicomponent systems. For one-component systems the Clapeyron and the Clausius-Clapeyron equations cover two-phase equilibria. The Gibbs phase rule provides information about the number of intensive variables which are necessary to characterize the state of a system. A relationship for the osmotic pressure of an ideal binary solution was developed. The third law of thermodynamics was presented and discussed.

Exercises

16.1   The density of ice is 0.917 g cm^{-3} at 273° K and 1 atm pressure. The change of enthalpy on melting ice under these conditions is 80 cal g^{-1}. Calculate the slope of the melting curve (dP/dT) in atmospheres per degree.

16.2   (a) Benzene boils at 353° K at 1 atm pressure and the change of enthalpy on evaporation is 7600 cal mole^{-1}. Calculate the vapor pressure of benzene, assuming the vapor to behave as an ideal gas, at several temperatures between 280° and 353° K and plot the vapor pressure of benzene as a function of the temperature.

(b) One-half mole of benzene is contained in a vessel whose volume is 46.8 liters. Calculate the pressure of benzene over the same temperature range, assuming that all the benzene exists in the gaseous state and behaves as an ideal gas. Plot this pressure against the temperature.

(c) For the system described in part (b), at what temperature does the benzene first begin to condense?

(d) How many moles of benzene will exist in the liquid state at 300° K?

16.3 The change of enthalpy on evaporating one mole of water at $373°$ K is 9700 cal mole^{-1}. The molar heat capacity in cal deg^{-1} mole^{-1} of water vapor is given by the equation

$$\tilde{C}_P = 7.187 + 0.00237T - 0.208 \times 10^{-6}T^2$$

and that of liquid water is 18 cal deg^{-1} mole^{-1}. Calculate the vapor pressure of water at $298°$ K.

16.4 The vapor pressure of propene (C_3H_6) is 44.2 atm at $363°$ K; the slope of the vapor pressure curve at $363°$ K is 0.861 atm deg^{-1}, the molar volume of the liquid is 143 ml, and that of the saturated vapor is 242 ml. Calculate $\Delta \tilde{H}$ for evaporation at $363°$ K.

16.5 (a) Derive the Clapeyron equation.
(b) Derive the Clausius-Clapeyron equation. What assumptions are made in this derivation?

16.6 According to Trouton's rule the molar entropy of vaporization is 21 cal deg^{-1} for a "normal" liquid at its boiling point (T_b). (a) Using this value, show that the following equation holds (where P is measured at T): $\ln P(\text{atm}) = 10.5(1 - (T_b/T))$. (b) Test Trouton's rule for CH_4, CF_4, CCl_4, C_4H_{10}, C_6H_6, and C_2H_5OH. (c) Benzene (C_6H_6) normally boils at $353.25°$ K. Estimate the vapor pressure of benzene in mm Hg at $358.15°$ K, assuming Trouton's rule.

16.7 Starting with a pure solid, sketch a V-T diagram for a substance which (a) contracts on freezing and (b) expands on freezing, showing the transitions solid $\rightarrow$ liquid $\rightarrow$ vapor.

16.8 The Clausius-Clapeyron equation also holds for solid-solid phase transitions. The specific volume of monoclinic sulfur (stable above the transition temperature) is greater than that of rhombic sulfur by 0.0126 cc g^{-1}. The transition point at 1 atm is $368.65°$ K, and it increases at the rate of 0.035 deg atm^{-1}. Calculate the heat of transition in calories per gram.

16.9 The average heat of vaporization of water in the temperature range between $353°$ K and $373°$ K is 534 cal g^{-1}. Calculate the vapor pressure of water at $353°$ K and at $363°$ K. What approximations are made in this calculation?

16.10 The heat vaporization of chlorobenzene at its normal boiling point ($405°$ K) is 73.4 cal g^{-1}. What is the estimated pressure in mm Hg under which the liquid will boil at $398°$ K? Recalculate this result, taking $V_g - V_l$ as 278 cc g^{-1} at the normal boiling point.

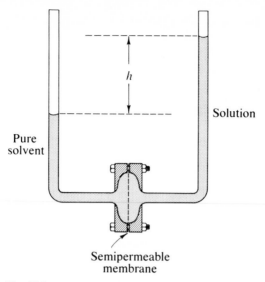

Fig. 16.8

16.11 Sketch the T–x diagram corresponding to Fig. 16.6. Does component 1 have a higher or lower boiling point than component 2? How many degrees of freedom are there above the curve *dac* in Fig. 16.6? Does it make sense to talk about the number of degrees of freedom along the curve *dac*?

16.12 An osmometer is usually set up as shown in Fig. 16.8. At equilibrium the height h is measured, the concentration of the solution is determined, and also the density of the solution is determined. From this information the osmotic pressure may be calculated. For the following aqueous solutions, all 1 percent by weight, calculate the height h and the osmotic pressure π for NaCl (mol wt = 58.44), AgNO$_3$ (mol wt = 169.88), and sucrose (mol wt = 342.29). Assume that the density of each solution is 1 g ml^{-1} and the temperature is 298° K. Express the height in centimeters and the pressure in millimeters of mercury. (*Note:* NaCl and AgNO$_3$ are completely ionized in solution.)

16.13 The vapor pressure of water in millimeters of mercury is given below for several temperatures.

T, °K	273	298	348	373	378
Pressure	4.6	23.8	289	760	906

Assume that the density of liquid water is constant at 1.00 g ml^{-1}.

(a) If 10 g of water is introduced into a previously evacuated 1-liter vessel, what weight of water will be liquid and what weight will be vapor at each of the temperatures listed in the table?

(b) What weight of water would be in the vessel at 378° K if all the water were vapor? At 273° K what weight of this amount of water will be liquid?

16.14 Calculate the standard entropy of formation at 298° K for the following substances:

(a) $H_2O(g)$ (e) $CO_2(g)$

(b) $H_2O(l)$ (f) $C_3H_8(g)$

(c) $C_6H_6(g)$ (g) $NO(g)$

(d) $C_6H_6(l)$ (h) $HCl(g)$

16.15 Using the standard entropies of formation calculated in Exercise 16.14 (a) and (b), and (c) and (d), obtain estimated values for the entropy and enthalpy of vaporization of H_2O and C_6H_6 at 298° K.

16.16 By using the standard absolute entropies in Table 16.2 and the enthalpies of formation in Table 8.3, calculate the standard Gibbs free energy of formation at 298° K for

(a) $HCl(g)$ (d) $C_2H_5OH(g)$

(b) $CO_2(g)$ (e) $C_6H_6(g)$

(c) $C_2H_2(g)$ (f) $H_2O(g)$

16.17 One gram of liquid water and 1 g of water vapor are in equilibrium in a rigid adiabatic container at 373° K and 1 atm pressure; 100 calories of heat are added, the volume remaining constant. Describe what happens, qualitatively and quantitatively.

Epilogue

A colleague of ours once remarked that the only people qualified to teach thermodynamics are those who had already taught the subject for 20 years. This paradoxical statement really means that the subject of thermodynamics requires repeated and continuous study and that it is only over the years that many of its concepts are gradually understood. You will undoubtedly apply what you have learned from this book to many varied circumstances. In other courses you may have opportunity to develop in much more detail those areas which were but lightly touched here or even completely ignored. This book is meant to be just a *beginning* for your studies in thermodynamics. We have attempted to explain the basic concepts at sufficient length to provide a solid foundation for the more specialized applications you will encounter in the future. In using thermodynamics you must always be cognizant of how the functions were defined, the exact state of each system, and the nature of the paths followed between various states. Careful attention to the fundamentals will simplify many problems.

Answers to Selected Problems

Chapter 2

2.2 Exact: a, b, c, f.

2.8 (a) $\pi r\theta/180$. (b) $\pi r^2/360$. (c) $-2\theta/r$. (d) $(\pi\theta/180) + 2$.
(e) $-180P/\pi r^2$. (f) $(1/r) + (360/\pi r\theta)$. (g) $2/r$. (h) $-\pi r^2/360$.

Chapter 3

3.3

| P atm | Ideal | | | van der Waals | | | Virial | | |
	PV liter-atm	Z		PV liter-atm	Z		PV liter-atm	Z	
10	22.414	1		22.80	1.018		22.32	0.995	
100	22.414	1		20.91	0.933		22.23	0.992	
1000	22.414	1		55.2	2.46		98.2	4.38	

3.7 54.2 kg.

Chapter 4

4.1 (b) $-40°$
4.2 (a) $P = P_f (0.879 + 0.0305°N)$. (b) $-27.8°N$. (c) 6.43 atm; $-24.3°N$.
 (d) $°K = 273 (0.879 + 0.305°N)$.
4.3 $0.7°$, $1.6°$, $1.7°$.
4.5 $28.7°$, $80.0°$.

Chapter 5

5.4 (a) $15.0°C$. (b) 75.4 g.
5.8 4.35 kg.

Chapter 6

6.3 (a) 840 cal. (b) 745 cal.
6.7 (a) 555 cal. (b) 1058 cal.
6.9 0.48 cal.

Chapter 7

7.1 (a) $W_1 = 558$ cal; $Q_1 = 677$ cal; $W_4 = 1060$ cal; $Q_4 = 1390$ cal.
 (b) $W_2 = 0$; $Q_2 = 1016$ cal; $W_3 = 0$; $Q_3 = 800$ cal.
7.6 (a) 0.388 mole; 0.5 liter. (b) $W_{acb} = -473$ cal; $W_{adb} = -9460$ cal.
7.7 $W = 69.5$ cal, $\Delta E = 30$ cal.
7.9 $Q = -1830$ cal.

Chapter 8

8.4 (b) 42,273 cal.
8.6 $\Delta H = 318$ cal; $\Delta E = 284$ cal.
8.7 (1) $\Delta H° = -326.70$ kcal.
 (5a) 15.54 kcal. (5d) 82.72 kcal.
8.8 $W = 354$ cal; $\Delta E = 1539$ cal; $\Delta H = 1893$ cal.
8.13 $\Delta E = -817$ cal; $\Delta H = -1065$ cal.

Chapter 9

9.1 (a) $Q = 0$; $\Delta E = -830$ cal; $\Delta H = -1503$ cal. (b). $W = 3920$ cal; $Q = 13,720$ cal; $\Delta H = 13,720$ cal.

9.2 $35°$ K.

9.3 $\mu_{JT}(\text{calc}) = 0.261°$ K atm^{-1}.

Chapter 10

10.3 53 cal.

10.7 (a) Isothermal expansion: $\Delta E = \Delta H = 0$; $Q = W = 4800$ cal. (b) Adiabatic expansion: $\Delta E = -3000$ cal; $\Delta H = -4195$ cal.

Chapter 11

11.2 $\Delta S = 0.089$ cal deg^{-1}.

11.3 $\Delta S = 45.9$ cal deg^{-1}.

11.5 $T_f = 352°$ K; $\Delta S = 8.92$ cal deg^{-1}.

11.7 $\Delta H = 328$ cal; $\Delta E = Q = 304$ cal; $\Delta S = 0.88$ cal deg^{-1}.

11.9 (a) $\Delta S_1 = 2.25$ cal deg^{-1}; $\Delta S_4 = 2.78$ cal deg^{-1}. (b) $\Delta S_2 = 2.57$ cal deg^{-1}; $\Delta S_3 = 2.03$ cal deg^{-1}.

Chapter 12

12.2 $\Delta E = 0$; $Q = 3600$ cal; $\Delta A = \Delta G = -3600$ cal; $\Delta S = 12$ cal deg^{-1}.

12.3 (a) $T_f = 81.5°$ K; $\Delta E = -3280$ cal.

12.7 $\Delta H = -747$ cal; $\Delta S = -2.72$ cal deg^{-1}; $\Delta G = -31$ cal.

12.12 $\Delta S = 4.57$ cal deg^{-1}.

Chapter 13

13.1 $x_{H_2O} = 0.718$; 50 wt % H_2O; 55.6 molal H_2O.

13.6 2.07 wt %, 18.5 g liter^{-1}, and 0.641 mole % in benzene.

Chapter 15

15.4 (b) $\Delta G_f^\circ = 1.152$ kcal mole^{-1}.
15.6 (a) $K = 2 \times 10^{-17}$. (d) $K = 1.41 \times 10^{15}$.
15.7 $\Delta G^\circ = 8716$ cal.
15.8 (c) $\Delta G^\circ = -108.7$ kcal.
15.10 $\Delta H^\circ = 38{,}810 - 15.41T + 2.07 \times 10^{-3}\, T^2$.
15.13 $\Delta G^\circ = 66.6$ kcal; $\Delta S^\circ = 82$ cal deg^{-1}.
15.16 0.772 V.
15.19 -27.3 kcal.
15.20 (b) 2.051 V; (c) 2.087 V.

Chapter 16

16.1 0.0984 atm deg^{-1}.
16.2 (c) 314° K. (d) 0.215 mole.
16.3 0.0294 atm.
16.8 3.2 cal g^{-1}.
16.10 635 mm; 604 mm.
16.12 For NaCl: 8700 cm, 6400 mm Hg.
16.14 (c) -37.54 cal deg^{-1}; (d) -72.12 cal deg^{-1}.
16.16 (a) -22.8 kcal mole^{-1} (b) -94.3 kcal mole^{-1}.

INDEX

327

INDEX